WILD PAGES

THE WILDLIFE FILM-MAKERS'
RESOURCE GUIDE 2012–13

EDITED BY JASON PETERS
AND PIERS WARREN

Published by:

Wildeye
United Kingdom

Email: info@wildeye.co.uk
Websites: http://www.wildeye.co.uk/wildpages
http://www.wildeye.co.uk/publishing

Copyright © Wildeye 2011
First published 2011

ISBN 978·1·905843·03·9

Cover photography by Jason Peters
www.jasonpeters.co.uk

CONTENTS

INTRODUCTION

Welcome to the 2012–13 edition of *Wild Pages: The Wildlife Film-makers' Resource Guide.*

The wildlife film-making industry is unique in many ways. The passion of the individuals involved, from camera operators to producers to distributors, is legendary. In many cases this leads practitioners to remain within the wildlife genre for all of their careers. Partly due to this, the industry has developed a community all of its own, with film festivals, production companies, and organisations devoted solely to wildlife imagery – whether it be productions for cinema, television, the internet, DVD/BD, phone applications and so on.

To find out who is in this community – whether you are looking for jobs, co-producers, footage, staff, work experience, film competitions or other opportunities – is not always easy. Trawling through the web and sending speculative emails can be very time-consuming and a hit-and-miss exercise. Festival directories may be invaluable, but few can afford to attend such events and the directories are usually only available to delegates.

Enter *Wild Pages*: a complete tool-kit of information for all wildlife film-makers – established and newcomers alike. Listings have been distributed into appropriate categories and many contain a description of the company/freelancer with full contact details, web-links etc. Where relevant, the companies have also been urged to give answers to those all-important questions such as whether they take people on work experience or consider co-productions, how to submit proposals and so on.

Keep *Wild Pages* on your desk, in your kit-bag or on your laptop or phone (there are eBook and Kindle editions available with active email/web-links) and access to the community will be constantly at your fingertips.

Good luck with your careers and productions and look out for the 2014–15 edition when the time comes!

Note that this is an international guide, with listings from all over the world: you may notice that different countries spell some words in different ways – organize/organise, program/programme, for example. We have left the spellings true to the contributors' origins.

Also note that the '+' on the telephone numbers requires the international access code which is usually 00, and numbers in brackets e.g. (0) would be omitted if dialling from abroad.

PRODUCTION COMPANIES

1080 Film and Television
Address: 26 Blackthorn Way, Poringland, NR14 7WD, UK
Phone: +44 (0)8484181338 & +44 (0)7973521409
Email: info@1080films.co.uk
Website: www.1080films.co.uk
Director of Photography – Mark Dodd (www.markdodddp.com)

1080 Films was set up in 2008 by Mark Dodd, an award winning photographer-filmmaker who has worked worldwide for twenty years with the BBC. We produce films for broadcast and commercial markets. The term 1080 represents the highest technical standard for high definition TV, a standard that reflects our objective of maintaining the highest production values. Give us a call to chat about your requirements; we are a small but friendly team with access to some of the best talent in the broadcast market: presenters, producers, location crew, editors, web designers. These skills are selected to provide a tailor-made package, specific to the requirements of your project.

360 Degree Films
Address: PO Box 418, Brunswick 3056, Victoria, AUSTRALIA
Phone: +613 9948 1922 Fax: +613 9948 1920
Email: info@360degreefilms.com.au
Website: www.360degreefilms.com.au
Producer – Sally Ingleton, Development Producer – Josephine Wright
Production Assistant – Emma Barnett, Production Book Keeper – Noga Mizrahi

360 Degree Films is a film and television production company based in Melbourne. Our motto is to make documentaries that matter. At the heart of our philosophy is the belief that it is possible to make insightful, entertaining films that inform, empower and inspire people so they see the world differently. Our films take audiences to all corners of the globe. Principal Sally Ingleton has been a major player in the Australian industry for the past twenty-five years. Her award winning documentaries cover many genres including nature, science, environment, social issues and the arts. In the past 5 years Sally has been commissioned by the following broadcasters: ABC, BBC, National Geographic, Arte France, France TV, ITV, SBS, RTBF, RTE, SVT, YLE, TSR, DR and AVRO. Apart from producing and directing, Sally has contributed and supported the Australian industry by regularly teaching at film schools and mentoring young filmmakers. Ideas and treatments can be forwarded to us by email. We currently don't have any positions available for work experience volunteers, however in the future please email your interest to us.

422 South
Address: 103 Whiteladies Road, Bristol, BS8 2PB. UK
Phone: +44 (0)117 923 8071
Email: adc@422.com
Website: www.422.com
Managing Director: Craig Howarth

We're an award-winning UK-based visual effects, animation and commercials company working for TV producers and advertising agencies around the world. We have designers, directors, visual effects specialists, animators, compositors and technicians in our core team, with an extended family of trusted, specialist freelancers close to hand.

42°N Films
Address: 284 Amory Street, Boston, MA 02130, USA
Phone: +1 617 987 8553
Fax: +1 413.828.6599
Email: information@42degreesnorth.com
Website: www.42degreesnorth.com/
Producer/Director/Writer: Kate Raisz – Kate@42degreesnorth.com

42 Degrees North specializes in translating complex ideas from science and natural history into compelling and dramatic media pieces for museums, television, and the web. Clients include Smithsonian National Museum of Natural History, NOAA, Discovery Channel, National Geographic, New England Aquarium and the Aquarium of the Pacific.

Abbey Gateway Productions
Address: 41 Brecknock Rd., Ground Floor, Bristol BS4 2DE, UK
Phone: +44 (0)7527 452 960
Email: ed.watkins@abbeygateway.co.uk
Website: www.abbeygateway.co.uk
Owner: Ed Watkins

We are a fully inclusive production team specialising in HD and digital cinema delivery. We cover all aspects of production from research and development through to production and post-production. We strive to provide the best possible production values on every project we undertake. Some of the companies we have done work for include NASA, NatGeo Wild, The National Park Service, PBS, Oxford University, and The US Army. We are looking for collaborators, sponsors and actively seek co-productions.

Africa Wildlife Films
Address: SOUTH AFRICA
Email: info@africawildlifefilms.co.za
Website: www.africawildlifefilms.co.za
Directors: Phil & Lynne Richardson

AfriScreen Films
Address: P.O Box HA 40 HAK, Maun 267, BOTSWANA
Phone: +267 6801123 & +267 6863720
Fax: +27 86 6200739
Main Email: office@afriscreen.com
Website: www.afriscreen.com
Producer – Tania "TJ" Jenkins
Director/Cinematographer – Mike Holding

AfriScreen Films is a Botswana-based natural history production company. Our core team have worked in natural history, feature film, TV drama series and corporate film. All the experience, diverse disciplines and skills learnt are now melded into AfriScreen Films, where we have accumulated: twenty-five+ years African wildlife filming expertise, twenty+ years feature film and TV drama experience, twenty+ years editing and post production skills and a lifetime of African bush skills and field operations. We produce our own films, film sequences for international productions and provide comprehensive fixing and facilitation services throughout Southern Africa. CVs welcome by email. Work experience offered for those with at least three years in the industry.

Aldabra Productions
Address: Corso Nazionale 5, La Spezia 19126, ITALY
Phone: +39 (0)187 513 975
Fax: +39 (0)187 510 241
Email: info@aldabraproductions.it
Website: www.aldabraproductions.it
Andrea Maggi: andream@aldabraproductions.it

Founder Andrea Maggi, has produced many award-winning programmes such as *Hippo Talk, A Dog's Life, Islanders, A Sea of Surprises, Islands without frontiers,* and many others with co-productions partners such as Discovery Channel, Canal+, RAI, NHK, NDR, etc.

Altayfilm GmbH
Address: Erknerstraße 46, Gruenheide 15537, Berlin, GERMANY
Phone: +49 3343473987
Email: mail@altayfilm.com
Website: www.altayfilm.com
CEO: Henry M. Mix
Producer: Yann Sochaczewski

Altayfilm is a natural-history film production company based in Berlin (Germany) specialized in producing blue-chip wildlife documentaries with a focus on Russia and the Far East.

Ambi Creations
Address: 10, Geetanjali apartments, N.Tanajiwadi, Shivajinagar, Pune 411005, INDIA
Phone: +91-9822522134 & +91-2025813034
Fax: +91-2025813034
Email: ambicreations@gmail.com
Website: www.ambicreations.com
Proprietor, Producer, Editor: Amol Chaugule
Producer, Director, Cinematographer/Cameraman, Editor: Bipin Chaugule

We offer video camera crew and production services almost anywhere in India and neighbouring countries for documentary, nature, wildlife and news filming crews. We are not looking for proposals, co-productions and we do not offer work experience.

Ammonite Ltd
Address: Bristol & Exeter House, Lower Station Approach, Bristol BS1 6QS, UK
Phone: +44 (0)117 927 9778
Email: info@ammonite.co.uk
Website: www.ammonite.co.uk
MD: Martin Dohrn – mdohrn@ammonite.co.uk

Ammonite is an independent film production company. We have been in existence since 1994 making high-quality, high definition films about science and natural history. Ammonite develops highly specialised and innovative equipment such as image intensified night vision cameras and motion control systems. Ammonite's kit can be hired. We also have an extensive library of high definition film clips available for sale.

11

Ant Farm Films
Address: Nottingham, UK
Phone: +44 (0)7948 377 224
Email: laura@antfarmfilms.net
Website: www.antfarmfilms.net
Owner/Editor/Camera: Laura Turner

I am an Apple-certified FCP editor, camera operator and filmmaker specialising in wildlife and conservation films. I have worked on documentaries, promos and charity videos, and as an editing tutor on the Wildeye Big Cat Film Safari in Kenya. I was also the in-house editor for CTV Perth, Australia, where a conservation documentary I edited won a WA Screen Award. In 2010 I set up *The Wildlife Garden Project*: a film and a website which aim to inspire people to make their gardens more wildlife friendly (www.wildlifegardenproject.com). Take a look at my websites or get in touch to discuss my services!

Aquavision TV Productions
Address: 144 Western Services Road, Woodmead, Johannesburg 2191, SOUTH AFRICA
Phone: +27(0)11 275 0900 & +27(0)11 275 0901
Email: HOD Library: Christo Ras – christo@aquavision.co.za
Executive PA: Julia Gaspar – julia@aquavision.co.za
Website: www.aquavision.co.za
Contacts: Pieter Lamberti (CEO), Dave Keet (General Manager), Sean O'Neill (Head of Production), Steve Eder (Executive Producer), Christo Ras (Head Librarian), Martin Ferreira (Head Audio Engineer)

Aquavision produces high quality high-definition natural history factual, cultural and reality documentaries. With an archive library with more than 5000 hours of natural history archive footage Aquavision is the largest NH stock library in Africa. For any of your African stock footage needs Aquavision must be your first stop. With its growing Local and International cinematography database its International NH stock footage is growing daily. For production management support for shoots anywhere on the African continent, Aquavision is able to assist; from the planning, organization, and fixing, of any aspect of the production. We are also available for work for hire, providing specialized cameramen and equipment for shoots. With more than ten edit suites we can deliver both off and on lines at any delivery specification. Looking for natural history/wildlife/cultural/reality film and festival entries. We are always actively looking for new talent, presenters, VO artists etc.

Aqua Vita Films
Address: 12 Dowry Square, Hotwells, Bristol, BS8 4SH, UK
Email: info@aquavitafilms.com
Website: www.aquavitafilms.com
Producer: Bernard Walton – bernard@aquavitafilms.com

Aqua Vita Films is a multi-award-winning independent television production company based in the UK. We specialise in producing high quality and innovative wildlife, science and adventure television documentaries for international broadcast.

Aquila Films
Address: 19 Bishops Road, London N6 4HP, UK
Phone: + 44 (0)208 340 9500
Main Email: info@aquilafilms.com
Website: www.aquilafilms.com
Executive Producer: Andrea Florence – andrea@aquilafilma.com

AQUILA FILMS is an established independent production based in London. We create powerful factual programming with strong stories that engage a wide audience. Specialising in producing high-impact adventure, science, travel and wildlife documentaries for key broadcasters worldwide including BBC and National Geographic. From blue-chip wildlife shows and 3D specials to high volume presenter-led series we aim to push the boundaries with inventive use of stunning computer graphics and multi-platform applications. Aquila collaborates with the world's best cameramen and some of the most creative and innovative directors and editors to produce shows with compelling visuals and strong storytelling.

Arctic Bear Productions
Address: CANADA
Email: abp@arcticbearproductions.com
Website: www.arcticbearproductions.com
Producers/Cinematographers: Adam Ravetch and Sarah Robertson

Are U Happy? Films
Address: Gerda-Weiler-Str. 1, 79100 Freiburg, GERMANY
Phone: +49-177-761 6263
Email: info@areuhappyfilms.com
Website: www.areuhappyfilms.com
Contact: Werner Schuessler – Director, Director of Photography

Currently in production: *Passion and Patience - Up Close with the World's Leading Wildlife Filmmakers*. We offer the following production services: experienced camera operator (Werner Schuessler) to hire and co-productions.

ArgoFilms
Address: USA
Email: info@argofilms.com
Website: www.argofilms.com
Contact: Allison Argo

ArgoFilms is dedicated to producing television programming that makes a difference.

Asian Wildlife Films
Country: THAILAND
Phone: +66 56 614 963 & +66 81 532 0303
Email: darrylsweetland@yahoo.com
Website: www.asianwildlifefilms.com
Cameraman/Biologist/Writer: Darryl Sweetland

Biologist, writer, and cameraman, Darryl has lived and worked in Thailand since 1996. He speaks, reads, and writes Thai. Darryl has extensive experience of looking for and filming Thai wildlife and most often this involves spending long periods in hides and camping in the forest, which is something he loves. From Oct 2007 to March 2010 Darryl was a regular contributor to www.earth-touch.com (Wild Touch – SABC2), and some of his work can be viewed in the Thailand section of their website. Darryl offers a wide range of services to film crews wishing to work in Thailand.

Banksia Films
Address: Av. Adolfo Ducke, 105 – Manaus, Amazonia, BRAZIL
Phone: +55 92 9152 0962 & +55 92 8205 4615
Fax: +55 92 3321 4138
Email: carolinabanksiafilm@gmail.com
Website: www.banksiafilms.com
Main Contact: Carolina Fernandez

FILMOGRAPHY: *J'ai vu Changer la Terre* – Directed by Pierre Bressaint, Adamis Productions/France; *Amyu – The army of a wasp men* – Directed by Jerome Raynaud, Zed Productions/France; *Extinctions – Onça Pintada* – Directed by Maurício Dias, Gullane Filmes; *La Peau Rouge* – Directed by Charlie Buffet, Zed Productions/France.
I want to get involved in films that make the difference. Films that educate people and respect the animals. Films categories: fiction and documentaries. I'm looking for collaborators to make films related with the biodiversity of the Amazon and I strongly consider co-productions. I offer work experience in the Amazon for who have the interest in coming to here. I'm not looking for a talent. I accept CVs by email.

BAOBAB TREE PRODUCTIONS

Baobab Tree Productions
Address: 21 Sydling Road, Yeovil, Somerset BA21 5LH, UK
Phone: +44 1935 410511 & +44 7707 007099
Fax: +44 1935 410511
Email: jenny@baobabtreeproductions.com
Website: www.baobabtreeproductions.com
Contact: Jenny Devitt

Small, flexible and versatile independent, specialising in wildlife and factual documentaries and features. Offering web-video production, and also specialist scripting/script editing and narration services. Script translation from French to English and re-versioning also available. We are not looking for proposals. Collaborators and co-producers considered for future productions. We do not offer work experience.

Bitis Documentales
Address: Polígono Industrial Las Salinas, C/ Aluvión, naves 4 y 5 El Puerto de Santa María (CÁDIZ) 11500, ESPAÑA
Phone: +34 699 942 868 & +34 956 873 475
Fax: +34 956 852 510
Email: joaquingacha@bitisdocumentales.com &
carmenrodriguez@bitisdocumentales.com
Website: www.bitisdocumentales.com
Producer/Director/Photography: Joaquín Gutiérrez Acha – joaquin.guti.acha@gmail.com

Bitis Documentales/Joaquín Gutiérrez Acha is a company specialized in the production of natural history documentaries for film and television. He has worked for companies such as National Geographic Television and Film, National Geographic Channel, National Geographic Digital Motion, BBC (NHU), Canal + France, Canal + España, Parthenon Entertainment, Wanda Vision, Terra Mater Factual Studio, Government of Spain and the Government of Andalusia. We have teams of production, postproduction, studies and our own vehicles. We are interested in producing nature documentaries for television and film. We are not interested in fiction, reality etc, only animal behavior and wildlife blue-chips. Usually our projects are funded by several companies. Yes, we are open for co-production. Now we are not looking new collaborators and in any case prefer to receive CVs by email.

Björn Welander Photography
Address: 7628 Bayside Road, Chesapeake beach, MD 20732, USA
Phone: +1 301 910 1930
Email: b.welander@gmail.com
Website: www.bjornwelander.com and www.baldibis.org
Producer/Camera/Editor: Björn Welander
Presenter/Co-producer: Neil Owen – neilcroc@hotmail.com
Script Writer: Amy Brown – amysusanbrown@gmail.com

We produce films with strong conservation messages that have the local people's angle and involve those who live and work in valuable conservation areas or where threatened species occur. Currently looking for proposals that shows a success story in conservation

15

and would work well as a presenter-led wildlife documentary. Conservation festival category. We are looking for sponsors that want to take an active part in our projects. We will consider co-productions. No work experience/internships for the moment since we have just relocated to Maryland, USA.

Camara Films
Address: Ave. San Juan Bosco, Edif. For You, Apt. 6-B, Altamira, Caracas 1060, VENEZUELA
Phone: +58 412 331 5252 & +1 954 543 8818 (Magic Jack)
Email: camarafilms@gmail.com
Website: www.camarafilms.com
Director/Founder: Ana Cristina Henriquez

We are an independent media production company based in Venezuela. We are interested in making films on the natural world as well as areas including science, people, adventure, children and health. We can provide location scouting, fixing and production film services for foreign companies in Venezuela and/or South America. We have experience in wildlife and nature consulting as well as a network of contacts throughout the Andes, the Caribbean coast, the llanos (plains) and the Amazon jungle.
Among others, we sell rights for AWARD winning documentary *Freshwater Lands* (50 min) on water and wetlands. BEST ECOLOGICAL DOCUMENTARY, The Big Apple Latin Film Awards. SPECIAL MENTION Ecofilms, Rodos International Film + Visual Arts Festival. FIRST PRIZE Environment and sustainable Development Category, IV Independent Hispano-American Video documentary Festival.
We like to provide production services for international TV networks and/or media production companies. We are looking for sponsors. We can consider co-productions that can cover crew/talent salaries. Not offering work experience at the moment.

Carles Castillo Nature Productions
Address: Nor C/Farigola, 5 "El Temple", Santa Mª de Palautordera 08460 SPAIN
Phone: +34 670898490
Email: info@carlescastillo.com
Website: www.carlescastillo.com

Thematic documentaries production company specialists in hunting, fishing, underwater and nature documentaries for thematic channels or other clients. We work for the main TV channels of different countries and we sell documentaries as DVDs (home video). We are looking for camera work in nature documentaries as well as making our own productions. Our categories in festivals are: wildlife, hunting, fishing. We are looking for sponsors and collaborators and consider co-productions. Currently we don't accept CVs.

Conservation Media
Address: P.O. Box 7061, Missoula, MT 59807, USA
Phone: +1 406-360-9684
Email: jroberts@conservationmedia.com
Website: www.ConservationMedia.com
Owner/Producer: Jeremy R. Roberts

We specialize in short conservation films for the web. We focus mainly on the natural history and conservation issues of the Northern Rocky Mountains of N. America. Also available as production support for any and all Northern Rocky Mountain natural history films. Will consider co-productions. We occasionally take interns and hire crew members.

Cristian Dimitrius Productions
Address: Rua das Tabocas 170, São Paulo 05445020, BRAZIL
Phone: +55 11 8906 7626 & +55 11 2892-6683
Email: cristian@diveadventures.com.br
Website: www.cristiandimitrius.com
Director: Cristian Dimitrius – cdimitrius@yahoo.com

Biologist, wildlife filmmaker, photographer, expedition leader and dive instructor. One of the few Brazilians who dedicates his full-time to document the natural history of our planet both topside and underwater, having more than 3,000 dives in the most diverse environments. Has been exploring places like Galapagos, Patagonia, Canada, Australia, Thailand, India, Africa, Antarctic and Bahamas. In Brazil, he has a lot of knowledge about the Brazilian Pantanal, Amazon, Coastal and Oceanic Islands. I work specially with pure wildlife films, wildlife photography and conservation-themed documentaries. He has also several articles published in diving and nature magazines.

Crossing the Line Films
Address: Barr an Uisce, Killincarrig Road, Greystones, Co. Wicklow, IRELAND
Phone: +353 12875394
Fax: +353 12875394
Email: johnmurray@ctlfilms.com
Website: www.ctlfilms.com
MD: John Murray
Producer: Siobhán Ward – siobhanward@ctlfilms.com
Development: Cepa Giblin – cepagiblin@ctlfilms.com

Crossing the Line Films is an award-winning production company specialising in travel, adventure, wildlife and historical documentaries. Our films have broadcast worldwide in over eighty different countries on RTÉ, BBC, Discovery, Nat Geo, Channel 5, ARTE, Travel, PBS, WGBH, History Channel, Adventure One, Sky, Voyage and many others. We also offer HD equipment rental, which includes specialist wildlife lenses and the only HD High Speed camera in Ireland – a Phantom. Not looking for proposals.

Compañia de Inventarios Naturales
Address: Pza. España 5 (2b) 40100, SPAIN
Phone: +34 921473795 & +34 615987502
Email: info@cintv.tv
Website: www.cintv.tv
Development Director: Victor M Fraile – vfraile@cintv.tv

CIN.TV (from the Spanish Compañia de Inventarios Naturales) is a wildlife, environmental and social documentaries producer whose main aim is to promote and extend the knowledge of the environment together with its care, conservation and respect. Its experience ranges from cinema to television, video and online distribution and successful productions are well known worldwide. CINTV has been awarded worldwide and sells regularly doc-series to the main networks of the sector. It offers and guarantees creativity,

17

constant innovation in all its products since its foundation in 1992. CINTV belongs to Vertice360 Group, a major media group in Spain.
Always looking for great ideas related to nature and man. Good talents too are welcome to contact with samples of their work. Co-production considered with good ideas and also with some financial lead. We accept CV through our main mail address.

Darlow Smithson Productions
Address: UK
Email: mail@darlowsmithson.com
Website: www.darlowsmithson.com

Deeble & Stone Productions
Country: UK
Website: www.deeblestone.com

Mark Deeble and Victoria Stone are Emmy award-winning film-makers, celebrated for their quality, story-driven wildlife films.

Deep Fried Films
Address: P O Box 659, Mossel Bay 6500, SOUTH AFRICA
Phone: +27 44 6903681
Fax: +44 86 7195309
Email: admin@deepfriedfilms.com
Website: www.deepfriedfilms,com
Owner/Admin: Fiona Ayerst – fiona@deepfriedfilms.com
Owner/Strategy: Ryan Johnson – ryan@deepfriedfilms.com

Fiona, originally from Kenya, is a camerawoman specializing in underwater work, especially with sharks, and Ryan is a freelance presenter who has done work for Nat Geo and BBC, inter alia. Ryan, originally a kiwi, is a marine biologist with a PhD and is in demand for documentaries featuring sharks. We live in the beautiful Garden Route area of the Western Cape in RSA and have access to many pristine areas and wild animals. Fiona runs a photography internship program in South Africa and details are available on www.fionaayerst.com We do co-productions and we offer an internship.

Dusty Foot Productions
Address: C-9/9037 Vasant Kunj, New Delhi 110070, INDIA
Phone: +91 11 26121673
Email: dustyfootindia@yahoo.com
Website: www.dustyfootindia.com
Contact: Rita Banerji

Dusty Foot Productions, established in 2002 and based in New Delhi, India, represents a team of young wildlife filmmakers who all share a common vision – of establishing a place recognized for films on wildlife and environment. This commitment comes not only as filmmakers but as individuals who love nature and are concerned about its future.

Earthmedia
Address: Oslo, Norway
Website: www.earthmedia.co.uk
Email: james@earthmedia.co.uk
Director/Cinematographer: James Ewen

Earthmedia is an award winning media production company run by James Ewen. James is a UK native with a wide-ranging experience of high-end documentary production. He turns his lens on many subjects but keeps natural history as the main focus of his work. James has worked in many countries and has extensive experience of filming in Africa.

Earth Native
Address: Los Angeles, USA
Email: tristan@earthnative.com
Website: www.tristanbayer.com
Producer/Director/Cinematographer: Tristan Bayer

Our mission is to find a path that leads towards a sustainable future. Nature guides us and teaches us, we follow and learn. Nature shows us and speaks to us, we watch and listen. If nature is under attack, we must protect and fight back. Lend your hand where others need help. Give your voice for those that can't speak. Listen when others call out. Call out so that others may join in. Share yourself so that others may share back. Be one with yourself. Be one with the Earth.

Echo Film Productions Inc
Address: 407 W Bannock Street, Boise, Idaho 83702, USA
Phone: +1 208 336 0349
Fax: +1 208 336 0858
Email: echofilm@mindspring.com
Website: www.echofilms.com
Producer: Tyler Nelson, Director: Norman Nelson

Echo Film Productions Inc. is a full-service high-definition video and 35mm production house specializing in outdoor recreation, wildlife programming, stock footage, corporate image video, freelance cinematography, commercials and home videos. During the last thirty years our production and cinematic approach to action subjects has won recognition and awards from a diverse group of national and international clients.

Erik Fernström Film & Video AB
Address: SWEDEN
Email: info@wildlifefilm.com
Website: www.wildlifefilm.com

One of the most active and experienced production companies in Scandinavia. We specialize in wildlife and exploring films.

Eten Entertainment
Address: Eten Entertainment.Manas Anand, 1-M-2, Dongripada, G.B Road, Thane, Mumbai, Maharashtra 400607 INDIA
Phone: +91 9833275515 & +91 2225862939
Email: etenentertainment@gmail.com
Producer/Director: Nandan Gaitonde

Production house producing travel show on wildlife in India, conservation and adventure. Inviting proposals to produce films on wildlife, conservation on joint venture. Looking for collaborators, sponsors including co-production. Not offering work experience.

Elkins Eye Visuals
Address: Northern California, USA
Phone: +1 408 266 1270 & +1 707 280 1648
Email: david@elkinseye.com
Website: www.elkinseye.com
Contact: David Elkins – Cinematogapher

David is highly creative and award-winning director of photography and camera operator with a wide range of experience on a variety of documentary, broadcast and commercial productions.

Extreme Wilderness Productions
Address: P.O. Box 3017, Prince George, BC V2N 4T8 CANADA
Email: Info@extremewilderness.ca
Website: www.rmp.ca
Contact: Troy Lorenz

Extreme Wilderness Productions is an outdoor adventure image capturing company, that explores the depths of the vast pristine northern wilderness in search the most beautiful breathtaking views and uniquely rare happenings seldom seen and captured on film in natures untamed wilderness.

EYESEALAND Visual Media
Address: Amsterdam, NETHERLANDS & Auckland, NEW ZEALAND
Phone: +64 9 5513603
Email: info@eyesealand.com
Website: www.eyesealand.com
Pieter Huisman – pieterhuisman@eyesealand.com
Laureline Smith – aurelinesmith@eyesealand.com

We are Pieter Huisman and Laureline Smith, the producing, directing, filming and editing team behind EYESEALAND visual media. We've worked individually and together on projects worldwide, including children's series, feature films, television and wildlife documentaries. It's this experience as professional videographers that we use to our advantage in producing for EYESEALAND visual media. Our passion is storytelling through striking visual images, revealing the details often missed and seen from a different perspective. We appreciate the big and the small in image and content; whether it's a personal story, exciting wildlife, educational material or a business testimonial, we'll aim for outstanding quality and get the message across to the intended audience as effectively as possible.

Feodor Pitcairn Productions
Address: 2860 Papermill Road, P.O. Box 513, Bryn Athyn, PA 19009, USA
Email: info@feodorpitcairnproductions.com
Website: www.feodorpitcairnproductions.com

Films@59
Address: 59 Cotham Hill, Clifton, Bristol BS6 6JR, UK
Phone: +44 (0)117 906 4300   Fax: +44 (0)117 923 7003
Email: info@filmsat59.com
Website: www.filmsat59.com

Films at 59 provides a creative and cost-effective range of pre- and post-production services for film and TV programme makers.

Fleisher Film
Address: USA
Email: staff@fleisherfilm.com
Website: www.fleisherfilm.com
President: Carol Fleisher

Frog Films
Country: Montana, USA & UK
Email: phil@philsavoie.com
Website: www.philsavoie.com
Contact: Phil Savoie – philshoots@gmail.com

Felis Creations
Address: #295 39th 'C' Cross 10th Main 5th Block, Jayanagar, Bangalore 560041, INDIA
Phone: +91 9448059209
Email: kadur.sandesh@gmail.com
Website: www.felis.in
CEO/Creative Director: Sandesh Kadur

Felis Creations is a media and visual arts company based in India that strives to create awareness through the use of visual arts, from paintings and still photography to the production of HD natural history documentaries for broadcast. Currently Felis offers a complete field production solution, able to acquire permits and deliver a completed program. Felis also offers HD stock footage and still images from remote and difficult regions of India. For more information please visit the website at www.felis.in. Every year a few exciting internship opportunities do come up. Interested individuals are requested to submit their CVs by email with links to their work online.

Foster Brothers Productions
Address: SOUTH AFRICA
Email: fosterfilm@iafrica.com
Website: www.senseafrica.com
Development and Research: Trisha Birkett
Producer/Director/Cameraman/Editor: Craig Foster – earthrise@iafrica.com
Producer/Director/Cameraman/Editor: Damon Foster – liquidp@iafrica.com

Brothers Craig and Damon Foster are widely regarded as South Africa's top documentary filmmakers. With nearly two decades of experience shooting and directing, and having received over fifty international awards, the Foster brothers have deservedly carved themselves a niche in global film circles.

Funk Productions
Address: Trabener Str 56, Berlin D14193, GERMANY
Phone: +49 (0)30 91 700 150
Email: daniela@natureheritage.org
Website: www.funkproductions.tv
Director: Daniela Rusowsky

FUNK PRODUCTIONS is a communications and video production company based in Jersey, Channel Islands and Berlin, Germany. We specialize in documentaries and participative videos that link the natural and cultural heritage, to support a sustainable development of human culture and the natural environments. We provide highly professional services with an holistic approach based on our environmental commitment and a vision to build a better future, which has lead to work in partnership with the environmental consultancy Nature Heritage. We have proved track record in filming for conservation and in developing awareness campaigns for the protection of endangered species. Visit our website to check or portfolio: www.funkproductions.tv www.natureheritage.org Contact us to know what we can do for you: info@natureheritage.org Open to co-productions.

Get Wet Productions
Address: 3 Oak Avenue, Noordhoek, Cape Town 7979, SOUTH AFRICA
Phone: +27 82 5641904 & +27 82 450 9399
Fax: +27 86 545 3133
Email: info@getwetproductions.com
Website: www.getwetproductions.com
Morne Hardenberg: morne@getwetproductions.com
Mark van Coller: mark@getwetproductions.com

Get Wet productions is an award-winning productions company specializing in underwater filming. We have worked on productions for BBC Natural world, Discovery, Animal Planet, Nat Geo, 60Minutes, CNN, ABC News and many more. Winner of the 2008 Guild of Television cameramen for sequences in the film *Sharkman – Great White* for Discovery channel. Best known for our work filming white sharks without protection of cages.

Green Renaissance
Address: 5 Roodehek Rd, Gardens, Cape Town 8001, SOUTH AFRICA
Phone: +27 (0)21 2000 415
Email: info@greenrenaissance.co.za
Website: www.greenrenaissance.co.za
Director: Michael Raimondo

Green Renaissance, is a film production company, specializes in helping non-profit organizations and environmentally-conscious businesses develop creative content that promotes green and conservation initiatives. Awards in the last year include 2011 – Best Short film at Wild Talk Film Festival, 2010 South Africa Environmentalist Award. We are always looking for environmental injustice stories (how big corporates are destroying the environment). As well as NGOs who are working with environmentally conscious corporates who are affecting change, we are looking to work with environmentally conscious corporations. From time to time we offer experienced film-makers short intern positions – please email applications. Minimum qualifications would be filmmakers who can film on DSLR cameras as well as editors who can operate Final Cut.

 **GREEN.TV**

Green TV
Address: 120 Long Acre, Covent Garden, London WC2E 9PA, UK
Phone: +44 207 240 0357
Ade Thomas · ade.thomas@green.tv
Website: www.green.tv
Editorial Director: Martin Atkin – martin.atkin@green.tv
Business Development Director: Alex Aleksander
Content and Syndication Director: Fi Ferrer

GREEN.TV is the online TV channel, producer, distributor and syndicator for environmental and sustainability films. We work with a range of non-profit and corporate clients including WWF, Greenpeace, UNEP, Alstom and Vestas to produce and distribute video content through our syndication partners. Together with our sister company Large Blue we offer a complete digital communications service. We're interested in presenter-led online and broadcast series with big potential for sponsorship and branded content – especially in the green tech, clean energy and low-carbon areas. We occasionally offer work experience – apply to one of the email addresses above.

Grey Films
Address: 82 F, Pocket K, Sheikh Sarai Phase II, New Delhi · 110 017, INDIA
Phone: +91 11 2925 70 26
Fax: +91 120 2535 219
Email: info@greyfilms.com
Website: www.greyfilms.com
Cinematographer, Producer & Director: Nalla – nalla@greyfilms.com
Head · Business Development & Operations: Akanksha Sood – akanksha@greyfilms.com
Research: Anvita Adeshra – anvita@greyfilms.com

Grey Films India Private Limited is one of India's leading production houses with specialization in wildlife and environment. We have independently designed productions, crafted cinematographic work and provided over 100 hours of programming content and high quality technical support for broadcast on national and international channels. We also undertake co-productions for documentary and feature films.

Guerrilla Films Uganda
Address: Entebbe, UGANDA
Phone: + 256 (0) 777 693586
Email: simon@guerrillafilms.co.ug
Website: www.guerrillafilms.co.ug
Contact: Simon Wood – simonpwood@hotmail.com

Uganda based production company specializing in HD videography. We shoot broadcast standard XDCAM 4:2:2 @50mbs. We specialize in: stock footage, wildlife documentaries,

23

social documentaries, video production, freelance camera operators, locations managers, local fixer, HD editing, transport. We have our own HD video equipment and edit suites.

Gulo Film Productions
Address: Simrockstraße 111, 22589 Hamburg, GERMANY
Phone: +49 4087082567 & +49 40823036
Fax: +49 408642611
Oliver Goetzl: oliver@gulofilm.com
Ivo Nörenberg: ivo@gmx.com

Wildlife Film Productions worldwide. Specialized on mammal behavior. ARRI Alexa Camera, time lapse Kit, 6m camera crane, borescope, endoscope, time-lapse dolly and X+Y head, HD-finger camera (2/3"), Zeiss macro lens, 3x HD remote cameras (1x Big Sensor), 100m cable car, Weisscam HS-2 MKII (slow motion up to 2.000 FPS in 1080).

Hairy Frog Productions Ltd
Address: 4 The Paddock, White Horse Lane, Trowse, Norwich, Norfolk NR14 8TD, UK
Phone: +44 (0)7885964790
Email: hairyfrog@lineone.net
Website: www.hairy-frog.co.uk
Director/Producer/Cameraman: Mike Linley – mike_linley@yahoo.co.uk

Wildlife production company with full HD kit (BBC specs) + GoPro hero in flat optic housing + video-microscope and endoscopes + Canon 7D time-lapse kit. Over 400 credits mainly as a producer for Survival/Anglia Television. Now also producing Wildlife Interactive Touch-screens. Over forty International awards to date. Specialist in herpetology, entomology and UK wildlife. Large video, sound and stills library. Always happy to co-produce. Limited work experience opportunities, depending on current projects.

Holy Mountain
Address: Unit 243, The Bon Marché Centre, 241-251 Ferndale Road, Brixton, London
SW9 8BJ, UK
Phone: +44 (0)7813 176850 & +44 (0)20 7738 7739
Email: info@holymountain.co.uk
Website: www.holymountain.co.uk
Sound: Alisdair McGregor – al@holymountain.co.uk
Director: Boz Temple-Morris – boz@holymountain.co.uk

We make radio plays that use sound as equal a driving force as dialogue to tell a story
and stimulate the imagination. We supply to BBC radio and are looking to expand this to
the film industry, as a test bed service for companies interested in achieving an audio
demonstration to aid the funding proposals of future film projects. We use experimental
sound creating techniques and music sensibilities to create finely tuned, psychologically
active products, with emotional balance and maturity. We are also looking for unusual
script synopses from writers new to radio to be considered for commission. These ideas
can be in any area of interest but should be leftfield in nature and intention. We are
looking for commissions and co-productions as well as to commission.

Homebrew Films
Address: 46 Orange Street, Gardens, Cape Town, SOUTH AFRICA
Email: info@homebrewfilms.co.za
Website: www.homebrewfilms.co.za
Chief Executive/Senior Producer: Jaco Loubser – jaco@homebrewfilms.co.za

Homebrew Films is a television production house specializing in natural environment,
lifestyle, youth, fashion, entertainment and cooking programmes.

Icon Films
Address: 3rd Floor, College House, 32 - 36 College Green, Bristol BS1 5SP, UK
Phone: + 44 (0)117 910 2030
Fax: + 44 (0)117 910 2031
Email: info@iconfilms.co.uk
Website: www.iconfilms.co.uk
Managing Director: Laura Marshall
Creative Director: Harry Marshall
Director of Production: Andie Clare
Commercial Director: Lucy Middelboe

Icon Films is an award-winning UK production company with a reputation for originality,
excellence, and entertainment across the breadth of factual genres including science,
history, exploration and natural history. We bring together international funders working
with BBC1, BBC2, BBC4, ITV1, ITV4, Channel 4, five, National Geographic Channels,
Discovery Networks and PBS. Our work is internationally distributed by ITV Studios
Global Entertainment, BBC Worldwide and Zodiak Rights. Recent productions include
Sandhurst (3 x 60 BBC4); *Beast Hunter* (5 x 60 National Geographic Channels); inserts for
The One Show (x 60 BBC One); *The Born Free Legacy* (1 x 60 BBC4 / BBCW); *One Million
Snake Bites* (1 x 60 BBC/Animal Planet US/BBCW); *Weird Creatures with Nick Baker* (23 x
50) Animal Planet International/Science/ITVStudios Global Entertainment) and *River
Monsters* (21 x 50 Animal Planet US/ITV Studios Global Entertainment) the highest rating
series in the history of Animal Planet US. Our documentaries have won Emmy, Grierson
and Hugo Awards together with numerous prizes and nominations at many of the leading
film festivals from Banff to Jackson Hole to Wildscreen. Icon Films offers two-week work
experience placements, continually looks for talent and accept CVs by email.

Imageworks
Address: PO Box 23, Northriding 2162, SOUTH AFRICA
Phone: +27(0)110225571 & +27 (0)836342182
Fax: +27 (0)865190670
Email: info@imageworks.co.za
Website: www.imageworks.co.za
Producer/Director: Anthony Irving – anthony@imageworks.co.za

We are producers and facilitators of wildlife and environmental programming across Africa. We have camera kits, edit suites, vehicles and camping equipment available for hire. We are looking for proposals and co-productions. Contact us by email for work experience opportunities.

India Wilds/Sabyasachi Patra
Address: Akarpuri Housing Colony, Near Vaital Temple, Rath Road, Bhubaneswar, Odisha 751002, INDIA
Phone: +91 9840932831 & +91 9980074003
Email: sabyasachi.patra@indiawilds.com
Website: www.indiawilds.com
Cinematographer and Director: Sabyasachi Patra
Production Manager: Mrudul Godbole – mrudul.godbole@gmail.com

We specialise in creating wildlife documentaries highlighting conservation challenges. We are currently documenting the Western Ghats in India and Human-elephant conflict in South India. *A Call in the Rainforest* is an 18 ½ minute film documenting the plight of Lion-tailed Macaques. A film on endangered Grizzled Giant Squirrels is currently in the production stage. We plan to make a film on elephant conflicts and Snow Leopard using an EPIC camera. Our services include camera operator, logistics support, sound recording, music and equipment rental of O'Connor 1030HDs, Hi Hat, Sachtler tripod, Sound Devices etc. We are currently looking for sponsors for our human-elephant conflict project and Snow Leopard project.

In The Light Productions
Address: California, USA
Email: info@inthelightproductions.com
Website: www.inthelightproductions.com
Filmmaker: Sylvie Rokab

Jen Grace Productions
Address: 501 S 15th Ave #3, Bozeman, Montana 59715, US
Phone: +1 406 249 2153
Email: minisuperjennifer@yahoo.com
Website: www.jengrace.com
Contact: Jen Grace

Producer, director, writer, multimedia designer Jen Grace has an MFA in Science and Natural History Filmmaking from MSU. Specializing in conservation, sports and dance film and live production. Clients include the Smithsonian Institution, The Jim Henson Company, Patrick Leonard, 4H and the Montana Ballet Company. Winner IWFF, Jackson Hole, Lunafest, College Television Awards, HATCHfest. Collaborators/sponsors/co-productions all welcome on children's, experimental and conservation subjects. I do not offer work experience/internships.

Jim Karnik Films/Fieldnotes.com
Address: 7142 Avenida Melodia, Encinitas, CA 92024, USA
Phone: +1 760-525-6045
Email: jim@fieldnotes.com
Website: www.fieldnotes.com
Producer: Jim Karnik

Since 1987 I have focused my efforts on helping conservation organizations increase public awareness of California's incredible natural diversity through film and photography. In particular, short web mini-documentaries have proven very effective. Through close collaboration with clients, I strive to create films that inform, motivate and inspire. Services include all aspects of production including: proposal development, scripting, field production, editing, graphic design, DVD authoring, distribution, kiosk/theater presentation system consultation. I am always interested in exploring new project ideas and proposals. Documenting conservation and research field activities as well as capturing the spectacular beauty of wild places is my main interest. I am seeking sponsors for my on-going mini-doc coverage of nature conservation and research efforts in the Pacific Southwest of the USA. I work mainly with conservancies and non-profits. There may be some opportunities for internships.

John Rubin Productions Inc.
Address: USA
Email: info@johnrubin.com
Website: www.johnrubin.com

Jungle Run Productions
Address: Jalan Raya Sanggingan #1. Ubud 80571, Bali Indonesia 80571, INDONESIA
Phone: +62 8123813887 & +62 361979109
Fax: +62 361975378
Email: info@jungle-run.com
Website: www.jungle-run.com
Head Creative Dude/Director/DOP: Joe Yaggi – joe@jungle-run.com
Production Coordinator: Shinta Okta – shinta@jungle-run.com

Jungle Run Productions offers complete production services for Indonesia and SE Asia including: HD crews & kit, location and production management, film permit facilitation, fixers, translators, full post-production and graphics, stock footage. We also have excellent contacts for: aircraft & watercraft, scientists and business leaders, government and NGO sector, search and rescue.
We're keen to collaborate with serious producers and broadcasters to make great factual programs in Indonesia and SE Asia. We've worked throughout the region in some of the most remote regions that Asia serves up. Jungle Run has been operating since 1993 and is fully licensed for television production and distribution in Indonesia.
We often receive applications for internships and we're willing to consider people for these positions. Even better though is seasoned professionals interested in coming over to share their skills and experiences with a very keen and vibrant Indonesian team.

Kathleen Swalling Photography and Film
Address: 483 Route des Nants, Chamonix Mont-Blanc 74400, FRANCE
Phone: +33 637 381 294 (Business) & +971 501 678 018 (Technical)
Email: info@kathleenswalling.com
Website: www.kathleenswalling.com
Producer/Director/Line Production/Location Manager/Fixer: Kathleen Swalling – kathleen@kathleenswalling.com
Technical Director/Fixer: Andrew Chapman – andrew@kathleenswalling.com

Services: Producer, Associate Producer, Line Producer, Location Manager. Wildlife, Marine/Island specialist. Media inspiring awareness and engagement with the natural and cultural world. Experience: *Revolution on the Reef part 1 and 2* (concept development, location manager, line producer, script supervisor, main character), *Lord Howe Island: Paradise at the End of the World* (location manager, line producer, 2nd underwater camera). Unique: capabilities stretch from boardroom to remote fieldwork. Science, Art, Law. Fisheries Prosecutor, Island Manager, Senior Lawyer/Strategist for Great Barrier Reef. Highly experienced diver, former competitive triathlete. Other: filmmaker, photographer, skier, mountaineer, team and individual sports. Board Member: Filmmakers for Conservation. Languages: English (highly proficient) and French (B1- Intermediate). Collaboration on marine/adventure related projects in above roles. Interested in conservation-themed, pure wildlife and adventure films.
Inspiring collaboration or co-production with experienced broadcasters and production companies welcomed. We offer sponsorship partners extensive exposure through our networks in Arabia, Australia, Europe, and additional global exposure through our website. During its first year of operation, receiving up to 500 different individual monthly visitors from across over 50 nations of the world and approximately 40-50,000 hits per month. This is probably due to our strong global networks that have been enhanced by collaborative projects undertaken in Arabia, Australasia, and Europe. We are currently seeking to expand our networks within the United States.
We accept CVs via email to info@kathleenswalling.com. Students in postgraduate studies in natural history filmmaking or those with strong experience in these areas are welcome to apply for placement/internship. We offer work experience placements and internships and are actively seeking to partner with talented camera operators, editors and technicians. Good spoken and written English desirable. At time of print, we are seeking an experienced web sales developer and a potential transmedia partner.

Lemuria TV
Address: Tisá 398, 40336, CZECH REPUBLIC
Phone: +420 602410580
Email: jiri.balek@lemuriatv.cz
Website: www.lemuriatv.cz
Owner/Cameraman/Editor: Jiri Bálek

Small TV studio that produces wildlife films.

Light & Shadow GmbH
Address: Badestraße 19a, 48149 Münster, GERMANY
Email: info@lightandshadow.tv
Website: www.lightandshadow.tv
Director/Cinematographer: Christian Baumeister – christian@lightandshadow.tv

Light & Shadow is a young and accomplished independent film production company known for stunning wildlife photography and unique stories. Headed by internationally-acclaimed director/cinematographer Christian Baumeister, Light & Shadow has shot in countries the world over, with a focus on Latin America. Co-producers include BBC, Discovery Channel, National Geographic Channel, NDR, ZDF, Arte, ORF and others.

Liquid Motion Film
Address: Current Wakatobi archipelago, INDONESIA
Email: production@liquidmotionfilm.com
Website: www.liquidmotionfilm.com
Producer/Cinematographer/Narrator/Co-Owner: Anita Chaumette
Director/Cinematographer/Editor/Co-Owner: Guy Chaumette

LMF is an internationally acclaimed, multi award-winning film production company, Leader in the field of high-end underwater cinematography and producer of choice for the worlds most prestigious TV broadcasters. With the highest honors in cinematography, photography, directing, editing and marine science, Liquid Motion Film has produced tailor-made, custom edited films for personal clients, corporate clients, corporate advertising, tourism, NGOs and global television. Clients & corporate partners include ARTE, RAI, NRK, TVE, National Geographic Television, Scubapro Uwatek UK Ltd, Fiji Islands Hotel & Tourism Association, Bermuda Institute of Ocean Science, Australia's University of Queensland; TV Productions include the critically acclaimed, Triple-Gold, winning *Reef* Series, landmark multi award-winning films *Jawfish Nursery*, *Colour Talks*, *Beyond The Blue* and *Fisheye Fantasea*, *The Perfect Reef*, *The Circle of Life* and *Talking With Fishes* and the Grand Prix de Monaco, & National Geographic Television exclusive, *Water Colours* Series. We are open to co-production and commissioning ideas, as well as corporate and private films.

Living Planet Productions/The Brock Initiative
Address: Dumpers Cottage, Chew Magna, Bristol, BS40 8SS, UK
Phone: +44 (0)1275 333187 +44 (0)7968 365816
Fax: +44 (0)1761 221702
Email: livingplanetproductions@gmail.com & info@brockinitiative.org
Website: www.brockinitiative.org

29

Executive Producer: Richard Brock

I try to get stuff out there that will make a difference. There are now more ways of doing that than ever before. It can be in any format, anywhere, anyhow. I will provide free footage on wildlife and environmental matters from around the world. I am always interested in issues where "Filming with Attitude" might help the planet. Just let me know.

Lost World Films Ltd
Address: Plymouth, UK & San Francisco, USA
Email: andy@lostworldfilms.com
Website: www.lostworldfilms.com
DOP: Andy Shillabeer

LunaSea Films
Address: Maine, USA
Email: hdcamera@me.com & lunaseafilms@me.com
Website: www.lunaseafilms.com
Cinematographer/Director: David Wright
Producer: MiMi McGee

MadRat Productions
Address: 2517 Leoti Dr, Colorado Springs, CO 80907, USA
Phone: +1 719 200 2590
Email: cavingincolorado@yahoo.com
Website: www.cavingincolorado.tv
Owner: Floyd Fernandez

MadRat Productions is a video capturing service and production service company. Dealing with 'cave location shooting', as well as other extreme environment, We specialize in video capturing including but not limited to underwater, ice caves, dust filed, high altitude environments. I graduated from Rocky Mountain College of Art and Design with a Bachelors in Fine Art. I spent six years creating and video taping Installation Art. Installation Art is the reconstruction of an interior space. I've spent four years creating internet video on the activities of the Nation Speleological Society, and activities of its local grotto, the Southern Colorado Mountain Grotto. These activities have ranged from dust-filled rooms, to water soaked passageways, to overnight excursions underground. This helped me gain the knowledge and experience to handle extreme weather situations. I have now turned professional for two years. My projects include making organization DVDs for the Williams Canyon Project, Restoration Church in Fountain, and The Abundant Harvest community Garden Project. I also created the Glenwood Springs hosting Video for the 2011 convention for the National Speleological Society.
Equipment: HDR-FX1 Sony Camera, CamRade DS-HDR Z1 Desertsuit for the HDR-FX1, CowboyStudioShoulder SupportPad for VideoCamcorder, CameraDV/DC, Lastolite Professional EzyBalance Grey/White card 20", Sony MDR-7502 headphones, Zoom H2 Portable Recorder, Audio Technica Shotgun Microphone, Sunpak Platinum plus mono pod, Sony VCT-870RM Tripod, Nite Rider Moab Light, Sima SL-20LX universal LED On Camera light, Dell Studio 1555 Laptop, Adobe Master CS3.

Marca D'agua Produções
Address: Rua Min Americo Marco Antonio, 278 - São Paulo 05442-040, BRAZIL
Phone: +55 11 9451 0098 & +55 11 3675 8954 Fax: +55 11 3675 8954
Email: marca.dagua@uol.com.br
Director: Tulio Schargel – tuliodoc@gmail.com

By observing the interactions within marine life, I fell in love with nature. Now, after more than twenty years shooting life underwater, I can say I am a fulfilled biologist. I got out of the water with my camera when I started to direct and photograph adventure documentaries in 1997, always connected to nature. Between 2004 and 2011 I co-produced twelve nature documentaries with Brazilian and international production companies and broadcasters – CBC, Arte, NatGeo, SBS, etc. If it is good idea, related to Brazil I could be interested in a co-production for 2013/2014. I'm looking for a commissioning broadcaster, pre-buy or a co-producer partner for a new film on Jaguars, being produced in 2011/12/13.

Marco Polo Films
Address: GERMANY
Email: office@marco-polo-film.de
Website: www.marco-polo-film.de
Contacts: Annette Scheurich CEO & Klaus Scheurich CEO

Mavela Media
Address: SOUTH AFRICA
Email: wildhoot@mweb.co.za
Website: www.wildcast.net
Producer/Cameraman: Kim Wolhuter

Melting Penguin
Address: 32 Rudgleigh Rd, Pill, Bristol BS20 0DS, UK
Phone: +44 (0)7973 293339
Email: jon@meltingpenguin.com
Website: www.meltingpenguin.com
Director: Jonathan Clay

Melting Penguin is the company of filmmaker and photographer Jonathan Clay, a freelance producer, director and cameraman specialising in natural history, environmental and adventure documentaries for television.

Michael Dillon Film Enterprises
Address: 91 Barker Rd, Strathfield, NSW 2135, AUSTRALIA
Phone: +61 297469554 & +61 419249582
Email: mcdillon@ozemail.com.au
Website: www.michaeldillonfilms.com.au
Cameraman/Producer/Director: Michael Dillon

Specialise in adventure and wildlife documentaries. Many Australian Cinematography awards, plus Emmy nominations for Survivor and National Geographic Special *Those Wonderful Dogs*. For full CV see website. Cameras include Aaton XTR Prod plus various HD video cameras and lenses ranging from wide to 800mm plus macro probe and snorkel lenses. Looking for any projects that involve adventure, wildlife, conservation. Mostly enter into International Adventure Film Festivals. Accept CVs by email for work experience placements.

Mountainside Films Ltd.
Address: PO Box 2781, Sidney, British Columbia V8L 5Y9, CANADA
Phone: +1-250-217-7573
Main Email: mountainsidefilms@gmail.com
Suzanne: suzanne@mountainsidefilms.com
Michael: michael@mountainsidefilms.com
Website: www.mountainsidefilms.com
Suzanne Chisholm, Director, Producer, Camera
Michael Parfit, Director, Writer, Editor, Camera

31

David Parfit, Music, Sound, Technical Supervisor

Mountainside Films Ltd. is an independent documentary film production company based near Sidney, British Columbia, Canada. Its principals are Michael Parfit and Suzanne Chisholm. We specialize in stories of the relationships between humans and our natural world. We are committed to accuracy, honesty, clarity, visual impact and compelling storytelling. We manage all aspects of film production, including research, development, shooting, sound recording, writing, editing, and music composition. We shoot and deliver in high definition. Our work has taken us to all seven continents. We are comfortable working on the ice floes of the high Arctic, on the plains of Africa, in the cloud forests of the Andes, and in our own ocean backyard on the rugged west coast of Canada. We often travel to remote locations in a single-engine plane, piloted by Michael. Our award-winning work has been shown in theatres across Canada, in IMAX theatres worldwide, on PBS, BBC, CNN, CBC, National Geographic Channel, France 2, Al-Jazeera, and NHK, and in film festivals in more than twenty countries. We have been honoured with awards from prestigious festivals and organizations around the globe. We are not currently looking for film ideas or proposals, as we do most of our development and production in-house. At this time we are not offering work opportunities.

Mowgli Productions
Address: L-34A 3rd Floor, Malviya Nagar, New Delhi 110017, INDIA
Phone: +91 9818734947
Email: md@mowgliproductions.com
Website: www.mowgliproductions.com
Managing Director: Amber Sharma

Mowgli Productions, a part of Mowgli Productions Pvt Ltd is Indian motion picture production wildlife and nature documentary production and distribution company. The company was founded by Amber Sharma after his nickname Mowgli and based out of New Delhi. Mowgli Productions provides camera equipments, crew and other production related services at very nominal cost. Help other countries' productions houses to shoot film, documentary or TV shows at Indian sub-continent. We consider co-productions and are looking for collaborators/sponsors.

Natural History Media
Address: Sandton, Johannesburg, SOUTH AFRICA
Phone: +27 827803840 +27 768409454
Email: contact@naturalhistorymedia.com
Website: www.naturalhistorymedia.com
Writer/Producer/Director: Vanessa Lucas – v.lucas@naturalhistorymedia.com
Cameraman/Zoologist: Nick Ball – n.ball@naturalhistorymedia.com

Natural History Media specialises in wildlife, conservation and environmental documentary filmmaking and photography. In addition, we produce regular short ENG segments for international news agencies on environmental, conservation and wildlife current affairs throughout Africa and worldwide. With backgrounds in zoology and eco-tourism we can provide expertise and access to a variety of unique locations and offer professional location management services, facilitating shoots before, during and after filming. Natural History Media has a large HD stock library, with a broad range of footage and photography from around Africa and the UK. We have full HD broadcast cameras, audio and accessories. We are always interested in hearing new ideas and stories and are always happy to provide our expertise and contacts to develop ideas in the wildlife, conservation, adventure and cultural genres. We would be looking for collaborators and sponsors and always consider co-productions. We would consider work experience and internship applicants, but not actively looking. Please send CVs by email.

Naturbilder
Address: Rypekroken 24, 3420 Lierskogen, NORWAY
Email: post@naturbilder.no
Website: www.naturbilder.no
Executive Producer: Arne Naevra – arne@naturbilder.no

Naturbilder is a Norwegian production company specializing in wildlife documentaries for TV. The majority of the programmes have been produced for NRK-1 in Oslo, and other public service TV channels in Scandinavia.

NaturaHD
Address: Atenas, 41- Alicante 03009, SPAIN
Phone: + 34 696791657 & +34 965172204
Email: info@naturahd.com
Website: www.naturahd.com
Director/Cameraman/Editor: Alberto Saiz
Director/Camera: Nacho Ruiz Rizaldos
Production manager: María Fernández
Production manager (Kenya): Jorge Alesanco

Independent film production company. Based in Europe (Spain) and Kenya (Masai Mara). We specialize in natural history films and documentaries. Our aim is to share a personal vision of the natural world and promote its conservation. Always looking for touching stories about natural history, environmental conservation, science and human interest.

NHNZ
Natural History New Zealand
Address: Box 474, 5 Melville St, Dunedin 9016, NEW ZEALAND
Phone: +64 (0)3 479 9799
Fax: +64 (0)3 479 9917
Email: info@nhnz.tv
Website: www.nhnz.tv
Head of Production: Andrew Waterworth
EVP Development and Marketing: Neil Harraway
EVP US Development and Production: Phil Fairclouph – pfairclough@nhnz.tv

NHNZ makes ground-breaking factual television about people, nature, adventure, history and science for National Geographic Channels, Discovery Channels including Animal Planet, A&E, NHK and numerous other international broadcasters. A world-leader in high volume 3D documentary production and the leading foreign producer of factual programming out of China, NHNZ is focused on innovation and revelation in producing unforgettable television.

Natural Perspectives
Address: RSD 414A, Finniss SA 5255, AUSTRALIA
Phone: +61 8 8536 0145 & +427 000 109
Email: nicholas@naturalperspectives.com.au
Website: www.naturalperspectives.com.au
Main Contact: Nicholas Crouch

Natural Perspectives is a small yet vibrant production company based in Adelaide, Australia, that specialises in natural history documentaries and other environmental multimedia. Coming from a background in ecological science and community education, we have a deep interest in environmental issues and our strong conservation ethic underpins our productions, in which we strive to minimise the footprint of our activities. We have expertise in all aspects of the production process, from concept to distribution, and will work closely with you to achieve your vision, no matter what the project.

Nature Conservation Films
Address: Torenlaan 1c, 1251 HE Laren (close to Hilversum), NETHERLANDS
Email: mail@ncf-nl.com
Website: www.ncf-nl.com
President: Evert van den Bos – evert@ncf-nl.com

Nature Conservation Films (NCF) is a nature film production company with offices in Laren, The Netherlands. NCF is among the front-runner in this field. Over the last twenty years, NCF has produced more than 100 programmes. Contact Evert van den Bos by email if you want to apply for a job.

Nature On Screen
Address: West Midlands, UK
Email: WildlifeFilmerAdam@live.co.uk
Website: www.NatureonScreen.webs.com
Wildlife Filmer Adam (Adam L Canning)

'Wildlife Filmer Adam' is a film-maker who directs, produces, presents, films & edits. Up for any kind of natural history documentary film. Have made documentaries for Reader's Digest in the form of a web-series called *Wildlife Monthly*. Experience: directing, producing, presenting, camerawork and editing, plus will happily assist with any of those roles. Keen to learn and experience new things. Would love to be sponsored and happy to do co-productions. Anyone who would like to write scripts for *Wildlife Monthly* are very welcome and anyone wanting their footage or pictures featured are welcome too.

nautilusfilm GmnH - Natural History Germany
Address: Postfach 1314, Dorfen 84403, GERMANY
Phone: +49 (0)8081·959 661
Email: info@nautilusfilm.com
Website: www.nautilusfilm.com
Director/Camera: Jan Haft
Production Management: Melanie Haft

nautilusfilm GmbH-Natural History Germany develops and produces blue-chip natural history and wildlife films.

NHU Africa
Address: Block A, Longkloof Studios, 21 Darters Rd., Gardens, Cape Town 8001, SOUTH AFRICA
Phone: +27 (0)21 422 0154
Fax: +27 (0)21 422 0012
Email: info@nhuafrica.com
Website: www.nhuafrica.com
Head of Production: Geta Palm – geta@nhuafrica.com
Production Manager: Shani van Straaten – shani@nhuafrica.com

Natural History Unit Africa (NHU Africa) commissions, co-produces and distributes wildlife and natural history documentaries and works with both international and local broadcasters. NHU Africa accepts proposals all year round. Please download our commissioning brief from our website. NHU Africa occasionally has positions available for production assistants and interns, please sign up with our newsletter for notifications of availabilities. We receive CVs via email, please direct your CVs to shani@nhuafrica.com

Nutshell Productions
Address: 3 Westfield Cottages, Medmenham, Marlow, Buckinghamshire SL7 2HQ, UK
Phone: +44 (0)1491 575 017
Email: madelaine@nutshellproductions.co.uk
Website: www.nutshellproductions.co.uk
Producer: Madelaine Westwood

Nutshell Productions produces wildlife and conservation films for international broadcasters and conservation charities. Recent productions are 3 x 1 hour series *Invisible Photographer* for Europe through Cello Media and *Red Kite Runner* for RSPB UK.

Based in the UK, we work with talented creative teams across the world. Nutshell Productions creates and hosts conservation film and production training courses for a range of clients including newcomers to the film industry and non-governmental organisations in the field. Nutshell Productions is always interested to receive well-researched conservation, sustainable development or associated proposals from charities, experts, and informed individuals. Nutshell Productions is open to co-production partners and currently works with a number of companies in Europe. If interested in work experience, send CVs by email.

Objetivo Verde S.L.
Address: C/ortega y gasset Nº 4, Seville 10600, SPAIN
Phone: +34 687433413
Email: info@objetivoverde.es
Website: www.objetivoverde.es
Contact: Jose Luis Calvo

Professional Wildlife Finders Extremadura. We are dedicated to photography and filming of nature, with more than fifteen years in the industry. We have a file in HDV format – hundreds of hours and thousands of photographs. Basically these files are about the animal life in the Iberian Peninsula. Birds, mammals, reptiles and plants, they have been the main focus of our goal, not neglecting the diverse landscapes of Extremadura and national geography.

Off The Fence
Head Office Address: Herengracht 105-107, 1015 BE Amsterdam, NETHERLANDS
Email: info@offthefence.com
Website: www.offthefence.com
CEO: Ellen Windemuth – Ellen@offthefence.com

OTF Productions
Address: 20 Elmdale Road, Tyndalls Park, Bristol BS8 1SG, UK
Email: info@offthefence.com   Website: www.offthefence.com
MD: Allison Bean – Allison@offthefence.com

OTF South Africa
Address: Unit 5a, Media Hive, 1 Glynville Terrace, Cape Town 8005, SOUTH AFRICA
Email: info@offthefencesa.com
Business Manager: Sherene Kingma – Sherene@offthefence.com

OTF Germany
Poststraße 37, 55126 Mainz, GERMANY
Executive Producer: Ralf Blasius – Ralf@offthefence.com

OTF Singapore
Address: 27C Tanjong Pagar Road, 088450 SINGAPORE
Managing Director: Tony Chow – Tony@offthefence.com

OFT New York
Address: 135 West 29th Street, Suite 1101, New York, NY 10001, USA
Senior Vice President: Adam Block – Adam.Block@offthefence.com

Established in 1994, Off the Fence is an independent television distribution and production company, specialising in nonfiction programming for the international marketplace. The company is based in Amsterdam, and has further offices in New York, Bristol, Singapore, Cape Town and Mainz.

One Tribe TV
Address: Fairview, Charlcombe Lane, Bath BA1 5TT, UK
Email: info@onetribetv.co.uk
Website: www.onetribetv.co.uk
Managing Director: Dale Templar
Researcher: Nicola Brown
CV Submissions: crew@onetribetv.co.uk (In the subject field please mark 'CV: Your Name – Your Job Title' e.g. 'CV: Martin Scorsese – Producer/Director'.)

Series Producer from the BAFTA award-winning BBC landmark series *Human Planet* now heads up her own independent production company One Tribe TV. Based in Bath and Bristol, One Tribe TV specialise in foreign and remote filming, producing natural history, travel, expedition, anthropology and science content. The company also provides media training, corporate video production, media consultancy, guest lecturing and professional speaking. Our clients include the BBC Academy, Royal Geographical Society and Cunard.
One Tribe TV are always on the look out for exciting ideas and proposals with engaging stories, compelling context and new concepts. Our content focuses on wildlife, science, adventure, and human-interest stories whether they're presenter-led formats or traditional documentary. In addition to film and television content, we have started a corporate production and media training arm. We are always looking to collaborate with other production companies that have strong, engaging and compelling ideas both internationally and within the UK. We are currently working on television projects with the BBC, Dragonfly, RGS, BFI and Adventure Lifesigns.

Oxford Scientific Films Limited (OSF)
Address: 2nd Floor, 21-22 Warwick Street, London, W1B 5NE, UK
Phone: +44 (0)20 3551 4600
Fax: +44 (0)20 3551 4601
Email: info@oxfordscientificfilms.tv
Website: www.oxfordscientificfilms.tv
Chief Executive: Clare Birks – cbirks@oxfordscientificfilms.tv
Executive Producer: Alice Keens-Soper – aliceks@oxfordscientificfilms.tv
Executive Producer: Caroline Hawkins – chawkins@oxfordscientificfilms.tv

Oxford Scientific Films is a BAFTA and Emmy-award-winning producer of contemporary factual, natural history, science and history. We are known for outstanding and innovative programmes that rate. We have a passion for storytelling and we are proud of the company's heritage as a technological pioneer. We offer Work Experience Placements. These placements are unpaid and last for a maximum of two weeks. Preference is given to graduates with degrees in history, science and zoology. A passion for factual television is a given. Please send your CVs to info@oxfordscientificfilms.tv

Parthenon Entertainment
Address: Station Approach, Chorleywood, Herts, WD3 5PF, UK
Phone: +44 (0)1923 286886
Email: info@parthenonentertainment.com
Website: www.parthenonentertainment.com
Director of Production: Danny Tipping
Head of Production, Bristol office: Alison Bradburn

Parthenon Entertainment Limited is a multi-media rights management company, which develops, produces and distributes a diverse portfolio of high quality factual and children's properties for the global marketplace.
Founded in 2002 by Carl Hall, former managing director of HIT Wildlife, Parthenon is ranked amongst the top independent UK producers and distributors and has built a reputation for delivering high rating series and specials for clients around the world. With operations in Europe and North America, Parthenon's international reach provides a presence across all key territories for the exploitation of its content and a platform for continued growth and development. We are always looking for proposals: Blue-chip natural history, wildlife and presenter-led series. We do consider co-productions and we are looking for collaborators. Work experience offered to those with relevant industry experience. Send CVs by email.

Pasternak Media LLC
Address: 3323 Laurel Court, Falls Church, VA 22042, USA
Phone: +1 703 992 0449 &: +1 703 216 1746
Email: kathryn.pasternak@gmail.com
Website: www.pasternakmedia.com
Executive Producer/Writer/Producer: Kathryn Pasternak

Pasternak Media LLC specializes in supervision of wildlife and conservation films for broadcast television. We work for, and directly with, producers of wildlife programming. We will help you develop and pitch your concept, and supervise it through completion. Focus is telling the best possible story. Acting as an outside voice, we give the broadcaster confidence that your film will meet their needs, and at the same time, help make sure your original vision doesn't get lost in the process. Kathryn Pasternak has won two National Emmy Awards and has been nominated for two more, including most recently for *Swamp Troop* which was the product of first time, African-based producers.

She has a twenty-year track record supervising projects for National Geographic Television, NGC, Animal Planet, and Smithsonian Networks. Looking for presenter-led, pure wildlife, and conservation-themed stories. Can consult on co-productions.

Pelagic Productions Ltd
Address: NEW ZEALAND
Email: steve@pelagicproductions.com
Underwater Camera operator: Steve Hudson

Plane Viewing Ltd
Address: 39 The Vineries, Burgess Hill, West Sussex, RH15 0ND, UK
Phone: +44 (0)1444 870894
Email: bryangrayson@ymail.com
Director/Cameraman: Bryan Grayson – bryangrayson@ymail.com
Cameraman/Editor: Nigel Jefferies – njefferies52@gmail.com

Wildlife filmmaker and cameraman. Credits from Animal planet *Shark Night* and the only UK selected contestant for the Animal Planet 2006 *Unearthed* series. Able to offer cameraman and editing service using Final Cut Pro. Looking for presenters in local area and storytellers

PolarArt Productions
Address: Barter Island, Arctic Ocean, Boc 96, Kaktovik, Alaska 99747, USA
Email: info@polarartproductions.com
Website: www.polarartproductions.com
Contact: Jennifer and Arthur C. Smith III

"Embedded" in the wilds of north Alaska, PolarArt Productions is on-location 24/7. Based on an island in the Arctic, we produce the freshest natural history and documentary content available for broadcast, commercial, interpretive, and theatrical markets. Our RED ONE camera is on the front line of digital cinema. Four times the resolution of high-definition. Slow motion up to 120 frames per second. Ever vivid second captured in 4:4:4 RAW. The Arctic has never looked better.

Popular Pictures
Address: C/Tallers 77, Barcelona 08001, SPAIN
Phone: +34 644263856
Email: info@popular-pictures.com
Website: www.popular-pictures.com
Cameraman/Producer: Matthias Popp

Bilingual camera crews in Spain. We are reliable production partner for international broadcasters and AV productions in Spain. Well-trained professionals, bilingual crews and top of the range professional equipment are some of our (many) strengths.

Pro Natura Documental
Address: Humaitá 7059 (C1408EGJ) Capital Federal, ARGENTINA
Phone: +54 1115 5150 9742
Email: info@pronaturadocumental.com
Website: www.pronaturadocumental.com

Throughout a broad experience, PRO NATURA DOCUMENTAL, created in 1983 by Ricardo Cobas and Daniel Sánchez, and directed nowadays by the latter, has specialised in issues related to natural sciences and the Man in Argentina. Nature, history, anthropology, and geography are dealt with in detail, especially in the region known as PATAGONIA, supplying all the information that comes from the most prestigious Institutions in the country.

R.E.M Films
Address: 100 Huguenot Ave, Apt 6A, Englewood, NJ 07631, US
Phone: +1 1 508-237-4830
Website: www.vimeo.com/user1319269
Email: envirodiver@yahoo.com
Owner: Rick Morris

I am a nature and marine science director/producer, cameraman and editor. I focus on underwater films but shoot all nature and wildlife as well as news and studio work. Won several film festivals with my work on the Census of Marine Life and now work as a studio cameraman in NYC on *Countdown with Keit Olbermann*. I have several series ideas and don't need more ideas to develop just films to work on and funding. My festival categories are nature and wildlife, science, exploration, sustainability and oceans. I only look for experienced filmmakers and have no internships. Seldom look at resumes.

The Really Interesting Picture Company
Address: USA
Email: Tom.Veltre@TheReallyInterestingPictureCompany.com
Website: www.thereallyinterestingpicturecompany.com
Contact: Thomas Veltre

Richmond Productions, Inc.
Address: 216 Valhalla Drive, Solvang, CA 93463, USA
Phone: +11 1 805-688-2718
Email: video@richmondproductions.com
Website: www.richmondproductions.com
Producer: Earl Richmond

Wildlife video production company specializing in scientifically based marine education and conservation programs. 19 Telly Awards, Monterrey Blue Ocean Film Festival Finalist. Large library of marine mammal stock footage. natural history and research library of blue whale footage. Credits include: National Geographic, BBC, PBS, Animal Planet. Currently in production of PBS series on persons compassionate about the oceans and their life's work. Currently seeking program sponsors for PBS series. Marine education and conservation, documentaries and shorts.

Riverbank Studios Pvt. Ltd.
Address: C-18, Chirag Enclave, New Delhi 110048, INDIA
Phone: +91 11 26216508 & +91 11 26410684
Email: info@riverbankstudios.com
Production Head: Doel Trivedy · doel@riverbankstudios.com
Website: www.riverbankstudios.com
Director: Mike Pandey – mike@riverbankstudios.com
Director: Gautam Pandey – gautam@riverbankstudios.com

Riverbank Studios was set up in 1973 by internationally recognized filmmaker Mike H Pandey. Based in New Delhi with over thirty-five years of experience in filmmaking, the studio is a wholly integrated set up equipped to handle the entire film pipeline from pre-production, production to post production including animation and VFX. Our productions are diverse; wildlife and environment, corporate and advertisement films, feature films, entertainment series for television, children,s programming, animation and public awareness campaigns. Shooting all over India we have developed a tremendous bank of footage and stories that represent various facets of the country's incredible natural and social heritage. Some of our other services are: HD production and post-production facilities; rentals, production and line production for International crews; stock footage; animation and VFX.
We do co-productions and are looking to collaborate on environmental/conservation films. We offer work experience placements/internships and accept CVs by email. Minimum qualification should be either education in filmmaking or work experience in filmmaking.

 a million
voices for
nature

The Royal Society for the Protection of Birds
Address: The Lodge, Sandy, Bedfordshire SG19 2DL, UK
Phone: +44 (0)1767 680 551
Fax: +44 (0)1767 683 262
Email: filmunit@rspb.org.uk
Website: www.rspb.org.uk
Head of RSPB Film Unit: Mark Percival
Assistant Producer: Robin Hill
Cameraperson: Toby Hough

The Royal Society for the Protection of Birds is a conservation organisation with over one million members. Producers of wildlife films since 1953, the RSPB Film Unit continues to create blue-chip wildlife and conservation programming today for event presentation, broadcast, DVD sales, online distribution and clips sales. Our aim is to showcase the RSPB's most important conservation work and to capture the spectacle of the natural world with award-winning clarity- achieved by a commitment to the principles of ethical wildlife filmmaking.

Credits include: *Eagle Odyssey* (ten awards incl. Wildscreen and Jackson Hole) *Waterlands* (nine awards incl. Japan Wildlife Film Festival)

The RSPB Film Unit is open to developing co-productions on the themes of saving nature, stopping species extinction, stopping climate change, and landscape restoration/re-creation. We periodically offer production internships (6-12 months) usually as camera or field assistant. For more information please contact via email.

Saint Thomas Productions
Address: FRANCE
Email: prod@saint-thomas.net
Website: www.saint-thomas.net

Scorpion TV
Address: 38 Thornaby House, Canrobert St. London E2 0BE, UK
Phone: +44 (0)7804077624
Email: office@scorpiontv.com
Website: www.scorpiontv.com
Sales Executive/Camera Operator/Editor: Juan Solera – juanantonio.solera@gmail.com

We are a distribution company based in UK over ten years and distributing documentaries internationally. We have BBC, Channel 4 and other winning awards documentaries. Also, we would love to co-produce in wildlife projects. We are already in touch with some producers looking for film ideas. We would love to make adventure, human interest and current affairs documentaries, as they are the main subject in the titles that we distribute. We are looking for collaborators and we definitely consider co-productions as we say above. We accept CVs by post for work experience and/or internships.

Screaming Reels Productions
Address: P.O. Box 63 682, Nairobi 00620, KENYA
Phone: +254 733 731 332 & +254 722 566 061
Website: www.screamingreelsproductions.com
Director, Camera: Ross Samuels – ross@screamingreelproductions.com
Director, Editor: Nathalie Samuels – nathalie@swiftkenya.com

We produce high quality videos up to full HD, 422. We are looking for sponsorship and broadcast opportunities for our project called *The Wildlife Sentinels*. We'd be interested to compete for filmforward We are looking for collaborators and sponsors and we do accept CVs by email.

Scubazoo Images Sdn Bhd
Address: P.O. Box 15475, 88864 Kota Kinabalu, Sabah, MALAYSIA
Phone: +6 088 232068 & +6 019 861 8610
Fax: +6 088 237068
Email: info@scubazoo.com
Website: www.scubazoo.com
Founder/CEO: Simon Christopher – simon@scubazoo.com
Co-Founder/Managing Director: Jason Isley – jason@scubazoo.com

Scubazoo is an independent production company that prides itself on providing quality footage, as well as solutions to your crewing and location management needs. We specialize in filming natural history programs and are renowned for our underwater cinematography and photography. We also have an extensive library of stills and high definition video footage of iconic underwater marine life such as sharks, turtles, rays and whales shot in locations around the world with a large selection being sourced on the rich reefs of South East Asia's Coral Triangle. Scubazoo is based in Kota Kinabalu, Sabah, Malaysian Borneo, and we have over fourteen years production experience in Borneo and beyond. Whether you are a corporate body, an NGO, or a broadcast production company, Scubazoo is ideally placed to handle your filming and production requirements.
We offer work experience as a stock library intern: Scubazoo are looking for young, motivated individuals to join our stock footage and photography team in Kota Kinabalu. Applicants should be: * College student or recent college graduate * Students of biological sciences or interested in marine life
Details of the position: * Full time (40 hours/week) * Unpaid * Duration of 12 weeks * Intern responsible for travel expenses * Preference will be given to Malaysian candidates.
The position is unpaid. Interns will work under our stock footage and stock photo library managers, gaining experience in skills such as keywording, CMS, basic photoshop, Final Cut Pro editing and more. This is a great opportunity to learn real world skills and work as part of a team in a dynamic business environment. Applicants should send a cover letter and CV to info@scubazoo.com or roger@scubazoo.com

SHAKE THE TREE
P R O D U C T I O N S

Shake The Tree Productions
Address: Hall Farm House, Rectory Road, Suffield, Norfolk NR11 7EW, UK
Phone: +44 (0)1263768203
Email: carolinebrett@mac.com
Website: www.shakethetree.co.uk
Company Director: Caroline Brett
Company Secretary: Alan Miller

Caroline Brett (BSc Hons/Zoology, Bristol Uni.) is a highly experienced and award-winning producer/director/writer. She worked for twenty-one years for the prestigious Survival series including in Arctic Canada, in the rain forests of Sierra Leone and on a remote Vietnamese island. She also produced the highly successful *Predators with Gaby Roslin* and *Wild about Essex with Tony Robinson*. Caroline has recently made films on black caiman in Brazil, the history of the pearl trade in Bahrain, street children in India and ponies in Scotland, the later two she also filmed. She has photographs at the Specialist Stock Library, has numerous articles and seven books published and while working for Save Our Seas, the foundation won many wildlife film festival awards including Jackson Hole and Wildscreen. I consider film proposals mainly on wildlife, animals and conservation for DVD, internet, TV and cinema. I consider co-productions.

Signature Infotainment Pvt. Ltd.
Address: 498, DDA, Pocket 2, Sector 9, Dwarka, New Delhi 110075, India
Phone: +91 11 2507 4996 & +91 98 18902101 Fax: +91 11 2507 4996
Email: Director – Praveen Singh: praveen@signatureinfotainment.com
Business Development – Akanksha Sood: akanksha@signatureinfotainment.com
Producer/Director and Cameraperson: Praveen Singh

We specialize in HD production of wildlife, conservation, environment and social documentaries. Have made films for National Geographic, Discovery, NHK, NDR Germany, etc. Awards and nominations include 'Student Emmy', IWFF, Missoula,Vatavaran (Indian Wildlife Film Festival), Explorer's Club, Asian Festival of First Film. Offer production services and co-production.
We do undertake and develop ideas/proposals with filmmakers for production for international broadcasters. Festival categories – wildlife, environment and conservation documentaries, human-wildlife conflict. We seek collaborators, co-production partners.
We accept CVs by email and offer internships that are volunteers or low paid depending on projects. Minimum qualifications is undergraduate but must have knowledge and be passionate about the natural world, conservation.

SlothouwerFilms: For Nature Conservation
Address: Amsterdam, NETHERLANDS
Email: info@slothouwerfilms.com
Website: www.slothouwerfilms.com

SlothouwerFilms is specialized in producing films that improve commitment to nature conservation programmes. The use of small, high quality cameras and mobile editing equipment makes SlothouwerFilms a flexible film company. For maximal output, SlothouwerFilms works in a close cooperation with conservation organisations in which SlothouwerFilms is responsible for the scenario, camera and editing. So far Indonesia has been the main work area, but that does not mean other countries are excluded. Normally, on site, a film team consists of two people. Occasionally a third person is required for sound or editing on location. SlothouwerFilms makes it possible to implement film as an effective communication strategy, for a reasonable price. Contents, location and duration determine the costs to produce a film.

Spier Films
Address: 3rd Floor, Union Building, 25 Commercial St. Cape Town 8000, SOUTH AFRICA
42 Vicarage Crescent, Battersea, London SW11 3LD, UK
Phone: +27214610925 (SA) & +442085224296 (UK)
Email: mike@spierfilms.com
Website: www.spierfilms.com
MD: Michael Auret
Producer/Sales: Heather Millard – heather@spierfilms.com
Producer/Sales: Amy Nelson

Production, financing and sales company with offices in Cape Town, Reykjavik and London. We are looking to work with directors with great stories to tell for an international audience but also with producers who are developing either one-off docs or series and would like us to work with them to raise finance and to make sales and pre-sales. We are looking for all types of film ideas and finished films. We prefer stories with some human interest or stories that are conservation related which we can campaign around, but the bottom line is entertaining television and that is what we are looking for. Whether fast-paced, presenter-led or slow moving wildlife we can help to raise finance and to sell the finished product. We are open to co-productions and we attend most festivals and markets including IDFA, Hot Docs, Mipcom, MipTV and some of the factual congresses. We are always looking for collaborators and sponsors. We have a small operation but could offer work experience for graduates and CVs can be emailed to us.

Stormwater Productions
Address: Sydney, AUSTRALIA
Email: info@stormwaterproductions.com
Website: www.stormwaterproductions.com
Director/Producer/Camera: Marie Davies

Studio Ray Productions
Address: 3101 West Place, Sarasota, Florida 34234, USA
Phone: 011-1-941-228-7288
Email: earthcare@aol.com
Website: www.studiorayproductions.com
Producer: Darryl Saffer

We produce nature-related documentaries completely in-house. Our current projects include a series on wild orchids (www.wildorchidman.com) and a look at the faith-based responsibilities of stewardship. We shoot, edit, and create the graphics and music. We

can only consider funded projects that incorporate a conservation-based theme.
We are always willing to consider sponsors and co-productions. We do work under the fiscal sponsorship of two not-for-profit organizations in the USA. We do not have any openings for interns at this time.

Swellendam TV
Address: P.O. Box 668, Swellendam 6740, SOUTH AFRICA
Phone: +27 285141783 & +27 0824143256
Email: swellendamtv@telkomsa.net
Website: www.swellendamtv.co.za
Producer: Cathy van Eeden

We film community projects and sporting events. We try to focus on projects that will uplift the community in some way. We also train video journalists from our previously politically disadvantaged communities. At present we are filming the rhino plight in South Africa. We are looking for educational ideas to educate the public about rhino poaching. It would be great if we could find a sponsor for a really big documentary about the rhino plight.

Table Mountain Films
Address: SOUTH AFRICA
Email: Joe Kennedy – joe@tablemountainfilms.com
Katharina Pechel – katharina@tablemountainfilms.com
Richard Matthews – richard@tablemountainfilms.com
Website: www.tablemountainfilms.com

Tigress Productions
Address: 1-2 Oakfield Court, Oakfield Road, Clifton, Bristol BS8 2BD, UK
Email: general@tigressproductions.co.uk
Website: www.tigressproductions.co.uk

Tom Burn Photography
Address: Dorset, UK
Website: www.tomburnphotography.net
Email: t.burn24@gmail.com
Owner/Photographer: Tom Burn

Wildlife photographer and videographer based in Dorset, UK. Available for hire to work in many different production roles, with the main focus being camera operator. Completed Wildeye Introduction to Wildlife Filmmaking and the Wildlife Film Academy Course. I am eager to support or co-produce wildlife films in the UK or abroad.

Tree & Sky Media Arts
Address: 1360 Sunflower Dr, Missoula, 59802, MT, USA
Phone: +1-406-721-5283 & +1-406-546-2999
Email: customerservice@treeandsky.com
Website: www.treeandsky.com
Producer/Director/Cinematographer: Rob Whitehair – rob@treeandsky.com
Producer/Cinematographer: Pam Voth – pam@treeandsky.com

Award-winning wildlife and natural history film production company. Producers of broadcast and theatrically released documentaries.

Two Hand Productions
Address: 6 Leeward House, Square Rigger Row, Plantation Wharf, London SW11 3TX, UK
Phone: +44 (0)207 924 7800 Fax: +44 (0)207 924 7962
Email: info@twohandproductions.com
Website: www.twohandproductions.com
Managing Directors: Luke Gallie & Jonathan Frisby

Two Hand Productions was founded by managing directors Luke Gallie and Jonathan Frisby in 1996. Since that time the company has produced a wide variety of programmes from wildlife and adventure formats to documentaries, children's television and light entertainment. Two Hand Productions is a dynamic production company that utilises some of the industry's brightest young talent.

UDENA (Latin America and Spanish Natural History Unit)
Address: 26 Berkeley Square, Bristol BS8 1HP, UK
Phone: +44 7920 196 552 & +34 91 771 02 51
Email: info@udena.es
Website: www.udena.es
Managing Director: Angel Garcia-Rojo · angel.g@udena.es

UDENA (Latin America and Spanish NHU) offers a range of services to natural history filmmakers operating in Latin America or Spain. From pre-production research to on-site support, and everything in between, our team of native Spanish/Portuguese speaking NH professionals are here to help you achieve the best possible results with the minimum of fuss in the shortest possible time and at competitive rates. We are currently looking for film ideas/proposals for docs/films that are focusing on the wildlife of Latin America or Spain. Ideally presenter led and with human-interest. We are always looking for collaborators and sponsors. We do co-productions and we can find money for good film ideas on wildlife documentaries about Latin America or Spain. We offer work experience and we are always looking for new talents, especially for new charismatic people that could act as presenters. We accept CVs via email. We are interested in people with passion for wildlife film-making. Qualifications are always helpful.

Untamed Science
Address: 2430 Belmeade Dr; Charlotte NC 28214, USA
Phone: +1 719 502 0530
Email: untamedscience@gmail.com
Website: www.untamedscience.com
CEO · Story developer: Rob Nelson

European Lead: Jonas Stenstrom
Producer: Dan Bertalan

Our films are targeted at science students of all ages from kindergarten through graduate students. Our goal is to get those students interested in the sciences. That means that we're interested in working with producers who see the potential of high-action science films designed specifically for students. Often we work in extreme sports, chemical explosions and exotic travel. We're particularly interested in teaming up with solo-producers that can produce pieces remotely. We currently have six presenters all based in different corners of the US and one in Sweden. We're interested in producers that can be in front of the camera as well as behind it. We always look for collaborators, sponsors and co-producers. In the past we have offered work experience for young filmmakers. More than anything we want to see a film they have made. It should include small bits with them in front of the camera. Minimum requirements are an undergraduate biology degree.

Va.Le.Cinematografica 78
98 Lungotevere Thaon di Revel, 00196 Rome, ITALY
Phone: +39 063231665 Fax: +39 063231665
Email: cv.valefilm@gmail.com
Website: www.claudio-valerio.com
Contact: Claudio Valerio

Underwater/topside crew for documentaries

Reece de Ville Productions
Country: UK
Phone: +44 770943532
Email: reeceadeville@gmail.com
Website: www.reecedeville.com
CEO: Reece de Ville

I am a freelance filmmaker who has worked with the BBC, Absolute Radio, Mark Kermode, Thea Gilmore, Middlesex and Bournemouth Universities and many more. I shoot/edit exciting pieces for broadcast, online, advertising, wildlife studies and promos. Previous work includes advertisements for Apple Europe, broadcast packages for the BBC and promos for various digital companies. I'm exceptionally patient, which comes in handy when awaiting the perfect wildlife shot! I'm looking for wildlife projects that tell unique and vital stories – whether that's species conservation across the globe to individual animal study through to macro shot insects and creatures rarely seen on film. Also, if you're looking to create documentaries such as *Project Nim*, for example, with previously shot footage, I can be your editor and help pull together a stunning film. I'm looking to collaborate on projects that have the potential to be fascinating – from company promos to wildlife documentaries, day in the life pieces and features. I've a keen interest in working across the wildlife genre and have worked on projects for the National Trust in England and have shot various local wildlife pieces across the country. I love creating interesting and vibrant work and can offer my clients a cost-effective one-man shoot/edit package with HD cams, rapid editing and an open mind! I am open to projects large or small – lets chat! I'm happy to work with all collaborators and sponsors who are interested in creating rewarding pieces. You can hire me as a one-man shoot/edit or as part of a larger crew – happy to discuss your project and talk about what I can offer. I don't currently offer work experience placements or internships, but I'm happy to chat to anyone who'd like advice or has questions about the industry. I believe it's vital to share knowledge and even more vital to be approachable! I'm always looking to build up a contacts list of sound designers, cameramen, musicians etc, so drop me a line.

Virgo Productions
Address: Z1 the Works, 32 Parer Place, Kelvin Grove, QLD 4059, AUSTRALIA
Phone: + 61 7 3175 9995 & +61 404 162 250
Email: cathyhenkel@virgoproductions.com.au
Website: www.virgoproductions.com.au
Producer/Director: Cathy Henkel
Head of Production: Tara Wardrop – tarawardrop@virgoproductions.com.au

Virgo Productions is a boutique screen industries company, specialising in feature documentaries that tell inspiring, positive, global stories with cross-platform delivery to engage audiences through cinema, television, online and DVD release. Best known for *The Burning Season*, which won the IF Award for Best Documentary and the Audience Choice Award at the Brisbane International Film festival and was nominated for an EMMY Award (Outstanding Documentary on a Business Topic), two ATOM Awards and a Golden Panda Award. In 2009 Cathy was awarded Documentary Producer of the Year at SPAA for her work on *The Burning Season*. We are not looking for proposals. Virgo's festival categories are conservation documentary, and business documentary. We are looking for sponsors with an interest in a proactive response to conservation. We consider co-productions. We do not offer work experience.

Visionquest Entertainment international Pty Ltd
Address: P.O. Box 2097, Kelvin Grove, Queensland 4059, AUSTRALIA
Phone: +61 7 3369 5430 & +61 402 058 863
Fax: +61 7 33698119
Email: norm@visionquest.com.au
Website: www.visionquest.com.au
CEO/Producer: Norm Wilkinson

We are producers and executive producers. We are constantly looking for new ideas in all areas, including children's, of natural history, science, adventure and history storytelling. We are always looking for co-productions, consider sponsors/collaborations and prefer CVs to be delivered by email.

49

VFX Productions
Address: P.O. Box 49265, 3A Al Qouz, Shaikh Zayed Road, Interchange 3, Behind Times Square, Dubai DXB, UAE
Phone: +971 43471248 & +971 506521931
Fax: +971 43479335
Email: vfxdubai@gmail.com
Website: www.vfxme.com
Producer/Director: Yusuf Thakur – yusufwings@gmail.com

Visual Effects & Productions (VFX) is twelve year-old company based in Dubai and headed by Yusuf Thakur. We have been producing natural history based documentaries since our inception and have produced four HD based films in 2011. The last two have been shot on 4K RED ONE camera, which we own. All our work is based on subjects in the Middle-East and specifically UAE. We have comprehensive production and post-production facilities including real time 2K/4K edit suites. Our work in the past has won awards at Jackson Hole, IWFF Montana, and Earth-vision. We have one of most comprehensive footage library on subjects from the region, 90% of which is HD/2K/4K. We would like to produce, work, collaborate, co-produce films on conservation, pure wildlife, children's based program. We would specifically work on films based on the Middle-East, and the Indian Subcontinent. Past films have been based on birds, dugongs, islands, mangroves and deserts. We attend pure wildlife film festivals. Would love to work with broadcasters/sponsors on co-productions. Will except Interns who will work in the Middle East region. Email CVs.

Wide Eye Productions
Address: PO Box 222, Quinns Rocks, Perth, WA 6030, AUSTRALIA
Telephone: +61 8 93052437
Email: info@WideEyeProductions.com.au
Website: www.WideEyeProductions.com.au
Contact: Terry Delahunt

A Perth, Western Australia, based production company. As well as working on our own projects, we also provide production services, crew and equipment to local or visiting production companies. We specialise in HD/4K+ acquisition. Not currently looking for proposals. We do consider co-production opportunities. Not currently offering work experience. Please refer to our website for further updates.

Wild Dog Productions
Address: 1680 Windsor Road, Henley On Klip, Gauteng, SOUTH AFRICA
Phone: +27 163661610
Fax: +27 163661611
Email: wilddogs@icon.co.za
Website: www.wilddogs.co.za
Producer: Robert Waldron
Editor: Thelma Roos

International award-winning wildlife and natural history producer, programmes flighted on National Geographic Channel, Discovery Channel, Animal Planet USA and more. Not currently looking for proposals. We do co-produce and are looking for collaborators. We offer work experience to graduates.

Wild Horizons Ltd (WHL)
Address: 59 Cotham Hill, Cotham, Bristol BS6 6JR, UK
Phone: +44 (0)117 906 4320
Fax: +44 (0)117 923 7003
Email: info@wildhorizonsltd.com
Website: www.wildhorizonsltd.com
Founder: Keith Scholey

Here at WHL, we are dedicated to producing the highest quality wildlife films for television and feature films. Our company includes a world-class team of wildlife film production specialists, who have been involved in many of the best natural history programmes, including *Planet Earth*, *Natures Great Events*, *South Pacific*, *Big Cat Diary* and *Life*.

Wild Horizons Productions
Address: 5757 West Sweetwater Drive, Tucson, Arizona 85745, USA
Phone: +1 520 743 4551 & +1 520 743 4848
Fax: +1 520 743 4552
Email: info@wildhorizons.com
Website: www.wildhorizons.com
Producer/Director of Photography: Thomas Wiewandt – tom@wildhorizons.com

Experienced independent natural history photographer-storyteller with PhD in behavioral ecology, based in the Sonoran Desert. Now engaged in multimedia production. Special interests include conservation projects, children's programming, and new nature media. Inquire about stock video clips, project research/consulting, or location scouting. Awards: Emmy nomination in cinematography, 4 CINE Golden Eagles, Gold Apple from National Educational Film & Video Festival. Not looking for proposals or offering work experience. We are seeking sponsors for work in progress and are interested in speaking with potential collaborators or co-producers.

Wild Images
Address: Suite 255, Private Bag X16, Constantia 7848, SOUTH AFRICA
Phone: +27217940804 & +27217946618
Fax: +27217946618
Email: info@wildimages.tv
Website: www.wildimages.tv
Director/Producer/Cameraman: Richard Matthews
Technical: Rob Cowling
Researcher: Bahia Fitchen – research@wildimages.tv

Wild Images is an independent media organisation specialising in aerial filming, wildlife sequence work and still image acquisition. Our main focus is in stabilised and inexpensive aerial filming from helicopters and light aircraft and we are building a stock library of superlative aerial images. Wild Images won an EMMY (2011) in Best Cinematography for work on National Geographic's *Great Migrations*. We have a range of specialist filming equipment available for hire. We are always open to new ideas for natural history or documentary films but now make these through our sister company Table Mountain Films. We regularly approach broadcasters to fund own programs and the programs from our collaborators. We offer some work experience positions. CVs should be emailed to us for consideration.

Wildlife Films
Address: BOTSWANA
Website: www.wildlifeconservationfilms.com
Contacts: Derek & Beverly Joubert

Film, photography and publishing by Derek and Beverly Joubert.

Wild Logic LLC
Address: USA
Email: katya.shirokow@wildlogic.net
Website: www.wildlogic.net
Managing Director: Katya Shirokow

Wildlife film producers and distributors.

Wild Planet Productions
Address: RAK Media City Free Zone, Ras al Khaimah, UAE
Website: www.wildplanetfilms.org
Managing Director: Jonathan Ai Khan – jak@wildplanetfilms.org
Operations Manager: Jody Anne Rodriguez – jody@wildplanetfilms.org
Producer/DOP/Cameraman: Majid Sarhaddi – majid@wildplanetfilms.org

Wild Visions, Inc.
Address: PO Box 42194, Phoenix, AZ 85080, USA
Phone: +1 602-516-1975
Email: mike@wildvisions.net
Website: www.wildvisions.net
President/Owner: Michael Pellegatti

Wild Visions, Inc., located in Phoenix, Arizona, is a full service, award-winning, video production company specializing in HD productions. We have twenty-one years experience in producing network television productions, sports, documentary, interviews, commercials, infomercials, product promotion videos, public service announcements (PSA), web and internet videos, and corporate video productions for local, national, and international clients. When Wild Visions was started, the focus was on wildlife, nature, and outdoor video productions. Filming the splendor of God's natural world has always been inspiring, motivating, and breathtaking. We are looking for proposals and sponsors for adventure, conservation-themed, environmental, and social commentary films. Looking for collaborators/sponsors and would consider a co-production with the right individuals and film topic.

Willstock Films
Address: UK
Email: contact@willstock.co.uk
Website: www.willstock.co.uk
Producer/Director: Will Clark

Zoozoo
Address: Balagervej 53, Viby J 8260, DENMARK
Phone: +45 29172266
Email: myles.thompson@yahoo.com
Website: www.zoozoo.dk
Contact: Myles Thompson

We produce short films at low cost for universities and corporations with a focus on wildlife and the environment. We research, write, shoot, and edit rapidly and painlessly – all in one affordable package.

STOCK FOOTAGE

ABC Library Sales
Address: 8 Gordon Street, Elsternwick, VIC 3185, AUSTRALIA
Phone: +61 3 9524 2273
Email: librarysales@your.abc.net.au
Website: www.abccontentsales.com.au/librarysales/index.htm
Library Sales Managers: Anne Gilbee & Cyrus Irani

ABC Library Sales is home to one of Australia's largest collections of natural history footage. We do not offer work experience.

Absolutely Wild Visuals
Address: AUSTRALIA
Email: sales@wildvisuals.com.au
Website: www.absolutelywildvisuals.com

Aquavision TV Productions
Address: 144 Western Services Road, Woodmead, Johannesburg 2191, SOUTH AFRICA
Phone: +27(0)11 275 0900 & +27(0)11 275 0901
Email: HOD Library: Christo Ras – christo@aquavision.co.za
Executive PA: Julia Gaspar – julia@aquavision.co.za
Website: www.aquavision.co.za
Contacts: Pieter Lamberti (CEO), Dave Keet (General Manager), Sean O'Neill (Head of Production), Steve Eder (Executive Producer), Christo Ras (Head Librarian), Martin Ferreira (Head Audio Engineer)

Aquavision produces high quality high-definition natural history factual, cultural and reality documentaries. With an archive library with more than 5,000 hours of natural history archive footage, Aquavision is the largest NH stock library in Africa. For any of your African stock footage needs Aquavision must be your first stop. With its growing Local and International cinematography database its International NH stock footage is growing daily. For production management support for shoots anywhere on the African continent, Aquavision is able to assist; from the planning, organization, and fixing, of any aspect of the production. We are also available for work for hire, providing specialized cameramen and equipment for shoots. With more than ten edit suites we can deliver both off and on lines at any delivery specification. Looking for natural history / wildlife / cultural / reality film and festival entries. We are always actively looking for new talent, presenters, VO artists etc.

BBC Motion Gallery
Address: 201 Wood Lane, Media Centre, Garden House, 1st Floor South, London W12 7TQ, UK
Phone: +44 (0)20 8433 2861 & +44 (0)20 8433 2862
Email: motiongallery.uk@bbc.com
Website: www.bbcmotiongallery.com
Head of Sales & Marketing: Linda Reeve

BBC Motion Gallery is the footage licensing division of BBC Worldwide, offering media professionals in advertising, commercials, television, film, interactive and corporate video production access to over a million hours of motion imagery for licensing worldwide. BBC

Motion Gallery footage encompasses subjects including natural history, sport, news, locations, art, music, celebrities and historic events. Clips from the archive have appeared in several films, usually of a historical nature. Users are able to access tens of thousands of BBC Motion Gallery clips online, or enlist a team of professional researchers to tap into the repository of content stored offline.

Brock Initiative/Living Planet Productions
Address: Dumpers Cottage, Chew Magna, Bristol, BS40 8SS, UK
Phone: +44 (0)1275 333187
Fax: +44 (0)1761 221702
Email: info@brockinitiative.org
Website: www.brockinitiative.org
Executive Producer: Richard Brock

I try to get stuff out there that will make a difference. There are now more ways of doing that than ever before. It can be in any format, anywhere, anyhow. I will provide free footage on wildlife and environmental matters from around the world. I am always interested in issues where "Filming with Attitude" might help the planet. Just let me know.

Echo Film Productions Inc
Address: 407 W Bannock Street, Boise, Idaho 83702, USA
Phone: +1 208 336 0349
Fax: +1 208 336 0858
Email: echofilm@mindspring.com
Website: www.echofilms.com
Producer: Tyler Nelson
Director: Norman Nelson

Specializing in birds of prey, North American wildlife, habitat and environmental issues. Beautiful stock footage shots of salmon leaping, birds in slow motion flight, habitats. Stock footage in HD and SD from digital and film sources.

Environmental Investigation Agency (EIA)
Address: 62-63 Upper Street, London N1 0NY, UK
Phone: +44 (0)20 7354 7960
Email: ukinfo@eia-international.org
Website: www.eia-international.org
Head of Operations: Bill Dishington
Press Officer: Paul Newman – paulnewman@eia-international.org
Video Production/Training Co-ordinator: Paul Redman – paulredman@eia-international.org

EIA produces hard-hitting campaign films on a wide range of environmental crimes, as well as bespoke training films for enforcement agencies. It also has one of the world's largest archives of footage devoted to the illegal trade in wildlife products and other environmentally damaging commodities. The collection is data-based and is available on a professional basis to journalists, publishers and programme-makers.
All the funds raised from the sale of this archive help to fund future campaigns. The visual media you see on the website is indicative of what is available in the whole collection. We are always prepared to listen to programme pitches from media professionals with a view to highlighting our work. Applications for work experience welcomed: CVs by email please.

Felis Creations
Address: #295 39th 'C' Cross 10th Main 5th Block, Jayanagar, Bangalore 560041, INDIA
Phone: +91 9448059209
Email: sandesh@sandeshkadur.com
Website: www.felis.in
CEO/Creative Director: Sandesh Kadur

Felis Creations provides valuable stock footage and field production services across the Indian sub-continent. We specialize in natural and cultural history and have worked on major projects with the BBC, National Geographic, Discovery and Animal Planet.

Erik Fernström Film & Video AB
Address: SWEDEN
Email: info@wildlifefilm.com
Website: www.wildlifefilm.com

The video archive consists of several hundreds of hours with exclusive footage of wildlife from around Europe, Asia, North America and Africa. Footage on Digi-Beta, Beta SP and Mini-DV.

FootageBank HD
Address: 13470 Washington Blvd, #210, Marina Del Rey, CA 90292, USA
Phone: +1 310 822 1400
Fax: +1 310 822 4100
Email: info@footagebank.com
Website: www.footagebank.com
Founder and President: Paula Lumbard
Vice President: Carol Martin

Worldwide representation of blue-chip natural history cinematographers and footage. We are actively looking for footage for clip representation.

Footage Search
Address: 243 El Dorado Street, Suite 300, Monterey 93940, USA
Phone: +1 831 375 2313
Email: support@footagesearch.com
Website: www.footagesearch.com
CEO: Dan Baron

At Footage Search, leading broadcasters, advertising agencies, and production companies worldwide will discover a unique and outstanding service through our successful niche collections OceanFootage, NatureFootage and AdventureFootage. We welcome your interest and participation in our company and its success. Our goal at Footage Search is to provide comprehensive footage support for the needs of today's media professionals. From High Definition video and film to Ultra High Definition 4K, clients now have an opportunity to access the best quality ocean, nature and adventure stock footage online, through our OceanFootage, NatureFootage and AdventureFootage web sites.

Global Focus Royalty Free Stock Footage
Address: PO Box 3008, Northcliff 3008, SOUTH AFRICA
Phone: +27 82 400 5525
Fax: +27 11 789 4003
Email: sales@globalfocus.co.za
Website: www.globalfocus.co.za

Our footage is the perfect addition to your production. Travel, scenics, cities, landscapes, timelapses & wildlife. Shot around the globe in 4K, 2K, HD 1080p|25 & 29.97 fps footage, as well as SD PAL. Contact us for any of your footage needs.

Hairy Frog Productions Ltd
Address: 4 The Paddock, White Horse Lane, Trowse, Norwich, Norfolk NR14 8TD, UK
Phone: +44 (0)7885964790
Email: hairyfrog@lineone.net
Website: www.hairy-frog.co.uk
Director/Producer/Cameraman: Mike Linley – mike_linley@yahoo.co.uk

Wildlife production company with full HD kit (BBC specs) + gopro hero in flat optic housing + video-microscope and endoscopes + Canon 7D time-lapse kit. Over 400 credits mainly as a Producer for Survival/Anglia Television. Now also producing Wildlife Interactive Touch-screens. Over 40 international awards to date. Specialist in herpetology, entomology and UK wildlife. Large video, sound and stills library. Always happy to co-produce. Limited work experience opportunities, depending on current projects.

Annie Haycock
Address: 1 Rushmoor, Marteltwy SA67 8BB WALES, UK
Email: annie@rushmoorphotos.co.uk

Natural history photography, videography and writing. I like to sit, watch, and record the natural world, by whatever means is at my disposal at the time. The result is a collection of photos, video clips, some sound clips, and diaries of observations, mostly from here in Wales, but also from other places around the world.

Greg Hensley Productions
Address: 200 South E Street, Unit 113, New Castle, CO 81647, USA
Phone: +1 970 984 3158
E-mail: hensley@sopris.net
Website: www.gregnensley.com

Greg Hensley has over thirty years of footage filmed across America. Now shooting 35mm movie film, Greg Hensley captures American wildlife in the remote areas of the United States. Greg has unique time-lapse techniques, transforming the ordinary to the extra ordinary.

Landis Wildlife Films
Address: USA
Email: LandisWF@YCSI.net
Website: www.wolftracker.com/Landis

Bob Landis is an Emmy award-winning wildlife cinematographer. He has produced many films for programs such as *National Geographic* and *Nature*. His work has taken him to Denali, Kluane, and Algonquin National Parks, but his home is Yellowstone Park where he has excelled in the art of wildlife film-making for over thirty years. Yellowstone/Wildlife stock footage available.

Last Refuge Ltd.
Address: Batch Farm, Panborough, Wells, Somerset, BA5 1PN, UK
Email: info@lastrefuge.co.uk
Website: www.lastrefuge.co.uk

Film Footage Library: wildlife, environment, peoples, aerial, time lapse, medical, science and adventure.

Mark Emery Films
Address: USA
Email: info@markemeryfilms.com
Website: www.markemeryfilms.com

NaturalHistoryFilm.com
Address: Van den Woudestraat 41, 2361VP Warmond, NETHERLANDS
Phone: +31(0)643-029201
Fax: +31(0)87-7849920
Email: info@naturalhistoryfilm.com
Website: www.naturalhistoryfilm.com
Manager and Cameraman/Editor: Raldi Somers

NaturalHistoryFilm.com provides high quality stock footage of wildlife and nature worldwide. NaturalHistoryFilm.com works with producers that have experience in filming on remote locations, mostly in the polar regions and Africa. Our producers/cameramen are available for freelance assignments, which we can arrange upon request.

Nature Stock Shots
Address: Colorado Springs, CO 80904, USA
Phone: +1 719 685 5060
Fax: +1 719 685 3884
E-mail: info@naturestockshots.com
Website: www.naturestockshots

Nature Stock Shots is a nature stock footage library of film, video, and photographs. Top nature cinematographers have captured more than 400 hours of stock footage in North and South America, Kamchatka, and Bering Island, some of it never before photographed.

NHNZ Moving Images
Natural History New Zealand
Address: Box 474, 5 Melville St, Dunedin 9016, NEW ZEALAND
Phone: +64 (0)3 4799799 Fax: +64 (0)3 4799917
Email: images@nhnz.tv
Website: www.nhnzmovingimages.com
Emerging Media Manager: Caroline Cook – ccook@nhnz.tv
Stock Footage Content Specialist: Olly Rudd – orudd@nhnz.tv
Stock Footage Content Specialist: Jamie Thorp – jthorp@nhnz.tv

NHNZ Moving Images; we live in an HD World. Our library represents exceptional HD stock footage across all genres produced by NHNZ and over twenty other leading filmmakers from around the world, including the National Geographic Channels Library. We are focused on finding the best shots to meet your creative, editorial and technical requirements, your deadlines and budget. This means offering you free research for most enquiries, offering full-length shots for you to view online, no minimum sale requirements, and we sell by the second. Our footage is made for the international broadcast market and is of the highest production values.

Oxford Scientific Films (OSF)
Address: 2nd Floor, Waterside House, 9 Woodfield Rd, London, W9 2BA, UK
Phone: +44 (0)20 7432 8200 Fax: +44 (0)20 7432 8201
Email: uksales@osf.co.uk
Website: www.osf.co.uk

Oxford Scientific (OSF) is a leading independent distributor of stock footage and still imagery. As a specialist in natural history and science, OSF represents some of the world's leading and most talented wildlife film-makers and photographers.

Richmond Productions, Inc.
Address: 216 Valhalla Drive, Solvang, CA 93463, USA
Phone: +11 1 805-688-2718
Email: video@richmondproductions.com
Website: www.richmondproductions.com
Producer: Earl Richmond

Wildlife video production company specializing in scientifically based marine education and conservation programs. Nineteen Telly Awards, Monterrey Blue Ocean Film Festival Finalist. Large library of marine mammal stock footage. natural history & research library of blue whale footage. Credits include: National Geographic, BBC, PBS, Animal Planet. Currently in production of PBS series on persons compassionate about the oceans and their life's work. Currently seeking program sponsors for PBS series. Marine education and conservation, documentaries and shorts.

a million
voices for
nature

The Royal Society for the Protection of Birds
Address: The Lodge, Sandy, Bedfordshire SG19 2DL, UK
Phone: +44 (0)1767 680 551
Fax: +44 (0)1767 683 262
Email: filmunit@rspb.org.uk
Website: www.rspb.org.uk
Head of RSPB Film Unit: Mark Percival
Assistant Producer: Robin Hill
Cameraperson: Toby Hough

The Royal Society for the Protection of Birds is a conservation organisation with over one million members. Producers of wildlife films since 1953, the RSPB Film Unit continues to create blue-chip wildlife and conservation programming today for event presentation, broadcast, DVD sales, online distribution and clips sales. Our aim is to showcase the RSPB's most important conservation work and to capture the spectacle of the natural world with award-winning clarity, achieved by a commitment to the principles of ethical wildlife filmmaking.
Credits include: *Eagle Odyssey* (ten awards incl. Wildscreen and Jackson Hole) *Waterlands* (nine awards incl. Japan Wildlife Film Festival).
The RSPB Film Unit is open to developing co-productions on the themes of saving nature, stopping species extinction, stopping climate change, and landscape restoration/re-creation. We periodically offer production internships (6–12 months) usually as camera or field assistant. For more information please contact via email.

SCIENCEphotoLIBRARY

Science Photo Library
Address: 327-329 Harrow Road, London W9 3RB, UK
Phone: +44 (0)20 7432 1100
Email: info@sciencephoto.com
Website: www.sciencephoto.com/motion
Head of Motion: Ben Jones
Head of Sales: Mark Abbott – mark.abbott@sciencephoto.com
Head of Marketing: Julia Moore

Science Photo Library is a leading stock archive of footage and images of the natural world, and all aspects of science. We license stock footage to a diverse range of clients in production, publishing and the commercial sector. Our collection is growing all the time, and we are happy to arrange commissions for specific projects.

Scubazoo Images Sdn Bhd
Address: P.O. Box 15475, 88864 Kota Kinabalu, Sabah, MALAYSIA
Phone: +6 088 232068 & +6 019 861 8610 Fax: +6 088 237068
Email: info@scubazoo.com
Website: www.scubazoo.com
Founder/CEO: Simon Christopher – simon@scubazoo.com
Co-Founder/Managing Director: Jason Isley – jason@scubazoo.com

Scubazoo is an independent production company that prides itself on providing quality footage, as well as solutions to your crewing and location management needs. We specialize in filming natural history programs and are renowned for our underwater cinematography and photography. We also have an extensive library of stills and high definition video footage of iconic underwater marine life such as sharks, turtles, rays and whales shot in locations around the world with a large selection being sourced on the rich reefs of South East Asia's Coral Triangle. Scubazoo is based in Kota Kinabalu, Sabah, Malaysian Borneo, and we have over fourteen years production experience in Borneo and beyond. Whether you are a corporate body, an NGO, or a broadcast production company, Scubazoo is ideally placed to handle your filming and production requirements.
We offer work experience as a Stock Library Intern: Scubazoo are looking for young, motivated individuals to join our stock footage and photography team in Kota Kinabalu. Applicants should be: * College student or recent college graduate * Students of biological sciences or interested in marine life.
Details of the position: * Full time (40 hours/week) * Unpaid * Duration of twelve weeks * Intern responsible for travel expenses * Preference will be given to Malaysian candidates. The position is unpaid. Interns will work under our stock footage and stock photo library managers, gaining experience in skills such as keywording, CMS, basic photoshop, Final Cut Pro editing and more. This is a great opportunity to learn real world skills and work as part of a team in a dynamic business environment. Applicants should send a cover letter and CV to info@scubazoo.com or roger@scubazoo.com

SpecialistStock

Specialist Stock
Country: UK
Phone: +44 (0)1275 375520
Email: info@specialiststock.com
Website: www.SpecialistStock.com
Director: Tom Walmsley – tom@specialiststock.com

Specialist Stock offers a number of services (www.SpecialistStock.com/services). As a comprehensive collection of photo and footage libraries we license material and multimedia photostories to the global media industry. Through our Comprehensive Research Facility we search our global supplier network for any subject matter and sort out the licenses. Finally we give consultations and seminars to individuals and businesses who are 'Adopting a Video Workflow' by going through the options, technical details and business plan. Visit separate website: www.SpecialistMediaTraining.com.

Gareth Trezise
Address: The Hipped Barn, Cholwell Farm, Stowey Road, Clutton, Bristol BS39 5TG, UK
Phone: +44 (0)7921 517420
Email: garethtrezise@wildlifeinmotion.com
Website: www.wildlifeinmotion.com

Independent wildlife film-maker, freelance cameraman. Stock footage. Promos. Specialist areas: long-lens, macro/studio, animal behaviour, wild/dangerous animals, butterflies. Some previous projects include working with Richard Brock – Living Planet Productions and Martin Warren – Butterfly Conservation. Principal cameraman for butterfly sequences and Sir David Attenborough on *Better Butterflies*. Principal cameraman on *Big Cat Safari* with Jonathan Scott. Additional camera work for *The Egret Has Landed* produced by Richard Brock, narrated by Tony Soper.

VFX Productions
Address: P.O. Box 49265, 3A Al Qouz, Shaikh Zayed Road, Interchange 3, Behind Times Square, Dubai DXB, UAE
Phone: +971 43471248 & +971 506521931
Fax: +971 43479335
Email: vfxdubai@gmail.com
Website: www.vfxme.com
Producer/Director: Yusuf Thakur – yusufwings@gmail.com

Visual Effects & Productions (VFX) is a twelve year-old company based in Dubai and headed by Yusuf Thakur. We have been producing natural history based documentaries since our inception and have produced four HD films in 2011. The last two have been shot on 4K RED ONE camera, which we own. All our work is based on subjects in the Middle East and specifically UAE. We have comprehensive production and post-production facilities including real time 2K/4K edit suites. Our work in the past has won awards at Jackson Hole, IWFF Montana, and Earth-vision. We have one of the most comprehensive footage libraries on subjects from the region, 90% of which is HD/2K/4K. We would like to produce, work, collaborate, co-produce films on conservation, pure wildlife, children's-based programs. We would specifically work on films based on the Middle East, and the Indian Subcontinent. Past films have been based on birds, dugongs, islands, mangroves and deserts. We attend pure wildlife film festivals. Would love to work with broadcasters/sponsors on co-productions. Will accept interns who will work in the Middle East region. Email CVs.

Video-film.no
Country: Norway
Phone: +47 93438903
Email: firmapost@video-film.no
Website: www.video-film.no
Contact: Per Johan Naesje

Our firm offers stock video of wildlife from Scandinavia. Many different species of "hard to find" footage. More info on our website.

Wild Horizons Productions
Address: 5757 West Sweetwater Drive, Tucson, Arizona 85745, USA
Phone: +1 520 743 4551 & +1 520 743 4848
Fax: +1 520 743 4552
Email: info@wildhorizons.com
Website: www.wildhorizons.com
Producer/Director of Photography: Thomas Wiewandt – tom@wildhorizons.com

Experienced independent natural history photographer-storyteller with PhD in behavioral ecology, based in the Sonoran Desert. Now engaged in multimedia production. Special interests include conservation projects, children's programming, and new nature media. Inquire about stock video clips, project research/consulting, or location scouting. Awards: Emmy nomination in cinematography, four CINE Golden Eagles, Gold Apple from National Educational Film & Video Festival. Not looking for proposals or offering work experience. We are seeking sponsors for work in progress and are interested in speaking with potential collaborators or co-producers.

Wild Images
Address: Suite 255, Private Bag X16, Constantia 7848, SOUTH AFRICA
Phone: +27217940804 & +27217946618
Fax: +27217946618
Email: info@wildimages.tv
Website: www.wildimages.tv
Director/Producer/Cameraman: Richard Matthews
Technical: Rob Cowling
Researcher: Bahia Fitchen – research@wildimages.tv

Wild Images is an independent media organisation specialising in aerial filming, wildlife sequence work and still image acquisition. Our main focus is in stabilised and inexpensive aerial filming from helicopters and light aircraft and we are building a stock library of superlative aerial images. Wild Images won an EMMY (2011) in Best Cinematography for work on National Geographic's *Great Migrations*. We have a range of specialist filming equipment available for hire. We offer some work experience positions. CVs should be emailed to us for consideration.

Wild Scape
County: UK
Email: peewit2@tiscali.co.uk
Website: www.ablackcountryladexplores.me.uk
Contact: Dave Hollis

Wild Scape produce wildlife DVDs of British and European wildlife. We are small company who are dedicated to producing high quality images that can inspire their viewers. We are always on the look out for good ideas and tie-ups with other individual and production companies. We are only interested in producing wildlife films please. We are always interested in sponsorship and co-productions with like-minded organisations.

DISTRIBUTORS

Fergus Beeley Ltd (FBL)
Address: 59 Cotham Hill, Bristol BS6 6JR, UK
Phone: +44 (0)117 906 4311
Email: info@fergusbeeley.com
Website: fergusbeeley.com

Fergus Beeley Ltd (FBL) brings a specialist team of expertise together, to develop business models that enable profitable distribution of short-form film content across multiple platforms. The company is also engaged in assisting emerging media markets in the Middle East. The company seeks contact with individual wildlife film-makers (including amateurs and NGOs) that could make and wholly own short-form conservation films for exploitation. We offer work experience but require that candidates have a good awareness of social media and marketing with video content.

Green Planet Films
Address: 564 Market St. Suite 610, San Francisco, CA 94104, USA
Phone: +1 415 377 5471
Email: service@greenplanetfilms.org
Website: www.greenplanetfilms.org

Green Planet Films is a non-profit distributor of nature and environmental DVDs from around the globe. We promote environmental education through film. We seek to preserve and protect our planet by collecting and distributing documentaries that can be used to educate the public about the science, beauty, and fragility of the natural world. Our mission is to grow our web-based DVD library, and provide a channel that connects these films to schools, organizations, businesses, government agencies, and individuals worldwide.

GREEN.TV

Green TV
Address: 120 Long Acre, Covent Garden, London WC2E 9PA, UK
Phone: +44 207 240 0357
Ade Thomas – ade.thomas@green.tv
Website: www.green.tv
Editorial Director: Martin Atkin – martin.atkin@green.tv
Business Development Director: Alex Aleksander
Content and Syndication Director: Fi Ferrer

GREEN.TV is the online TV channel, producer, distributor and syndicator for environmental and sustainability films. We work with a range of non-profit and corporate clients including WWF, Greenpeace, UNEP, Alstom and Vestas to produce and distribute video content through our syndication partners. Together with our sister company Large Blue we offer a complete digital communications service. We're interested in presenter-led online and broadcast series with big potential for sponsorship and branded content – especially in the green tech, clean energy and low-carbon areas. We occasionally offer work experience – apply to one of the email addresses above.

Lizard Entertainment
Address: PO Box 12317, Mill Street, Cape Town 8010, SOUTH AFRICA
Email: mike@lizardentertainment.co.uk
Website: www.lizardentertainment.co.za
Contact: Michael Zylstra

Lizard Entertainment is an independent distribution company, specializing in non-fiction programming for the international market. We are dedicated to assisting African filmmakers in getting their films 'out there', providing them with a channel to broadcasters around the world. We represent world-renowned filmmakers as well as newcomers to the industry, and take pride in being Africa's leading distributor and have a wide range of high quality programs available.

Octapixx Worldwide
Address: 200 Tiffield Road, Suite 101, Toronto, Ontario M1V 5J1, CANADA
Phone: +1 416 449 9400
Fax: +1 416 449 9498
Email: info@octapixx.com
Website: www.octapixx.com

Worldwide distribution of quality television programming representing top-notch producers and libraries from around the globe.

Off The Fence
Address: Herengracht 105-107, 1015 BE Amsterdam, NETHERLANDS
Phone: +31 20 5200 222
Fax: +31 20 5200 223
Email: info@offthefence.com
Website: www.offthefence.com
Managing Director, Distribution: Bo Stehmeier – bo@offthefence.com

Off the Fence (OTF) is an independent television distribution company specialized in non-fiction content for the international marketplace. Since 1994, we've been creating and marketing high quality programming, focussing on integrity and innovation. OTF's comprehensive catalogue contains an impressive 4,500 hours of nature & wildlife, people, places & culture, travel & adventure, science & technology, history and lifestyle. And our expertise doesn't stop there. We also develop, finance, produce and co-produce international non-fiction programmes.

Oxford Scientific Films (OSF)
Address: 2nd Floor, Waterside House, 9 Woodfield Rd, London, W9 2BA, UK
Phone: +44 (0)20 7432 8200 Fax: +44 (0)20 7432 8201
Email: uksales@osf.co.uk
Website: www.osf.co.uk

Oxford Scientific (OSF) is a leading independent distributor of stock footage and still imagery. As a specialist in natural history and science, OSF represents some of the world's leading and most talented wildlife film-makers and photographers.

Parthenon Entertainment
Address: Station Approach, Chorleywood, Herts, WD3 5PF, UK
Phone: +44 (0)1923 286886
Email: info@parthenonentertainment.com
Website: www.parthenonentertainment.com
Director of Production: Danny Tipping
Head of Production, Bristol office: Alison Bradburn

Parthenon Entertainment Limited is a multi-media rights management company, which develops, produces and distributes a diverse portfolio of high quality factual and children's properties for the global marketplace.
Founded in 2002 by Carl Hall, former managing director of HIT Wildlife, Parthenon is ranked amongst the top independent UK producers and distributors and has built a reputation for delivering high rating series and specials for clients around the world. With operations in Europe and North America, Parthenon's international reach provides a presence across all key territories for the exploitation of its content and a platform for continued growth and development. We are always looking for proposals: blue-chip natural history, wildlife and presenter-led series. We do consider co-productions and we are looking for collaborators. Work experience offered to those with relevant industry experience. Send CVs by email.

Scorpion TV
Address: 38 Thornaby House, Canrobert St. London E2 0BE, UK
Phone: +44 (0)7804077624
Email: office@scorpiontv.com
Website: www.scorpiontv.com
Sales Executive/Camera Operator/Editor: Juan Solera – juanantonio.solera@gmail.com

We are a distribution company based in UK for over ten years and distributing documentaries internationally. We have BBC, Channel 4 and other award-winning documentaries. Also, we would love to co-produce in wildlife projects. We are already in touch with some producers looking for film ideas. We would love to make adventure, human interest and current affairs documentaries, as they are the main themes in the titles that we distribute. We are looking for collaborators and we definitely consider co-productions. We accept CV by post for work experience and/or internships.

Spier Films
Address: 3rd Floor, Union Building, 25 Commercial St. Cape Town 8000, SOUTH AFRICA
42 Vicarage Crescent, Battersea, London SW11 3LD, UK
Phone: +27214610925 (SA) & +442085224296 (UK)
Email: mike@spierfilms.com
Website: www.spierfilms.com
MD: Michael Auret
Producer/Sales: Heather Millard – heather@spierfilms.com
Producer/Sales: Amy Nelson

Production, financing and sales company with offices in Cape Town, Reykjavik and London. We are looking to work with directors with great stories to tell for an international audience but also with producers who are developing either one-off docs or series and would like us to work with them to raise finance and to make sales and pre-sales. We are looking for all types of film ideas and finished films. We prefer stories with some human interest or stories that are conservation related which we can campaign around, but the bottom line is entertaining television – that is what we are looking for. Whether fast-paced, presenter-led or slow-moving wildlife we can help to raise finance and to sell the finished product. We are open to co-productions and we attend most festivals and markets including IDFA, Hot Docs, Mipcom, MipTV and some of the factual congresses. We are always looking for collaborators and sponsors. We are a small operation but could offer work experience for graduates – CVs can be emailed to us.

Terranoa
Address: 155 rue de Charonne, 75011 Paris, FRANCE
Phone: +33 (0)1 55 25 59 37
Email: communication@terranoa.com
Website: www.terranoa.com
General Manager: Emmanuelle Jouanole – ejouanole@terranoa.com

Terranoa is a documentaries distribution company. It has become a benchmark for innovative, high-profile factual productions to broadcasters worldwide and has attracted outside producers who share the values and quality of our brand. Each year the productions distributed by Terranoa are awarded internationally. Today with a catalogue of over 800 hours covering Science & History, Nature & Environment, Travel & Adventure and Sports, we supply broadcasters and other media platforms worldwide with an attractive choice of factual programmes.

Wild Logic LLC
Address: USA
Email: katya.shirokow@wildlogic.net
Website: www.wildlogic.net
Managing Director: Katya Shirokow

Wildlife film producers and distributors.

BROADCASTERS/CHANNELS

ABC - Australia Broadcasting Corporation
Address: GPO Box 9994, Sydney NSW 2001, AUSTRALIA
Email: erson.alan@abc.net.au
Website: www.abc.net.au
Head of Documentaries: Alan Erson

Animal Planet
Countries: Animal Planet USA; CANADA; UK & IRELAND; NORDIC; AUSTRALIA & NEW ZEALAND; GERMANY; POLAND; INDIA; ASIA: JAPAN; LATIN AMERICA
Websites: USA: www.animal.discovery.com
Canada: www.animalplanet.ca
Japan: www.animal-planet.jp
Latin America: www.tudiscovery.com
Rest of the world: www.yourdiscovery.com/web/animalplanet

There are several different Animal Planet channels around the world, owned by the Discovery Communications networks.

Babelgum
Address: Block J Eastpoint Business Park, Clontarf, Dublin 3, IRELAND
Phone: +353 18984924
Email: info@babelgum.com
Website: www.babelgum.com

Babelgum is a free, revolutionary Internet and mobile TV platform focusing on independent film and music, comedy, animation, nature and travel, all streaming full screen and in TV-like quality.

BBC Natural History Unit
Address: BBC Broadcasting House, Whiteladies Road, Bristol BS8 2LR, UK
Phone: +44 (0)117 973 2211
Website: www.bbc.co.uk/nature
Head of BBC NHU: Andrew Jackson – andrew.jackson@bbc.co.uk
Commissioning Editor, Science & Natural History: Kim Shillinglaw

All proposals need to be sent through the e-commissioning system.

BBC VISION
Address: BBC Broadcasting House, Whiteladies Road, Bristol BS8 2LR, UK
Phone: +44 1179746704 & +44 7740818239
Email: chris.hutchins@bbc.co.uk
Website: www.bbcproductiontalent.co.uk
Contact: Christopher Hutchins

I am the Head of Production Talent for the BBC's Natural History Unit. Looking for talent, CVs can be posted on bbcproductiontalent.co.uk

Bonobo.tv
Country: UK/Worldwide
Phone: +44 (0)207 617 420
Website: www.bonobo.tv
Creative Director: Geoff Francis

Please get in touch to discuss any project or idea you may have. At Bonobo.tv we're always happy to hear from you.

Channel 4
Address: Channel 4 Headquarters, 124 Horseferry Road, London SW1P 2TX, UK
Website: www.channel4.com
Head of Specialist Factual: Ralph Lee
Commissioning Editor, Specialist Factual: Jill Fullerton-Smith
Editorial Administrator: Nicola Brodie – nbrodie@channel4.co.uk
Phone: +44 (0)207 306 8283
Commissioning Editor, Specialist Factual: Tanya Shaw
Editorial Assistant: Carrie Thomas – cathomas@channel4.co.uk
Phone: +44 (0)207 306 5537
Multiplatform Commissioning Editor, Doc's & Specialist Factual: Kate Quilton
Editorial Administrator: Serena Lloyd-Smith – slloydsmith@channel4.co.uk
Phone: +44 (0)207 306 8281

Channel 4's Specialist Factual team commission a distinctive portfolio of history, science, arts and religion programmes. From the channel's daily religion strand, *4thought.tv* to major series like *Inside Nature's Giants,* our aim is to offer viewers programmes that are engaging, challenging and rich in content. Our current priorities are threefold: First, we want to back projects of real scale that can stand out in a competitive schedule. So we're particularly keen on returnable formats and eye-catching propositions like *Blitz Street.* Second, we are aiming to generate more events, stripped or themed weeks and programmes with live elements. *Surgery Live* or *Alone in the Wild* are good, recent examples of innovation in this space. Third, we're working to find new faces around which our subjects can revolve. Across all our genres we want to find new characters who have outstanding stories, ideas, qualifications and communication skills and whom an audience will relate strongly to.

Channel 5 Television Ltd
Address: 10 Lower Thames Street, London EC3R 6EN, UK
Phone: +44 (0)20 8612 7700 & +44 (0)8457 05 05 05
Email: customerservices@channel5.com
Website: www.channel5.com
Head of Factual: Andrew O'Connell – andrew.o'connell@channel5.com
Commissioning Editor, Factual: John Hay – john.hay@channel5.com
Andrew oversees all factual, news and current affairs commissioning on Channel5, including the channel's distinctive wildlife and natural history documentary programmes.

What we are looking for: Wildlife: obs doc series following animal lovers who are experts in their field such as *The Man Who Lives with Bears, Alone with Grizzlies, Sharkman, Mr. and Mrs. Wolf.* Also light docs featuring nature and humans co-existing and/or living in strange situations such as *There's a Hippo in My House.* Nature Shock Strand: amazing and unusual tales of wildlife and the natural world, such as *The Whale that Ate the Great White* or *Cannibal Hippos.* Submit any proposals/treatments via email only.

71

CBC – Canadian Broadcasting Corporation
Science and Natural History, Documentary Unit
Address: PO Box 500, Stn A, Toronto, Ontario M5W 1E6, CANADA
Phone: +1 416 205-6894
Email: caroline.underwood@cbc.ca
Website: www.cbc.ca/natureofthings
Senior Producer: Caroline Underwood
Vance Chow · vance.chow@cbc.ca

The CBC is Canada's public broadcaster. The Documentary Science & Natural History Unit's flagship program *The Nature of Things with David Suzuki* is an award-winning series broadcast across Canada, as well as many countries around the world. The series explores issues, discoveries and events in the worlds of science, medicine, technology, wildlife and the environment. Analytic and humanist in perspective, it documents our increasingly complicated and interconnected world, seeking to interpret both advances and setbacks, at a time when the speed of change is ever accelerating.
Proposals can be submitted to vance.chow@cbc.ca. If there is interest in a project, you will be contacted for further discussion and refinement of the program proposal. (General response time 4-6 weeks).
We currently work with independent producers from Canada who have International Treaty Co-productions with non-Canadian independents or broadcasters.

Discovery Communications Europe
Address: Discovery House, Bldg 2, Chiswick Park, 566 Chiswick High Road, London W4 5YB, UK
Email: rachel_oreilly@discovery-europe.com
Website: www.discoveryuk.com
Production Manager: Rachel O'Reilly

Discovery Communications' Internship Programme offers students valuable industry knowledge and skills through opportunities such as hands-on training, project management, executive lectures and networking opportunities. The programme runs between June and September and is based at Discovery House, West London. Discovery also supports internship opportunities in its regional offices in continental Europe on an as-needed basis.
http://careers.discovery.com/emea/internship-programme/overview.html

Discovery Communications, Inc.
DCI World Headquarters
One Discovery Place, Silver Spring, MD 20910, USA
Phone: +1 240 662 2000
USA Sales Offices
101 West Big Beaver Road, Suite 405, Troy, MI 48084-4169, USA
Phone: +1 248 764 4400
10100 Santa Monica Boulevard, Suite 1500, Los Angeles, CA 90067, USA
Phone: +1 310 551 1611
One Capital City Plaza, 3350 Peachtree Road NE, Suite 1630, Atlanta, GA 30326, USA
401 North Michigan Avenue, Suite 3000, Chicago, IL 60611, USA
Phone: + 312 946 0909
4201 Congress Street, Suite 245, Charlotte, NC 28209, USA
Phone: +1 704 557 2400
850 Third Avenue, New York, NY 10022-7225, USA
Phone: +1 212 548 5555

Asia-Pacific Headquarters
3 Changi Business Park Vista, #03-00, Singapore 486051
Phone: +65 6510 7500
Western Europe Headquarters
Discovery House, Chiswick Park Building 2, 566 Chiswick High Road, London, W4 5YB, UK
Phone: +44 208 811 3000
Latin America/U.S. Hispanic Headquarters
6505 Blue Lagoon Drive, Suite 190, Miami, FL 33126, USA
Phone: +1 786.273.4700
Central & Eastern Europe, Middle East, Africa Headquarters
59 Zlota Street, Zlote Tarasay, Lumen Building, 00-120 Warsaw, POLAND
Website: www.corporate.discovery.com & www.dsc.discovery.com

Discovery Communications' Campus Connect Internship Program is a 12-week, unpaid, for-credit learning experience. The program offers students valuable industry knowledge and skills through opportunities such as hands-on training, project management, executive lectures and networking opportunities. Internships are available during the spring and summer semesters. http://careers.discovery.com/north-america/internship-program/overview.html

Earth Touch
Addresses:
4 Sunbury Crescent, Sunbury Park, La Lucia Ridge, 4051, SOUTH AFRICA
7 Poland Street, London, W1F 8PU, UK
Phone: +27 (0)31 582 0800
Email: info@earth-touch.com
Website: www.earth-touch.com

Earth-Touch aspires to be the pre-eminent multimedia company that brings matters of the Earth (including wildlife and the environment) into the offices, homes and daily lives of people around the world by using cutting-edge technology. Our mission is to both educate and entertain as we strive to raise awareness and provoke reaction to a range of environmental matters. We aim to achieve this mission by disseminating our media across multiple platforms, including television networks, video and DVD, the internet and mobile phones. We are a South African company with a head office in Durban and a satellite office in London, UK.

Eden TV channel - UKTV
Address: 245 Hammersmith Rd, London W6 8PW, UK
Phone: +44 (0)845 734 4355
Website: www.uktv.co.uk
Email: web@uktv.co.uk
GM Factual: Adrian Wills
Scheduler, Eden: Laura Morris

GREEN.TV

Green TV
Address: 120 Long Acre, Covent Garden, London WC2E 9PA, UK
Phone: +44 207 240 0357
Email: Ade Thomas – ade.thomas@green.tv
Website: www.green.tv
Editorial Director: Martin Atkin – martin.atkin@green.tv
Business Development Director: Alex Aleksander
Content and Syndication Director: Fi Ferrer

GREEN.TV is the online TV channel, producer, distributor and syndicator for environmental and sustainability films. We work with a range of non-profit and corporate clients including WWF, Greenpeace, UNEP, Alstom and Vestas to produce and distribute video content through our syndication partners. Together with our sister company Large Blue we offer a complete digital communications service. We're interested in presenter-led online and broadcast series with big potential for sponsorship and branded content – especially in the green tech, clean-energy and low-carbon areas. We occasionally offer work experience – apply to one of the email addresses above.

itvWILD
Address: ITV Studios Limited, Anglia House, Norwich NR1 3JG, UK
Email: contact@itvwild.com
Website: www.itvwild.com

Search thousands of wildlife videos from one of the largest collections in the world and enjoy exclusive features from ITV wildlife programmes. With thousands of animal videos available and hundreds of thousands of keywords and search terms, you'll be amazed at the videos we have available to watch!

National Geographic Channel
US Headquarters : 1145 17th Street N.W., Washington, D.C. 20036-4688, USA
European Headquarters: 3rd Floor, Shepherd's Building East, Richmond Way, London W14 0DQ, UK
Phone: +44 (0)207 751 7700
Email: askngs@nationalgeographic.com
Website: www.nationalgeographic.com
Programme proposals: www.ngcideas.com

Nat Geo Wild
Website: www.natgeotv.com/uk/wild

Nat Geo Wild provides a unique window into the natural world, the environment and the amazing creatures that inhabit Planet Earth. From the most remote environments to the forbidding depths of our oceans, from protected parks to domestic doorsteps, Nat Geo Wild uses spectacular cinematography and compelling storytelling to take viewers on unforgettable journeys. Nat Geo Wild is part of National Geographic Channels International (NGCI) and is available in Australia, Hong Kong, India, Indonesia, Israel, Jordan, Macau, Malaysia, Maldives, Myanmar, Papua New Guinea, Philippines, Singapore, South Korea, Taiwan, Thailand, UAE, U.K., U.S., France, Italy, Portugal, Turkey, Germany, Latin America and other territories in Europe. Nat Geo Wild HD launched in the UK in March 2009, and is also available in Greece, Latin America, Poland, and Russia. Further expansion is expected globally.

RTP – Radio e TV Portugal
Address: Rua do Belomonte, 405, Mafamide, Vila Nova de Gaia 4430-029, PORTUGAL
Phone: +351 962407468 & +351 967902766
Fax: +351 22716125
Email: Luis Henrique – luis.henrique@rtp.pt
Website: www.rtp.pt or bloguedoluis.blogspot.com

I'm an author and wildlife film-maker in the Portuguese Public TV Station, Radio e Televisão de Portugal. I've made documentaries in São Tomé e Príncipe, Cape Verde, Portugal, Azores, Spain, Amazónia (Brazil, Colombia and Peru.) Lots of experience and lots of work in the field. I'm currently filming two new series about birds in Portugal and about wildlife in the four seasons. I'm editing two documentaries about the fossil treasures in Santa Maria Island (Azores) and another about great whales migration off-shore Pico Island (Azores). Of course I consider co-productions. I'm always Looking to improve my skills with books, like Wildeye books that I have, and other authors like David Attenborough, and Chris Palmer for instance.

SKY 3D
Address: BSkyB Ltd, Grant Way, Isleworth, Middlesex, TW7 5QD, Attn: Sky 3D, NHC1, UK
Phone: +44 (0)20 7032 7387
Email: sarah.needham@bskyb.com
Website: www.sky.com/tv/3d/producing3d
3D Production Executive: Sarah Needham
Commissioning Editors:
Head of Features & Factual: Celia Taylor – Celia.Taylor@bskyb.com
Head of Factual Entertainment: Mark Sammon – Mark.Sammon@bskyb.com

We very much look forward to receiving your programme ideas, to seeing your creativity and innovation and hearing why your project needs to be 3D. We're looking for ideas that will have a life both on a 2D channel like Sky One, Sky Living, Sky Arts or Sky Atlantic and then shine in 3D on Sky 3D.

South African Broadcasting Corporation (SABC)
Address (Head Office): Private Bag X1, Auckland Park, Johannesburg 2006, SOUTH AFRICA
Phone: +27 (0)11 714 9111
Fax: +27 (0)11 714 9744
Website: www.sabc.co.za

SABC will receive only submitted material that is embodied in written form in hard copy. Facsimiles and email submissions will not be considered. SABC will consider your submission only at your request and only with your assurance that to the best of your knowledge you are the sole originator of the idea and that you have the legal right to submit it to SABC for evaluation.

Terra: The Nature of Our World
Address: School of Film & Photography, P.O. Box 173350, Visual Communications
Building #202, Bozeman, Montana 59717-3350, USA
Email: Ericebendick@lifeonterra.com
Website: www.lifeonterra.com

TERRA: *The Nature Of Our World* is a collaborative filmspace and laboratory exploring the questions and ideas on the cutting-edge of science and at the farthest horizons of the natural world. We are a worldwide crossroads, a forum for compelling issues, and a stage for the awesome diversity of our planet. The content for the podcast is contributed freely by numerous independent filmmakers and the series is produced by Eric Bendick and George Potter.

LOCATION MANAGERS/FIXERS

African Environments
Address: P O box 16080, Mawalla St, Olasiti, TANZANIA
Phone: +255 27 2508625 & +255 733 508625
Fax: +255 27 2508625
Email: janiceb@africanenvironments.com
Website: www.africanenvironments.com
Director: Janice Beatty
Email Contact:
beatty@africanenvironments.com & wkrause@africanenvironments.com

Tanzania is the perfect venue for film crews wishing to capture some of the finest wilderness and largest concentrations of wildlife in the world. Janice Beatty, one of the directors of African Environments, has been "film fixing" in Tanzania for ten years. African Environments has been outfitting and providing field support for film crews for more than sixteen years. We offer safari camps, location guides, mountain climbs, film fixing, location managing, staffing of camps, camera vehicles, drivers, trip leaders, driver/guides. We assist in all genres: documentaries (wildlife/other), feature films, exposé documentaries. We don't offer work experience but do accept CVs (no minimum qualifications).

Akanksha Sood Singh
Address: J 183, Jalvayu Vihar, Sector 25, Noida 201301, INDIA
Phone: +91 9891116777 & +91 9891116777 Fax: +91 1204542312
Email: soodakanksha@gmail.com

Line Producer, still photographer, researcher for wildlife documentaries and feature films to be shot in India.

Amazon Trekkers
Address: Chacara, Ave Autaz mirin 8612, Tancredo, Neves, MANAUS 69085000, Amazonas, BRAZIL
Phone: +55 92 91 075700 Fax: +44 1908 542149
Email: amazontrekkers@yahoo.co.uk
Website: www.amazontrekkers.com/
Main contact: John Chalmers, specialist in river-based exploration of the Amazon system.

I specialise in river-based exploration of the middle and upper Amazon. I work with a team of biologists and local guides when required. Having lived in Amazonas for over eight years I have a vast resource of who's who in this area. I have a fleet of motorised canoes (skiffs) and my main boat of 20m has eight air-conditioned cabins. The installed 15 kVA-silenced genset is available for lighting. Main clients have included Dutch ITV and BBC. I look to co-operate with the production of adventure, pure non-sensationalised wildlife, and conservation-orientated films. I work strictly within IBAMA and Brazilian Naval guidelines or dispensations obtained. All Brazilian AV documentation can be organised either in Manaus or Rio. I do not accept payment through Brazilian co-producers.

Banksia Films
Address: Av. Adolfo Ducke, 105 – Manaus, Amazonia, BRAZIL
Phone: +55 92 9152 0962 & +55 92 8205 4615
Fax: +55 92 3321 4138
Email: carolinabanksiafilm@gmail.com
Website: www.banksiafilms.com
Main Contact: Carolina Fernandez

LOCAL KNOWLEDGE: A fund of knowledge of Amazon Forest, its people, language, geography, flora, fauna and geology. A wide network of contacts, and introductions to experts in every field. Up-to-date knowledge on all wildlife projects, such as translocations and research being undertaken in the region.
PERMITS AND LICENCES: Licenses to film from the Ministry Information and Communications; permits to film in national parks and reserves, and any other permits necessary from immigration, museums, railways, etc.
ARRIVAL AND DEPARTURE FORMALITIES: All import, clearing, export and freighting of equipment, plus personal airport assistance with immigration, customs, etc.
EQUIPMENT: Assistance in hiring equipment locally: lighting, generators, etc and recruitment of local cameramen and other crew if required.
ACCOMMODATION AND TRAVEL: All hotel/lodge bookings at residents' rates. Arrangement of specialised camp facilities, vehicle hire, internal flights, air charter (including helicopters), and all travel including personal holiday itineraries. Confirmation of outward air tickets and all transfers to and from hotels/airports.
THE ADVANTAGES OF USING OUR SERVICES: All your requirements can be handled quickly and efficiently, and as cheaply as possible, under one roof. Our cheerful participation as part of your team will save you hours of finding your way around. Our personal involvement will ensure that you get the very best advice and information throughout your time in Brazil.
I want to get involved in films that make the difference. Films that educate people and respect the animals. Film Categories: fiction & documentaries. I'm looking for collaborators to make films related with the biodiversity of the Amazon and I strongly consider co-productions. I offer work experience in the Amazon for who have the interest in coming to here. I'm not looking for a talent. I accept CVs by email.

Blue Wilderness
Address: 9 Hilltop Road, Widenham, KZN 4170, SOUTH AFRICA
Phone: +27 (0)39 9732348 & +27 (0)83 3031515
Fax: +27 (0) 86 6485072
Email: info@bluewilderness.co.za
Website: www.bluewilderness.co.za
Contacts: Mark and Gail Addison

Blue Wilderness has specialised in getting natural history film-makers up close and personal with South Africa's marine wildlife for fifteen years, and have been involved in over 350 film productions. Blue Wilderness have taken some of the world's most prestigious awards, Emmy award (*The Blue Planet* series), World Wildlife Photographer (Doug Perrine), World Wildlife Photographer (Thomas Peschak), Nomination for Roscar award, Fuji Film awards, Golden Globe Awards, Avanti awards. From the ultimate mega events such as the squid spawning, sardine run to cage-free encounters with all Africa's sharks and marine wildlife contact Blue Wilderness. We facilitate the filming of all and any marine wildlife shows, from presenter-led to purest blue-chip. We offer location management, fixing, stock footage, freelance cameraman, freelance presenters, underwater camera equipment. We offer internship programmes, collecting and collating shark data.

78

DesertLife
Address: Alice Springs, Northern Territory, AUSTRALIA
Phone: +61 (0)447358045
Email mark@desertlife.com.au
Website: www.desertlife.com.au
Owner/Operator: Mark Carter

DesertLife is a unique business offering a range of wildlife-related services in Central Australia. Services include: bird and wildlife guide, media assistance, biodiversity surveys, ecotour guide training, specialist consultancy.

E.A. Rift Valley Safaris Ltd.
Address: P.O. Box 41017 GPO 00100 Nairobi, KENYA
Phone: +254 733600856/7 & +254 20 3882050
Email: earvs@net2000ke.com
MD: Clive Dougherty

Wildlife filming · location fixing guiding camps etc. We have dedicated wildlife filming vehicles with filming door and roof mounts, and over ten years fixing/guiding wildlife filming experience. Have worked with Mtv, Grenada TV, canal+, etc.

Facilitation Southern Africa
Address: Suite 36, Private Bag X12, Cresta 2118, SOUTH AFRICA
Phone: +27 83 259-6324 & +27 11 880-4302
Email: karenvbrooks@gmail.com
Website: www.tinyurl.com/6l83cmw
Producer/Researcher/Facilitator: Karen Brooks

Facilitation for all southern African countries: South Africa, Swaziland and Lesotho, Botswana, Namibia, Zimbabwe, Mozambique and Zambia. Madagascar. Wildlife films, documentaries and commercials. Over twenty-three years' experience in South African television.

Fixers Brazil
Address: Avenida Bartolomeu de Gusmão, 163, Santarém · Pará, BRAZIL
Phone: +55 93 9115 8111
Email: gilserique@gmail.com
Website: www.fixersbrazil.com
Contact: Gil Serique (Founder)

We offer best locations and fixing work all over Brazil. We also have a few film pitches and help film-makers on the four corners of Brazil. We are specialised in providing film-makers and photographers with the best wildlife sites in the country, from Amazon (where we are based) to Pantanal, Rio de Janeiro, Salvador.

Indonesian Nature Foundation (LINI)
Address: Jl. Tirta Nadi 21, Sanur, 80227 Bali, INDONESIA
Phone: +62 361 8427 168
Director LINI: Gayatri
Technical Advisor: Ron Lilley
Email: gayatri@lini.or.id
Website: www.lini.or.id

We have experience in facilitating filming at various marine sites around Bali and elsewhere in Indonesia. Also we have helped film crews (inc for NatGeo) to film reptiles (snakes) in Komodo National Park, and Bali. We have wide travel experience in Indonesia, including Papua. Our community-based conservation work with marine ornamental fish collectors and their communities in Bali, Sumatra, and currently with the endemic Banggai Cardinalfish in Sulawesi might be of interest to film-makers coming to Indonesia. Sponsors always welcome! We will accept volunteers experienced in reef restoration and capacity-building.

Jon Rees Locations
Countries: South East Asia
Phone: +60 12 827 8902
Email: jonrees.asialocations@gmail.com
Contact: Jon Rees

Location and production management, fixer, shoot-logistics for Borneo, Malaysia, Indonesia & Southeast Asia. Highly efficient, No-nonsense, permits, locations, logistics, research and in-country organization.

Jin Pyn Lee – Fixer
Elemantree Media
Address: Blk 6, 12-430, Telok Blangah Crescent, 090006, SINGAPORE
Phone: +65 62726769 & +61 423662233
Fax: +65 62726769
Email: jinpyn.lee@elephantandtree.com
Website: www.elemantreemedia.com

Freelance television producer, director, writer, fixer, production management. Specialize in Asian natural history and conservation (over twenty years involvement). Jin Pyn's career spans across broadcaster and independent production companies. Credits include BBC Worldwide, Channel News Asia, and Animal Planet, across all genres: short-form interstitials, long-form factual documentaries, and animation. Geographically the programs have been distributed all over the globe, including Korea's Kids Talk Talk, US's Somos TV and India's Edumedia. In Japan, Jin Pyn has won the best animation award, and her children's picture book was the first from Singapore to garner multiple languages.

Kathleen Swalling Photography and Film
Address: 483 Route des Nants, Chamonix Mont-Blanc 74400, FRANCE
Phone: +33 637 381 294 (Business) & +971 501 678 018 (Technical)
Email: info@kathleenswalling.com
Website: www.kathleenswalling.com
Producer/Director/Line Production/Location Manager/Fixer: Kathleen Swalling – kathleen@kathleenswalling.com
Technical Director/Fixer: Andrew Chapman – andrew@kathleenswalling.com

Services: Producer, Associate Producer, Line Producer, Location Manager. Wildlife, Marine/Island specialist. Media inspiring awareness and engagement with the natural and cultural world. Experience: *Revolution on the Reef part 1 and 2* (concept development, location manager, line producer, script supervisor, main character), *Lord Howe Island: Paradise at the End of the World* (location manager, line producer, 2nd underwater camera). Unique: capabilities stretch from boardroom to remote fieldwork. Science, Art, Law. Fisheries Prosecutor, Island Manager, Senior Lawyer/Strategist for Great Barrier Reef. Highly experienced diver, former competitive triathlete. Other: filmmaker, photographer, skier, mountaineer, team and individual sports. Board Member: Filmmakers for Conservation. Languages: English (highly proficient) and French (B1- Intermediate). Collaboration on marine/adventure related projects in above roles. Interested in conservation-themed, pure wildlife and adventure films.
Inspiring collaboration or co-production with experienced broadcasters and production companies welcomed. We offer sponsorship partners extensive exposure through our networks in Arabia, Australia, Europe, and additional global exposure through our website. During its first year of operation, receiving up to 500 different individual monthly visitors from across over 50 nations of the world and approximately 40-50,000 hits per month. This is probably due to our strong global networks that have been enhanced by collaborative projects undertaken in Arabia, Australasia, and Europe. We are currently seeking to expand our networks within the United States.
We accept CVs via email to info@kathleenswalling.com. Students in postgraduate studies in natural history filmmaking or those with strong experience in these areas are welcome to apply for placement/internship. We offer work experience placements and internships and are actively seeking to partner with talented camera operators, editors and technicians. Good spoken and written English desirable. At time of print, we are seeking an experienced web sales developer and a potential transmedia partner.

Jungle Run Productions
Address: Jalan Raya Sanggingan #1. Ubud 80571, Bali Indonesia 80571, INDONESIA
Phone: +62 8123813887 & +62 361979109
Fax: +62 361975378
Email: info@jungle-run.com
Website: www.jungle-run.com
Head Creative Dude/Director/DOP: Joe Yaggi – joe@jungle-run.com
Production Coordinator: Shinta Okta – shinta@jungle-run.com

Jungle Run Productions offers complete production services for Indonesia and SE Asia including: HD crews & kit, location and production management, film permit facilitation, fixers, translators, full post-production and graphics, stock footage
We've worked with broadcasters and producers from around the globe. Some of our clients include: broadcast clients: BBC (1, 2, 3, Panorama, & BBC World), National Geographic, Animal Planet, One Planet Pictures, ICON Films, Diverse Bristol, Ricochet, Disney Channel, ABC USA, MTV, Paramount Pictures, CNN, EBU, NOS Holland, E! TV. NGO collaborations include: The Nature Conservancy (TNC), WWF, CIFOR, IFC, UNDP, USAID. Field production support for British, Dutch, Brazilian, German, Indonesia, Taiwanese, American, Canadian and Singaporean television productions.
We're looking to collaborate with serious producers and broadcasters to make great factual programs in Indonesia and SE Asia. We've worked throughout the region in some of the most remote regions that Asia serves up. Jungle Run has been operating since 1993 and is fully licensed for television production and distribution in Indonesia.
We occasionally consider interns so please don't hesitate. We're especially keen to have seasoned professionals coming through to share their skills and experiences with our vibrant and talented Indonesian team.

Magic Touch Films
Address: PO Box 26321, Windhoek, NAMIBIA
Phone: +264 (0)61 309 155 & +264 (0)81 355 5931
Fax: +264 (0)61 221 337
Email: info@magictouchfilms.com
Website: www.magictouchfilms.com
Contacts: Wolfgang Knoepfler and Edna Awaras

Services: permits/work visas, recces/locations, risk assessments, insurance, crew hire, equipment hire, accommodation, transport and everything else your production requires!

Mystic Pictures Films
Address: Kitwe/Lusaka, Zambia 10101, ZAMBIA
Phone: +260 955 558 259 & +260 968 370 375
Email: info@mysticpictureszambia.co.zm
Website: www.mysticpicturesfilms.webs.com
Production Consultant: Joseph Muwowo: josephmuwowo9@yahoo.com

Mystic Pictures Zambia is a production house working with international film crews doing production related works in Zambia. We are production fixers, camera crew and off-line editors working with HD formats.

Nguruman Camping Safaris
Address: PO BOX 25253 · 00603, Nairobi, KENYA
Phone: +254 (0)733 722818 & +254 (0)721 431432
Fax: +254 20 3874434
Email: ngurumansafaris@bizland.com
Website: www.ngurumansafaris.com
Director: Feisal Malik

We are specialists in camping safaris around Kenya and have all the necessary equipment and expertise to successfully run camps in the wilderness. We set up and manage camps for film crews country-wide, as per your specifications. We have been in operation since 1999 and market experience has enabled us to successfully set up camps for film crews as we realize the difference between running a camp for tourists and that for a film crew who are on a schedule. We also have our own vehicles; as a result, we can also handle the groundwork for your transport logistics.

Vivian A. N. Nuhu – Coordinator
Address: P. O. Box OS3053, Osu-Accra, GHANA, WEST AFRICA
Phone: +233 244799749 & +233 302763308
Email: vannuhu@yahoo.co.uk

Coordinating notably for outside filming crews, including BBC and NHK, on wildlife locations, permits and local casts and logistics. As an experienced wildlife conservationist, specialized in communication and education, I have been, and still are, available as a presenter for wildlife adventure documentaries for general public and especially youth-cum-school groups. As a trained wildlife film-maker without own equipment/facilities have facilitated in the production of overseas documentaries for awareness creation in my home country, Ghana.
Not looking for proposals. Have already a number of ideas and proposals for wildlife adventure particularly for children and general Ghanaian public with conservation theme. Collaborators/sponsors most needed. Will welcome co-productions if it comes with funding.

Tanzania Rift Valley Tours Ltd.
Address: P.O. Box 11381 Arusha, Tanzania 11381, TANZANIA
Phone: +255 784468823 & +255 754468823
Email: trvtours@bol.co.tz
MD: Rashid Mtungi
Guide/Fixer: Clive Dougherty – earvs@net2000ke.com

Wildlife filming and trekking-filming, over ten years in the business. Have dedicated filming vehicles with filming doors and roof mounts. Have done several Kilimanjaro shoots and wildlife filming over the last decade.

83

Viewfinders EPZ Ltd
Address: PO Box 14098, Nairobi 00800, KENYA
Phone: +254 (0) 716 875928 & +254 (0) 716 875953
Email: info@viewfindersltd.com
Website: www.viewfindersltd.com
Managing Director: Jean Hartley

The original wildlife film fixers, founded in 1988. Top quality wildlife films are our speciality, also documentaries on nature, science, medicine, conservation, etc. Operating in Kenya, we are the leaders in our field.
For employment and work experience, it would be very rare for us to take on anyone who is not locally based with an exceptional knowledge of wildlife.

Wide Eye Productions
Address: PO Box 222, Quinns Rocks, Perth, WA 6030, AUSTRALIA
Email: info@WideEyeProductions.com.au
Website: www.WideEyeProductions.com.au

A Perth, Western Australia, based production company. As well as working on our own projects, we also provide production services, crew and equipment to local or visiting production companies. We specialise in HD/4K+ acquisition. Not currently looking for proposals. We do consider co-production opportunities. Not currently offering work experience. Please refer to our website for further updates.

FILM FESTIVALS

Albert International Wildlife Film Festival
(Festival International du Film Animalier)
Address: 55 rue de Birmingham, Albert 80300, FRANCE
Email: presse@fifa.com.fr
Website: www.fifa.com.fr

The festival is an official competition in which each selected movie is presented to an international jury composed of personalities known for their competence, commitment and knowledge of wildlife and environment.

American Conservation Film Festival
Address: PO Box 889, Shepherdstown, WV 2544, USA
Phone: +1 304 876 7373
Email: Info@conservationfilm.org
Website: www.conservatiofilm.org

The American Conservation Film Festival presents entertaining films with a wide range of issues that often focus on the relationships between people and the environment.

Big Sky Documentary Film Festival
Address: 131 South Higgins Ave. Suite 3-6, Missoula, Montana 59802, USA
Phone: +1 406 541 3456
Email: info@bigskyfilmfest.org
Website: www.bigskyfilmfest.org/bsdff/festival/films/category/natural_facts/9

Category: Natural Facts · Films about Nature, Wildlife and the Environment.

Bird and Nature Film Festival
(Festival de L'Oiseau et de la Nature)
Address: 20 rue du Chevalier de la Barre 80142 Abbeville Cedex, FRANCE
Phone: +33 3 22 24 02 02
Fax: +33 3 22 25 47 97
Email: contact@festival-oiseau-nature.com
Website: www.festival-oiseau-nature.com
Festival Director: Marie-Agnès Boche
Assistant: Sophie Delsaut: sophie@festival-oiseau-nature.com

Our festival takes place every April. The acceptable formats are: for the pre-selection DVD (zone 2 or region-free) or Mini DV or DVCam and for the competition BETA Digital only for professionals and Mini DV or DVCam for amateurs. Please send entry early November at the latest. Entries open between late August and early November every year.
Non-feature film only (no children's or animated films)
The entrants can register their videos in the following categories: bird/wildlife, environment, conservation, (any length and year of production) and amateur (dealing with same subjects, up to 13min duration).

BLUE Ocean Film Festival & Conservation Summit
Address: 798 Lighthouse Ave., #324, Monterey, CA 93940, USA
Phone: +1 831 920 3527
Email: info@blueoceanfilmfestival.org
Website: www.blueoceanfilmfestival.org

BLUE Ocean Film Festival is a global film festival and conservation summit for underwater filmmakers and marine researchers. A simultaneous community festival will share the best of the film competition with the public and will include presentations from the filmmakers and scientists who created them. Following the festival, a selection of winning films will tour the world, providing those who may not otherwise have access to these great films a chance to learn more about our oceans.

Blue Planet Film Festival
Address: 6200 Vista Del Mar Suite 313 Los Angeles, CA 90293, USA
Email: info@BluePlanetFilmFest.com
Website: www.blueplanetfilmfest.com

Blue Planet Film Fest is an environmental and animal-welfare-themed film festival that endeavors to do for environmental films what Sundance did for indie films: branding a genre and making these films a staple of the general public's cultural menu. Our festival is more than an entertaining weekend where films are screened and seen. Instead, we aim to raise mainstream awareness and incite viewers to action on the most important issues of our time - climate change and animal welfare issues. Blue Planet provides both a visual and visceral experience with interactive, hands on, off-site, events to connect attendees at a heart level with issues related to Animal Welfare, Wildlife, Environmental issues, Ecology, Conservation, Sustainable Living/Non Sustainable living, Globalization, Climate Change, Factory Farming/Agriculture issues, Water, Land.

China Ya'an Panda International Animal and Nature Film Festival
Address: A2202, A2-3, Zhaowei Huadeng Mansion, No.14, Jiu Xian Qiao Road,Chao Yang District, 100016 Beijing, CHINA
Phone: +86 10 84 56 21 71   Fax: +86 10 84 56 20 61
Email: animalandnature@gmail.com
Website: www.film-yaan.com/yaanen/index.asp

Cinemambiente Environmental Film Festival
Address: via Montebello, 15, 10100 Torino, ITALY
Phone: +39 011 8138860 Fax: +39 011 8138896
Email: festival@cinemambiente.it
Website: www.cinemambiente.it

Since its debut in Turin in 1998, CinemAmbiente — Environmental Film Festival has presented outstanding environmental films in a year-round program of initiatives that promote cinema and green awareness.

CMS Vatavaran Environment & Wildlife Film Festival and Forum
Address: Research House, Saket Community Centre, New Delhi 110017, INDIA
Phone: +91 11 2686 4020/2685 1660/ 2652 2244/55
Fax: +91 11 2696 8282 & +91 11 4379 0248
Email: vatavaran@cmsindia.org & info@cmsvatavaran.org
Website: www.cmsvatavaran.org
Festival Director: Alka Tomar — alka@cmsindia.org
Contact: Narender Yadav — narender@cmsindia.org

CMS VATAVARAN is India's homegrown international Competitive and Travelling Festival of Environment and Wildlife Films.

Darsser NaturfilmFestival
Address: Arche Natura, Bliesenrader Weg 2, 18375 Wieck, Darß, GERMANY
Phone: +49 (0) 38233 – 70 38 10
Email: post@arche-natura.de
Website: www.darsser-naturfilmfestival.de
Contact: Kai Lüdeke

Since 2005 the Darsser Naturfilmfestival has been a growing attraction for both filmmakers and lovers of nature in Germany, also thanks to its location at the Baltic Sea on the unique Fischland-Darss-Zingst peninsula in the northeast of the country. The relaxed atmosphere during the festival makes it easy for visitors to get in touch with directors and producers, especially in the discussions after each screening. Further highlights are six excursions into the "Nationalpark Vorpommersche Boddenlandschaft" (Western Pomerania Lagoon Area National Park), where everyone can experience the beautiful surroundings of the Darsser Naturfilmfestival.

EcoCinema
Country: ISRAEL
Email: ecocinema@gmail.com
Website: www.ecocinema.org.il

EcoCinema began operating in 2004, producing film festivals at cinematheques around the country. Its goals are to bring Israel to films dealing with the environment in all its forms, and help Israeli artists to make such films.

EcoVision
Address: 55/57 90139 Palermo, ITALY
Phone: +39 091 332 567
Fax: +39 091 324 397
Email: info@ecovisionfestival.com
Website: www.ecovisionfestival.com

International Festival of Cinema and Environment, held in Palermo.

Ecozine: The International Film Festival and Environment of Zaragoza
Address: EcoZine Cultural Association PO Box 293, 50,080 Zaragoza, SPAIN
Phone: +34 617 946 303 & +34 976 205 640
Email: infoecozine@gmail.com or direccionecozine@gmail.com
Website: www.festivalecozine.es

Ecozine takes place in May, and we want to bring stories that talk about our Earth and how humans interact with it, loving it and, unfortunately, many times, wounding her. Our fundamental goal remains to show, support and promote films made about the environment. Being a free and open space from which to inform, disseminate, raise awareness and, of course, contribute to a world ever more just and sustainable, which sometimes is difficult. We want to keep on being an open window to provide a space for all those realities, we talk about the difficulties but also the solutions with an active and critical cultural attitude that promotes respect and conservation of our natural environment and all walks of life that respects our environment.

EKOFILM - International Film Festival on the Environment and Natural and Cultural Heritage
Address: Soborská 6, 160 00 Prague 6, CZECH REPUBLIC
Phone: +420 233 323 333 & +420 724 187 037
Fax: +420 233 323 333
Email: ekofilm@ekofilm.cz
Website: www.ekofilm.cz

EKOFILM is the International Film Festival about the Environment and our Natural and Cultural Heritage. It brings the latest information about the state of nature and the environment in various countries of the world and in many instances even facts about the resolution of particular situations to a wide audience.

Envirofilm
Address: Slovak Environmental Agency, Tajovského 28, 975 90 Banská Bystrica, SLOVAK REPUBLIC
Phone: +421 48 4374 182
Fax: +421 48 4132 153
Email: envirofilm@sazp.sk
Website: www.envirofilm.sk/index-en.html
Festival Manager: Dagmar Rajčanová

The International Film Festival ENVIROFILM seeks to help today's man to see and hear again the hidden universe, the hidden wealth of our planet, our homeland. It wishes to knock on human senses to bring a message to the brain about the worsening state of our environment and about risks that grow every year. ENVIROFILM is a feast of human soul awakening; a meeting place of people who have not lost the sense for mankind interests yet. People who want to get enlightened positively to recognise real values. That is why I feel very well at each ENVIROFILM. I defer with respect to each filmmaker who brought and is bringing artistic values to ENVIROFILM and contributes to the enlightenment of today's man.

Environmental Film Festival in the Nation's Capital
Address: 1228½ 31st Street, NW, Washington, D.C. 20007, USA
Phone: +1 202 342 2564 Fax: +1 202 298 8518
Email: info@envirofilmfest.org
Website: www.dcenvironmentalfilmfest.org

Founded in 1993, the Environmental Film Festival in the Nation's Capital has become one of the world's largest and most influential showcases of environmental film and a major collaborative cultural event in Washington, D.C. Each March the Festival presents a diverse selection of high quality environmental films, including many Washington, D.C., U.S. and world premieres. Documentaries, narratives, animations and shorts are shown, as well as archival, experimental and children's films at venues throughout the city. Films are screened at partnering museums, embassies, libraries, universities and local theaters and are attended by large audiences. Selected to provide fresh perspectives on global environmental issues, most festival films are accompanied by discussions with filmmakers, environmental experts and special guests, including national decision makers and thought-leaders, and are free to the public. The festival's website serves as a global resource for environmental film throughout the year.

Grenoble International Nature & Environment Film Festival
Address: Maison de la Nature et de l'Environnement de l'Isère, 5, place Bir-Hakeim,
38000 Grenoble, FRANCE
Phone: +33 (0)4 76 42 64 08
Fax: +33 (0)4 76 44 63 36
Email: frapna-isere@frapna.org & festival@frapna.org
Website: www.festivaldufilm-frapna.org

The festival aims at showing beautiful wildlife and environmental films coming from all over the world in order to raise public awareness of ecological issues.

International Bat Film Festival (IBFF)
Address: Bat Wildlife Rehabilitator Consortium, PO Box 272, New Canaan 06840, USA
Email: batinfo@batfilmfest.com
Website: www.batfilmfest.com

The Film Festival and Award Ceremony serves as a forum to raise awareness of the benefits and details of bats in a fun, campy, scientific and unusual way, recognize film-makers who achieve best-in-class in these categories, engage the press and honor achievements of individuals. The purpose of raising awareness is for the ultimate survival of bats in North America. According to the USFWS, nine bat species are expected to become extinct within ten years in North America. Millions of bats from Maine to Virginia have died and White Nose Syndrome (WNS) is moving to all fifty States and Canada despite the best effort of scientists and the USFWS.

International Underwater Film Festival Belgrade
Address: Pop Lukina 4, Beograd 11000, SERBIA
Phone: + 381 64 8611455 & +381 11 2625032
Email: dive.bgd@vektor.net
Website: www.kpa.co.rs
President: Milorad Djuknic
Director: Bruno Bratovic

The International Underwater Film Festival in Belgrade is a unique opportunity to peek into the underwater world, to find out more about it through films, photos, meetings with authors and other underwater adventurers and enthusiasts. As usual, the festival program encompassed film contest and film revue, underwater photography contest and exhibition, children drawings exhibition, art students, poster contest and exhibition, lectures, presentations and many other events.

International Wildlife Film Festival (IWFF)
Address: 27 Fort Missoula Road, Suite 2, Missoula, MT 59804 USA
Phone: +1 406 728 9380
Fax: +1 406 728 2881
Email: iwff@wildlifefilms.org
Website: www.wildlifefilms.org

The International Wildlife Film Festival (IWFF) created and based in Missoula, Montana, hosts a wide-ranging line-up of special events, public screenings, seminars and panel discussions and evening receptions. The Missoula festival is not a trade show or marketplace; it is a forum for people to teach and learn about the natural history filmmaking business and wildlife issues. Our festival is an eclectic collection of people who have a great concern for wildlife and wildlands, and how television, film and video play important roles in understanding and protecting creatures and habitat worldwide. The mission of the International Wildlife Film Festival is to foster knowledge and understanding of wildlife and habitat through excellent, honest wildlife films and other media. The IWFF was the first juried wildlife film competition in the world.

Jackson Hole Wildlife Film Festival
Address: 240 S Glenwood, Suite 112, PO Box 3940, Jackson, WY 83001, USA
Phone: +1 307 733 7016
Fax: +1 307 733 7376
Email: info@jhfestival.org
Website: www.jhfestival.org

Launched in 1991, the Jackson Hole Wildlife Film Festival's biennial six-day conference is an international industry event drawing 650+ international leaders in science, conservation, broadcasting and media.

Japan Wildlife Film Festival (JWFF)
Address: Akagishita-machi 11-1 162-0803 Shinjuku-ku, Tokyo, JAPAN
Phone: +81(0)3 5261 9908
Fax: +81(0)3 5261 9760
Email: jwff@naturechannel.jp
Website: www.naturechannel.jp

The festival hopes to increase understanding and awareness of the urgent need to protect and care for the natural world. It was established in 1993, and is held biennially.

Madeira Film Festival
Address: Apartado 392, Estação Zarco 9001-905 Funchal, Madeira, PORTUGAL
Phone: +351 91 302 8330
Email: aitken@madeirafilmfestival.com
Website: www.madeirafilmfestival.com
Festival Director: Aitken Pearson

Through the persuasive strength of audio-visual communication the Madeira Film Festival's aim is to raise awareness of the Laurisilva forest of Madeira. The Madeira Film Festival intends to be Europe's most exclusive and independent festival. Held at the prestigious Reid's Palace Hotel, The Madeira Film Festival serves as a platform to showcase independent feature, short and documentary films from directors around the world. Indicative of Madeira's continued commitment to preserve the natural history, flora and fauna of the island, the festival will present a special environmental category screening worldwide nature-orientated films. We are actively seeking content to screen at our festival: films that have a relevance to nature from around the world. We are always open to appropriate sponsorship proposals.

Matsalu Nature Film Festival
Address: Tallinna mnt 25, 90303 Lihula, Läänemaa, ESTONIA
Phone: +372 477 5141
Email: tiit.mesila@matsalufilm.ee
Website: www.matsalufilm.ee/english/index.html
Festival director: Tiit Mesila

The objective of the festival is to present and give credit to new nature films and filmmakers and to contribute to the distribution of nature films. The festival promotes natural and sustainable lifestyle and respect for the traditions of indigenous peoples, deeply interwoven with nature. The festival is a meeting place for filmmakers, whose films deal with the biological diversity and its protection, preserving nature as a habitat.

Montana CINE International Film Festival
Address: International Wildlife Media Center, Montana CINE, 718 S Higgins Avenue, Missoula, Montana 59801, USA
Phone: +1 406 728 9380
Email: iwmc@wildlifefilms.org
Website: www.wildlifefilms.org

Montana CINE is a new cultural and environmental film festival that brings our world closer to home. It celebrates and explores the cultures and issues that affect our world, our environment, and human relationships in the natural world. As with the annual International Wildlife Film Festival (IWFF) Montana CINE (Cultures and Issues of Nature & the Environment) is an annual film festival held every fall in Missoula, Montana featuring award-winning films, seminars, receptions and workshops. This film festival completes a global picture of why and how we live in our world and interact with our environment. While the wildlife film festival has a special focus with wildlife as the central theme, the film subjects of Montana CINE are broad, featuring topics and issues that explore the human experience and people's relationships with nature and their environment.

Namur Nature Festival
Address: Rue Léon François 6-8, 5170 Bois-de-Villers, BELGIUM
Phone: +32 (0)81 432 420   Fax: +32 (0)81 432 249
Email: secretariat@festivalnaturenamur.be
Website: www.festivalnaturenamur.be/en/

NaturVision
Address: Kultur:Land GmbH, Forstwaldstr. 6, 94556 Neuschönau, GERMANY
Phone: +49 8558 97390   Fax: +49 8558 9739 26
Email: info@natur-vision.de
Website: www.natur-vision.de

Documentaries from around the world focusing on nature and wildlife are welcomed.

New York WILD Film Festival
Address: 23 W. 73rd St., #1201, New York, NY 10023, USA
Phone: +1 212 877 6364
Email: info@nywildfilmfestival.com
Website: www.nywildfilmfestival.com
Founder and Executive Director: Nancy Rosenthal –nancy@nywildfilmfestival.com

Brand new weekend documentary film festival in New York City, April 2012 looking for international films with content of exploration, adventure, wildlife, conservation, ecology, environmental, earth sciences and campaign-related. Looking for submissions in the above genres: feature-length to shorts. Looking for collaborators/sponsors and we are looking for interns/volunteers so please email us.

The Paws and Claws Film Festival
Address: Vancouver Island, BC SPCA, 3150 Napier Lane, Victoria, BC V8T 4V5, CANADA
Phone: +1 250 507 7380 & +1 800 665 1868
Email: gbugslag@spca.bc.ca
Website: support.spca.bc.ca/site/PageServer?pagename=pcff_home
Events Coordinator: Gina Bugslag

Paws and Claws is the first wildlife film festival in Western Canada, and aims to promote awareness, knowledge and understanding of wildlife, habitat, people and nature through excellence in film, television, and other media. The Paws and Claws film festival is a fundraiser that is in support of BC SPCA Wild ARC. Wild ARC - the Wild Animal Rehabilitation Centre is operated by the BC Society for the Prevention of Cruelty to Animals. As the only wildlife rehabilitation centre on southern Vancouver Island, Wild ARC treats over 1,800 wild animals annually from throughout the region.

Planet in Focus
Address: 55 Mill Street, Case Goods Warehouse, Building 74, Studio 402
Toronto, Ontario M5A 3C4, CANADA
Phone: +1 416-531-1769 Toll Free: 1-855-531-1769
Fax: +1 416-531-8985
Email: sarah@planetinfocus.org
Website: www.planetinfocus.org
Executive Director: Sarah Margolius

Canada's top environmental film and video festival is a place to stoke debate or simply be awed by the beauty of nature.

San Francisco Green Film Festival
Address: 1230 Market Street #13, San Francisco, CA 94102, USA
Phone: +1 415 742-1394
Email: info@sfgreenfilmfest.org
Website: www.sfgreenfilmfest.org

SFGFF is the Bay Area's *only* event dedicated to film and media that explore green issues and sustainable living. Our mission is to organize and present inspiring programs of films and discussions that link media arts with environmental action and advocacy. The films that we premiere explore the relationship between people and the planet and offer compelling insights into the environmental challenges we face as well as the creative social entrepreneurs who are crafting a vision for a greener future.

San Francisco Ocean Film Festival
Address: 1007 General Kennedy Avenue San Francisco, California 94129, USA
Email: info@oceanfilmfest.org
Website: www.oceanfilmfest.org

Ocean lovers of all species find a second home on both sides of the screen at the San Francisco Ocean Film Festival (SFOFF), the first, largest, and most influential showcase of its kind in North America. Themes range from marine science and industry to wildlife, conservation, coastal culture, exploration, adventure, and salt-water sports.

SunChild Wildlife Film Competition
Address: Aygestan 5rd str, # 48 Fizkulturnikneri str., 0070, Yerevan, ARMENIA
Phone: +374 10 555209
Fax: +374 10 552181
Email: info@sunchild.org
Website: www.festival.sunchild.org

The SunChild Festival was established in 2007 by the Foundation for the Preservation of Wildlife and Cultural Assets (FPWC). The festival is a biennial event and the only wildlife/environmental festival in the entire South Caucasus region.

teleNatura
Address: University of Navarra, University campus, Pamplona 31080, SPAIN
Phone: +34 948 425600
Fax: +34 948 425636
Email: telenatura@unav.es
Website: www.unav.es/telenatura
Festival Directors: Bienvenido Leon & Santiago Echeverría

Conservation of Nature and the Environment Film Festival. Documentary, reportage, amateur production, NGO production. The festival's mission is twofold: firstly it tries to promote knowledge and respect for nature through the exhibition of quality films, secondly it offers a showcase which can help producers exhibit their work, thus promoting the production of nature films. Since it was founded in 2002, Telenatura has achieved excellent reception from producers, with over 800 films from 50 countries in competition. The public has also welcomed the festival, attending the screenings year after year in Pamplona. In addition, a selection of the awarded films have been shown in other festivals in several Spanish cities (Madrid, La Coruna and Zaragoza), as well as in Argentina, Costa Rica and New Zealand. In 2011 a new twin festival was born: teleNatura Costa Rica.

UK Green Film Festival
Email: info@ukgreenfilmfestival.org
Website: www.ukgreenfilmfestival.org

The UK Green Film Festival is a not-for-profit, national film festival showcasing films and filmmakers engaging with environmental and climate change themes. Launched in May 2011, look out for bonus screenings around the country later in the year, and for our next major festival in May 2012.

Wild & Scenic Environmental Film Festival
Address: 216 Main Street, Nevada City, CA 95959, USA
Phone: +1 530 265 5961
Fax: +1 530 265 6232
Email: miriam@syrcl.org
Website: www.wildandscenicfilmfestival.org
Producer of Wild and Scenic Events: Miriam Limov

The Wild & Scenic Film Festival is the largest of its kind in the US. Held annually the second week of January in the Nevada City, CA, the three-day event is a gathering of award-winning films, filmmakers, speakers, celebrities, and activists who bring a human face to the environmental movement and the actions being taken in our communities. The founding organization, SYRCL (South Yuba River Citizens League), is now sharing their success with other environmental groups to host 115 tour venues nationwide.

Wildlife Vaasa - International Nature Film Festival
Address: Vaasa, FINLAND
Phone: +358 400 800 302
Email: terranova@vaasa.fi
Website: www.wildlife.vaasa.fi

Wildscreen Film Festival
Address: Ground Floor, The Rackhay, Queen Charlotte Street, Bristol BS1 4HJ, UK
Phone: +44 (0)117 328 5952
Email: info@wildscreen.org.uk
Website: www.wildscreen.org.uk
Chief Executive: Richard Edwards

The Wildscreen Film Festival is an initiative of the UK-based charity Wildscreen – which uses the power of wildlife films and photos to promote a greater understanding of the natural world and the need for its conservation. To find out more about Wildscreen's key international initiatives please visit www.wildscreen.org.uk or the 'Organisations' section within this directory. Wildscreen Film Festival Panda Award categories: Animal Behaviour, Campaign, Children's Choice, Cinematography, Earth Sciences, Best Editing, Environment, Innovation, Best Music, New Media, Newcomer, People & Animals, Popular Broadcast Programme, Presenter-led, Best Script, Best Series, Short Film, Sound, Theatrical, Wildscreen's Award to promote filmmakers from developing countries, Jury's Special Prize, Christopher Parson's Award for Outstanding Achievement, and Golden Panda. For sponsorship opportunities please contact the Wildscreen Festival & Events Team. Each Wildscreen Festival a small dedicated team of volunteers are chosen through an application process – to be considered for such a role please contact the Wildscreen Festival & Events Team.

Wild Talk Africa
Address: Block A, Longkloof Studios, 21 Darters Rd, Gardens, Cape Town 8001, SOUTH
AFRICA
Phone: +27 (0)21 422 0154
Fax: +27 (0)21 422 0012
Email: shani@wildtalkafrica.com
Website: www.wildtalkafrica.com
Festival Director: Sophie Vartan
Festival Manager: Shani van Straaten

Situated in the home of wildlife filmmaking, Wild Talk Africa is a premier international
film festival and conference. Wild Talk Africa provides a relaxed and authentic platform
for networking and exchanging ideas between the international filmmaking fraternity and
the local African industry, as well as showcasing its talent and superior
infrastructure. Stay connected to the industry as we bring some of the world's top
broadcasters and cutting edge technology to Cape Town, and be part of the growth and
future of filmmaking within this wild continent.
Festival Categories/Awards: Best of the Festival, Cinematography, Limited Budget, Best
Children's Natural History Production, Best Environmental Production,
Expedition/Adventure, Short Film, Presenter, Alternative Broadcast, Editing, Best Script,
Best Series, Best Music and Sound Design, Best Newcomer, Best African Production.
Wild Talk Africa is looking for festival volunteers and interns as of 2012. If you want to
work with Wild Talk Africa please contact shani@wildtalkafrica.com

Wlodzimierz Puchalski Nature Film Festival
Address: WFOiPE ul. Kilinskiego 210 93-106 Lodz, POLAND
Phone: +48 42 689 23 45
Fax: +48 42 689 23 46
Email: wfo@wfo.com.pl
Website: www.wfo.com.pl/eng/about.html

The festival is a biennial event (odd years) that takes place in Lodz. The festival
programme includes an international competition of films that deal with nature and
environmental issues. The festival screens more than forty films in competition and
awards several prizes.

EDUCATION/TRAINING

American University's Center for Environmental Filmmaking
Address: 4400 Massachusetts Avenue, NW, Washington DC 20016-8017, USA
Phone: +1 202 885 3408
Fax: +1 202 885 2019
Email: palmer@american.edu
Website: www.environmentalfilm.org
Director: Professor Chris Palmer

Films and new media are essential educational and political tools in the struggle to protect the environment. Our mission is to train filmmakers to produce films and new media that effectively strengthen the global constituency for conservation. The world faces immense environmental challenges. We are fouling our own nest to an unprecedented degree. Powerful, emotive, and affecting images and films can play a key role in raising the importance of conservation and bringing about change. We are committed to raising awareness and empowering action through the innovative use of media.

Bristol Wildlife Filmmakers
Address: 44 Clarendon Road, Redland, Bristol BS6 7ET, UK
Phone: +44 (0)117 924 9426 & +44 (0)1275 375861
Email: karen.partridge@blueyonder.co.uk
Website: www.bristolwildfilm.co.uk
Co-Founders: Karen Partridge and Sarah Pitt – sarah.pitt@metronet.co.uk

Bristol Wildlife Filmmakers run professional courses for filmmakers, wildlife educators and wildlife enthusiasts. We work on location and courses are timed to coincide with natural wildlife events. Our tutors are all professionals working in the international natural history broadcast industry and include producers, directors, editors and camera people. We also offer tailor-made courses designed to meet the needs of business and conservation bodies. So, if you want to ENGAGE with NATURE through FILMMAKING and don't know where to start – talk to us! Tap into world-class expertise and learn how to craft wildlife films that will inspire others. We are not looking for proposals and we do not offer work experience/internships.

Canopy Access Limited
Country: UK
Website: www.canopyaccess.co.uk
Directors: James Aldred & Grant Harris

Canopy Access Limited provides safety at height for working on ropes in the rainforest canopy.
CAL was set up in 1998 to provide camera assistance and technical rigging solutions for the wildlife TV industry and has been providing access, training and consultancy on a full time basis ever since.

CBCF
Community-based Biodiversity Conservation Films
Address: 1758, Kijabe Farm, Naivasha 20117, KENYA
Phone: +254 725711057
Email: info@communityconservationfilms.org
Website: www.communityconservationfilms.org
Technical Director: Elijah Chege – cbcfkenya@gmail.com

We produce environmental films/documentaries, offer a minimum of two weeks film production training, community film showing, film distribution. We sell stock footage and stills. We are looking for conservation-themed films. We are working towards being conservation filmmaking agents in East Africa, We are also looking for collaborators and sponsors. We are happy to co-produce.

Hairy Frog Productions Ltd
Address: 4 The Paddock, White Horse Lane, Trowse, Norwich, Norfolk NR14 8TD, UK
Phone: +44 (0)7885964790
Email: hairyfrog@lineone.net
Website: www.hairy-frog.co.uk
Director/Producer/Cameraman: Mike Linley – mike_linley@yahoo.co.uk

Wildlife Production Company with full HD kit (BBC specs) + GoPro hero in flat optic housing + video-microscope and endoscopes + Canon 7D time-lapse kit. Over 400 credits mainly as a Producer for Survival/Anglia Television. Now also producing Wildlife Interactive Touch-screens. Over forty International awards to date. Specialist in herpetology, entomology and UK wildlife. Large video, sound and stills library. Always happy to co-produce. Limited work experience opportunities, depending on current projects.

Jeff Goodman – Underwater Wildlife Video and Edit Courses
Address: The High Barn, Sancreed, Penzance, Cornwall TR20 8QY, UK
Phone: +44 (0)1736 788705
Email: jeffgoodman@supanet.com
Website: www.jeffgoodman.co.uk/underwatercoursesintropage.html

Jeff Goodman, director and award-winning cameraman, leads a series of courses aimed at improving the art of good underwater video production while at the same time realising the incredible wealth and diversity of our planet's marine life. Learn the skills of camera work, editing and story creation first. Share a camera with a friend if you like. The courses are very flexible and can be tailored to fit individual requirements from the absolute beginner to the semi pro.

MFA Program in Science and Natural History Filmmaking
Address: School of Film & Photography, P.O. Box 173350, Visual Communications Building #202, Bozeman, Montana 59717-3350, USA
Phone: +1 406 994 2484 Fax: +1 406 994 6214
Email: naturefilm@montana.edu
Website: www.naturefilm.montana.edu

The graduate program in Science and Natural History Filmmaking at Montana State University is the first program of its type in the world and remains the largest and the most well-known.

Nature Kenya
Address: 44486, Nairobi 00100, KENYA
Phone: +254 0700886424
Email: Mbengeus@yahoo.com
Website: www.communityconservationfilms.org
Contact Film-maker: Mary Mbenge

Making films for children in local languages. Children's conservation films. Co-production is very welcome and sponsors too because I do it voluntarily. Work experience offered to those with an interest in conservation.

One Tribe TV
Address: Fairview, Charlcombe Lane, Bath BA1 5TT, UK
Email: info@onetribetv.co.uk
Website: www.onetribetv.co.uk
Managing Director: Dale Templar

Series Producer from the BAFTA award-winning BBC landmark series *Human Planet* now heads up her own independent production company One Tribe TV. Based in Bath and Bristol, One Tribe TV specialise in foreign and remote filming, producing natural history, travel, expedition, anthropology and science content. The company also provides media training, corporate video production, media consultancy, guest lecturing and professional speaking. Our clients include the BBC Academy, Royal Geographical Society and Cunard.
One Tribe TV are always on the look out for exciting ideas and proposals with engaging stories, compelling context and new concepts. Our content focuses on wildlife, science, adventure, and human-interest stories whether they're presenter-led formats or traditional documentary. In addition to film and television content, we have started a corporate production and media training arm. We are always looking to collaborate with other production companies that have strong, engaging and compelling ideas both internationally and within the UK. We are currently working on television projects with the BBC, Dragonfly, RGS, BFI and Adventure Lifesigns.

99

Skillset
Address: Focus Point, 21 Calendonian Road, London N16 6XS, UK
Phone: +44 (0)207 713 9800
Email: info@skillset.org
Website: www.skillset.org
Partnerships Managers: Sarah Trigg and Rebecca Davies

Skillset is the industry body which supports skills and training for people and businesses to ensure the UK creative industries maintain their world class position. If you're working in one of these industries, we have information and resources to help you take your career to the next level.

SpecialistStock

Specialist Stock Media Training
Country: UK
Phone: +44 (0)1275 375520
Email: info@specialiststock.com
Website: www.SpecialistMediaTraining.com
Director: Tom Walmsley – tom@specialiststock.com

Specialist Stock offers a number of services (www.SpecialistStock.com/services). As a comprehensive collection of photo and footage libraries we license material and multimedia photostories to the global media industry. Through our Comprehensive Research Facility we search our global supplier network for any subject matter and sort out the licenses.
Finally we give consultations and seminars to individuals and businesses who are 'Adopting a Video Workflow' by going through the options, technical details and business plan.

UK Wildlife Film School
Address: Fort William, SCOTLAND, UK
Website: www.wildlifefilmschool.com
Managing Director: Ric Swift

The UK wildlife Film School has been established to give you first-hand experience of working in the field, and filming 'real wildlife', in some of the most beautiful and remote locations on offer throughout the UK. Our courses are not run in nature reserves, or animal rescue centres, where you will find that the animals are kept in an enclosed space. All the animals you will encounter will be 'real wildlife', living in their own natural environments. Please see our website for further details: www.wildlifefilmschool.com (please mention *Wild Pages*, in your email, when responding from this entry/publication)

We are a film school and as such do not produce items for broadcast; therefore, we are not looking for any film ideas or film proposals. We are always interested to hear from possible sponsors, both from the UK and overseas. We do not offer work experience placements. We are always looking of for talented staff to join our list of freelance instructors. For the type of staff we are looking for, take a look at the staff write-ups, on the staff pages of our website. If you feel you hold similar work experience, please feel free to email a covering letter, CV and wildlife related work history to info@wildlifefilmschool.com

Wildeye – The International School of Wildlife Film-making
Address: Wildeye, Heather Lodge, The Moor, Reepham, Norwich NR10 4NL, UK
Phone: +44 (0)1603 871141
Email: courses@wildeye.co.uk (for information about courses and bookings) or info@wildeye.co.uk (for general enquiries)
Website: www.wildeye.co.uk
Principal: Piers Warren

Wildeye run a number of courses, workshops and training expeditions for aspiring wildlife film-makers and enthusiastic amateurs. If you are just starting out we suggest you start with the Introduction to Wildlife Film-making weekend in Norfolk, UK. From there you can go on to take more specialist weekend courses such as wildlife camera operator, creative video editing or wildlife sound recording. We also run a variety of exciting wildlife training tours and expeditions all over the world. We have now had many hundreds of students on our courses from all over the world and are thrilled to hear of those that are now accomplished in the industry, award-winners, or simply making better wildlife films for their own enjoyment. We have had numerous tutors over the years, all experienced professionals with an enthusiasm for sharing their knowledge, often gained through many years of dedicated work in the wildlife film-making industry. Many of our tutors are multi-award-winners who continue to work in production.

Wildlife Film Academy
Address: Block A, Longkloof Studios, 21 Darters Rd. Gardens, Cape Town 8001, SOUTH AFRICA
Phone: +27(0)21 422 0154
Fax: +27 (0)21 422 0012
Email: info@wildlifefilmacademy.com
Website: www.wildlifefilmacademy.com
Head of Production and Wildlife Film Academy Registration: Géta Palm – geta@nhuafrica.com
Head of Operations: Khanyo Nzunzu – khanyo@wildlifefilmacademy.com

A practical filming location in a game reserve in southern Africa to give you hands on camera experience. Lectures on how to conceptualize script and make your film come to life. Tutorials and lectures developed by renowned wildlife filmmakers who know how hard it is to make a start in the wildlife filmmaking industry. Individual access to editing suites and personal tutors to enable you to complete your own film at the end of the course, which you can use as a promo for a bigger project. We notify students who have completed the course about any industry jobs and openings.

Wildscreen Outreach
Address: Ground Floor, The Rackhay, Queen Charlotte Street, Bristol BS1 4HJ, UK
Phone: +44 (0)117 328 5952
Fax: +44 (0)117 328 5955
Email: info@wildscreen.org.uk
Website: www.wildscreen.org.uk/initiatives-outreach
Chief Executive: Richard Edwards

Wildscreen Outreach is an initiative of the UK-based charity Wildscreen which uses the power of wildlife films and photos to promote a greater understanding of the natural world and the need for its conservation. To find out more about Wildscreen's key international initiatives please visit www.wildscreen.org.uk or the 'Organisations' section within this directory.

Wild Work Productions
Email: info@wildworkproductions.com
Website: www.wildworkproductions.com
Contact: Marleen van der Werf

Wild Work Productions runs filmmaking workshops especially for scientists and conservationists. In the hands-on workshops you and your team learn to communicate your work and be trained in the essential skills for making professional (web) films. During the workshop, you will also be able to make your own film about your work, which will be perfectly suitable for online informational, promotional and funding purposes. For more information, please email us.

ORGANISATIONS

21st Paradigm
Address: 1714 NW Quincy Ave, Bend, Oregon, 97701, USA
Phone/Fax: +1 541 868 7646
Email: info@21Paradigm.com
Website: www.21paradigm.com
Contact: Vanessa Schultz

21st Paradigm is a non-profit group that produces award-winning films to raise awareness of crucial issues censored by mainstream networks. A way of thinking for the 21st Century that respects the intrinsic value of all life – that is, the right of other life forms to exist regardless of their instrumental values to humans. Not only the pretty birds but also the predators and reptiles, the ugly and unloved have a right to be left in peace, to exist not only for the pleasure and health and instruction of humans but for their own sake.

Aaduki Multimedia Insurance
Address: Bridge House, Okehampton, Devon EX20 1DL, UK
Phone: +44 (0)1837 658880
Fax: +44 (0)1837 658503
Email: info@aaduki.com
Sales Manager: Vince Brown
Website: www.aaduki.com

Specialist insurance provider for the photographic and video-making community. Aaduki can cover photographers and video makers as well as camera operators, both professional and amateur for cover for equipment, including loss or damage, public liability and other covers relevant to the client. Aaduki is one of the leading providers in the community and prides itself on its friendly, efficient service.

Adventures With Elephants
Address: P O Box1500, Bela Bela, 0480, SOUTH AFRICA
Phone: +27 14 7347700
Email: info@efaf.co.za
Website: www.efaf.co.za
Manager: Sean Hensman

AWE Offer hands on educative interactive elephant experiences with six African elephants as well as safaris, night safaris and swims. We have trained elephants for a number of films, documentaries, re-enactments and other. We are looking for any filming that anyone would like to do with elephants, we hope to do more educational filming. Please contact us via email for any work experience queries.

The Brock Initiative
Address: Dumpers Cottage, Chew Magna, Bristol, BS40 8SS, UK
Phone: +44 (0)1275 333187 +44 (0)7968 365816 Fax: +44 (0)1761 221702
Email: info@brockinitiative.org
Website: www.brockinitiative.org
Executive Producer: Richard Brock

I try to get stuff out there that will make a difference. There are now more ways of doing that than ever before. It can be in any format, anywhere, anyhow. I will provide free footage on wildlife and environmental matters from around the world. I am always interested in issues where "Filming with Attitude" might help the planet. Just let me know.

CAVU
Address: 941 W. Byrd, Ste 101, Universal City, TX 78148, USA
Phone: +1 210 858 8580 (US) & +506 2228 3047 (COSTA RICA)
Email: contact@cavusite.org
Website: www.cavusite.org
Cinamatographers: Garrick Dutcher & Kai Benson
Director of Photography: Alvaro Rodriquez
Editor: Tony Hale

When people are informed and engaged, healthy societies and renewable natural resources thrive. Outreach campaigns are CAVU at its best. Each one works to create a level playing field and unite communities by fully employing CAVU's unique combination of tools: flight, film and education. Film is the principal medium of communication in a CAVU outreach campaign. Films share the power of flight and embody the transformative nature of education by using the voices of local stakeholders

Channel G
Website: www.channelg.tv
Executive Director: Cynthia A. Phillips

Using the power of media and communication to help non-profits enact progressive social change! Channel G is a non-profit media company that provides a platform for non-profits and filmmakers to share their stories of positive global change. Channel G partners with non-profits to tell their stories through the medium of short films, showcasing their projects to the world in a professional manner: from story development, to production, and a sophisticated marketing and distribution system that delivers these films to millions of viewers via the Internet, television, film festivals and various other vehicles. These short films highlight the universal themes of the critical social issue at hand, and the greater mission of the work being done by our non-profit partners in the areas of the environment, sustaining community, health & wellness, social justice, and the arts.

CBCF
Community-based Biodiversity Conservation Films
Address: 1758, Kijabe Farm, Naivasha 20117, KENYA
Phone: +254 725711057
Email: info@communityconservationfilms.org
Website: www.communityconservationfilms.org
Technical Director: Elijah Chege – cbcfkenya@gmail.com

We produce environmental films/documentaries, offer a minimum of two weeks film production training, community film showing, film distribution. We sell stock footage and stills. We are looking for conservation-themed films. We are working towards being conservation filmmaking agents in East Africa, We are also looking for collaborators and sponsors. We are happy to co-produce.
CBCF's Goals:
1. To train indigenous young conservationists in Kenya, Tanzania and the rest of East Africa to make biodiversity conservation films for the sake of effective environmental education,
2. To make these films in partnership with local communities about issues linked to their local livelihoods,
3. To distribute these films among education organisations (NGO and government) within East Africa and beyond.
4. To evaluate the effectiveness of digital films as a means of education and capacity-building in schools, communities and countries where we exist.

EarthWatch Institute
Addresses: Mayfield House, 256 Banbury Road, Oxford, OX2 7DE, UK
Phone: +44 (0)1865 318 838 Fax: +44 (0)1865 311 383
Email: info@earthwatch.org.uk
114 Western Ave, Boston, MA 02134, USA
Phone: +001 (978) 461-0081 Fax: +001 (978) 461-2332
Email: info@earthwatch.org
Website: www.earthwatch.org

Our mission is to engage people worldwide in scientific field research and education to promote the understanding and action necessary for a sustainable environment. Earthwatch is an international environmental charity that is committed to conserving the diversity and integrity of life on earth to meet the needs of current and future generations. We work with a wide range of partners, from individuals who work as conservation volunteers on research teams through to corporate partners, governments

105

and institutions. Earthwatch has a global reach, with offices in Oxford (UK), Boston (USA), Melbourne (Australia) and Tokyo (Japan).

Environmental Investigation Agency (EIA)
Address: 62-63 Upper Street, London N1 0NY, UK
Phone: +44 (0)20 7354 7960
Email: ukinfo@eia-international.org
Website: www.eia-international.org
Head of Operations: Bill Dishington
Press Officer: Paul Newman – paulnewman@eia-international.org
Video Production/Training Co-ordinator: Paul Redman – paulredman@eia-international.org

EIA produces hard-hitting campaign films on a wide range of environmental crimes, as well as bespoke training films for enforcement agencies. It also has one of the world's largest archives of footage devoted to the illegal trade in wildlife products and other environmentally damaging commodities. The collection is data-based and is available on a professional basis to journalists, publishers and programme-makers. All the funds raised from the sale of this archive help to fund future campaigns. The visual media you see on our website is indicative of what is available in the whole collection. We are always prepared to listen to programme-pitches from media professionals with a view to highlighting our work. Applications for work experience welcomed; CVs by email please.

Filmmakers For Conservation (FFC)
Country: UK/Worldwide
Website: www.filmmakersforconservation.org
Email: paulm@filmmakersforconservation.org
Coordinator: Paul Mahoney

106

Filmmakers For Conservation is a global community of passionate people who work in, or have an association with, the global film and television industry. The organisation was born almost a decade ago out of a growing sense of frustration among many producers and directors that there was very little funding and airtime being made available for films that dealt with conservation and the environment.

Films That Make A Difference!
Country: UK/WORLDWIDE
Email: jason@wildeye.co.uk
Website: www.filmmakersforconservation.org/conservation-filmmaking/film-library.html
Project Coordinator: Jason Peters

An online directory of effective conservation films. A project set up in collaboration with Wildeye, The Brock Initiative, AU's Centre for Environmental Filmmaking and Filmmakers for Conservation. It is hosted on the FFC website and is an expanding catalogue of films that have made, or are intent on making, a difference. The database can be used by anyone looking for models for their own productions, for proof that filmmaking can make a difference, and will potentially lend strength to funding applications etc. The database will, over time, become a valuable resource for showing how best to make a difference using film. We will not tell people how to do this, the films will speak for themselves!

Fisher Forestry Environmental Management
Address: 308 Jasmine Drive, Conway, SC 29527, USA
Phone: +1 843 902 3388
Email: WideWorldofWildlife@hotmail.com
Website: www.wideworldofwildlife.webs.com
Registered Forester & Wildlife Natural Resource Manager: Jim Fisher II – FisherForestry@gmail.com

Establishing and maintaining wildlife food plots. Tagging and distribution of Canadian Geese, capturing nuisance alligators, snakes, and other wildlife for relocation. Experience in herpetology, biology, botany, and the safe handling of all forms of wildlife. Handled Expert Witness Testimony in court. Have handled all indigenous snakes in the Southeast United States for the over twenty-three years and have never been bitten by a venomous or non-venomous snake or spider. A Documentary Exploration Film of Nature with Naturalist Jim Fisher's *The Wide World of Wildlife – Eastern Cottonmouth Snake.*

Friends of the Earth (Bristol UK Branch)
Email: clairepagan@hotmail.com
Website: www.bristolfoe.org.uk
Press Officer: Claire Evans – press@bristolfoe.org.uk

107

Friends of the Earth make films with an environmental theme. The Bristol group's films have been played at the Arnolfini and on TV. They are usually short films. You can see an example of an FoE film here: www.bristolfoe.org.uk/?Content=Campaign=Get-Serious-About-CO2

We would be interested in receiving ideas for films that are in line with the goals of FoE. See www.bristolfoe.org.uk and www.foe.co.uk for more information. Bristol FoE considers co-productions and sponsors, contact us if interested. We can sometimes offer work experience. Prefer CVs by email. Some prior experience is usually necessary for roles such as camera operator. However, there are other roles (such as Production Coordinator) for which minimal experience is required.

Great Apes Film Initiative (GAFI)
Address: 3 Westfield Cottages, Medmenham, Marlow, Buckinghamshire SL7 2HQ, UK
Phone: +44 (0)1491 575 017
Email: madelaine@gafi4apes.org
Website: www.gafi4apes.org
Director: Madelaine Westwood

The Great Apes Film Initiatives uses the power of film and media in support of conservation. Many people living in depleted habitats alongside critically endangered species have never seen wildlife or conservation films and therefore have no access to accurate information on protection measures or local solutions that could make an enormous difference to their lives. GAFI distributes film to three target groups a) Government ministers b) National television audiences c) Local communities, schools, wildlife management centres, park rangers and the army – anyone who can be empowered to make a difference. So far 300 million people have seen the films through road shows, river shows, TV broadcast and now by the innovative pedal powered cinema shows which brings films to remote communities where there is no electricity. GAFI also trains NGOs to make their own films on local issues in local languages. In 2011 GAFI has extended its template to include elephant and tiger conservation, and it is intended to include all endangered species by 2015. GAFI actively encourages film submissions for its library that are rights free or assigned. Any format is invited, animation and non-languages versions are particularly welcome or versions in a number of languages. GAFI has a legal agreement document that is used for all films giving security to copyright owners. GAFI makes local issue conservation films for its partners, and co-productions are welcome. GAFI took its first volunteers to the field in July 2011 to assist with pedal powered cinema screenings and filming promotional material for websites. Any interested volunteers should contact Madelaine Westwood.

108

HAWNT Media
Address: P.O. Box 1872, Byron Bay, NSW 2480, AUSTRALIA
Phone: +61 421573262
Email: info@hawntmedia.com
Website: www.hawntmedia.com
Director: Rowena Mynott

HAWNT Media is a company specialising in natural history photojournalism. Services offered include natural history research for wildlife films, scientific advice, photography and writing. We currently have an aquatic wildlife documentary focusing on sharks in production. We produce natural history and science writing and photography as well as magazine publishing.
We invite communication from sponsors and are open to collaborations. We are always interested in hearing from people that might like to contribute. CVs and publication content can be sent via email or post. We would prefer contributors to be experienced writers, photographers and/or scientists but are happy to hear from anyone interested in being part of our publication. We would also consider work experience placements.

Highland Images
Address: The Cabin, Silverbridge, Garve, Ross-shire IV23 2PU, Scotland, UK
Phone: +44 (0)1997 414215
Email: highlandimages@btinternet.com
Website: www.highlandimages.com
Owner: Andrew Allan

Wildlife filming and photography holidays in the Highlands of Scotland, specialising in Ptarmigan, Red Deer and Wild Goats. Accommodation and Equipment supplied.

International League of Conservation Photographers (iLCP)
Address: 2011 Crystal Drive Suite 500 Arlington, VA 22202, USA
Phone: +1 703 341 2786
Website: www.ilcp.com
Chief Operating Officer: Mark Christmas – mark@ilcp.com
Director of Communications and Multimedia: Jenny Nichols – jenny@ilcp.com

As a project-driven organization, our mission is to translate conservation science into compelling visual messages targeted to specific audiences. We work with leading scientists, policy makers, government leaders and conservation groups to produce the highest-quality documentary images of both the beauty and wonder of the natural world and the challenges facing it ... Making a difference, one image at a time.

International Association of Wildlife Film-Makers (IAWF)
Website: www.iawf.org.uk
Chairman: Andy Shillabeer
Secretary: Mandy Leith

The International Association of Wildlife Film-makers (IAWF) was founded in 1982 to encourage communication and co-operation between people who are often isolated in the field. We are an association for professional camera men and women and sound recordists earning most of our income from making wildlife films. Our worldwide membership includes many of the leading names in our industry.

International Conservation and Education Fund (INCEF)
US Address: 236 11th Street, SE, Washington DC 20003-2124, USA
Phone: +1 (202) 548-0115
Congo Address: BP 1506, Rue de la Musique Tambourinee, Quartier Nfoa, Centreville, Brazzaville, REPUBLIC OF CONGO
Phone: +242 5930529
Email: Cyn@incef.org
Website: www.incef.org
Founder/Executive Director: Cynthia Moses Director of Production: David Weiner
Republic of Congo Manager: Bonne Année Matoumona

The International Conservation and Education Fund (INCEF) is an American 501(c)3 non-profit organization dedicated to the concept that a commitment to strategic communication is a prerequisite to positive changes in attitudes and behavior regarding the nexus of wildlife conservation, public health and economic development in underdeveloped and/or overly exploited areas of the planet. INCEF's approach focuses on the use of locally produced and disseminated video as an educational tool to foster improvement of the health and well-being of human and wildlife populations. We do this by: • Building capacity among local media professionals and emerging filmmakers to produce quality digital productions in local languages that are culturally appropriate • Building capacity of local education teams to disseminate these videos and measure impact • Analyzing impact measurements of our outreach to understand the efficacy of our efforts and to adapt production and dissemination plans to fit the needs of the communities we serve

Indonesian Nature Foundation (LINI)
Address: Jl. Tirta Nadi 21, Sanur, 80227 Bali, INDONESIA
Phone: +62 361 8427 168
Director LINI: Gayatri Technical Advisor: Ron Lilley
Email: gayatri@lini.or.id
Website: www.lini.or.id

We have experience in facilitating filming at various marine sites around Bali and elsewhere in Indonesia. Also we have helped film crews (inc for NatGeo) to film reptiles (snakes) in Komodo National Park, and Bali. We have wide travel experience in Indonesia, including Papua. Our community-based conservation work with marine ornamental fish collectors and their communities in Bali, Sumatra, and currently with the endemic Banggai Cardinalfish in Sulawesi might be of interest to film makers coming to Indonesia. Sponsors always welcome! We will accept volunteers experienced in reef restoration and capacity-building.

Make A Difference Media Inc
Address: 140 Island Way, Suite 259, Clearwater, FL 33767, USA
Phone: +1 727 466 8016
Email: info@makeadifferencemedia.org
Website: www.makeadifferencemedia.org
Founder: Debbie Kinder – dk@makeadifferencemedia.org
Vice President/CFO: Charles Kinder – ck@makeadifferencemedia.org
President: Laura Vagnone – v@makeadifferencemedia.org

To use the power of media for the greater good. Our purpose is to create and support programs and events for television, radio, internet, classrooms and community outreach that educate, enlighten, inspire a healthier, more compassionate and responsible humanity. If you have any questions or would like to get more information about a Make A Difference Media project contact us today.

Marine Conservation Society
Address: Unit 3, Wolf Business Park,
Alton Road, Ross on Wye HR9 5NB, UK
Phone: +44 (0)1989 566017
Email: richard@mcsuk.org
Website: www.mcsuk.org

MCS is the voice for everyone who loves the sea. We work to secure a future for our living seas, and to save our threatened sea life before it is lost forever. Our wonderful seas, shores and wildlife are under threat. Almost nowhere in UK seas is marine wildlife safe from harm. We need to establish vital marine protected areas where wildlife can recover and flourish. Levels of beach litter have doubled over the last decade. MCS works to clear our seas of the rising tide of rubbish that is so dangerous to sea life, including seabirds, whales and dolphins. 88% of Europe's fish stocks are overfished or depleted. Once common fish such as skate and cod are now rare. MCS works to reduce the overfishing which is devastating the life in our seas, and promotes sustainable seafood alternatives. Our work ensures that the sea's rich wildlife can be restored, fish stocks grow more plentiful, and our beaches and seawater become cleaner.

MJH Media
Address: 4 Benchleys Road, Hemel Hempstead, Hertfordshire HP1 2AQ, UK
Phone: +44 1442 381593 & +44 7805 039290
Fax: +44 1442 381593
Email: martinjohnhammond@mjhmedia.co.uk
Website: www.mjhmedia.co.uk
MD: Martin Hammond

MJH Media is an independent media consultancy. The company offers services to companies, trade associations and individuals. It offers training programmes, event management and fund-raising services to a broad range of industry organisations and professionals. Martin Hammond MD served with Kodak for thirty-six years prior to establishing the company and brings a wealth of contacts and experience to his work. MJH Media provides services to a number of the world's biggest film and television festivals for many years including Jackson Hole Wildlife Film Festival and Wildscreen. Full details of Martin's wildlife, environmental and conservation experience can be found at www.mjhmedia.co.uk. Interested in all film, television and media festivals with a particular interest in wildlife, environmental and conservation festivals. I offer some work experience opportunities. I accept CVs by email.

NHBS - Environment Bookstore
Address: 2-3 Wills Road, Totnes, Devon TQ9 5XN, UK
Phone: +44 (0)1803 865913   Fax: +44 (0)1803 865280
Email: customer.services@nhbs.co.uk
Website: www.nhbs.com
Managing Director: Nigel Massen – nmassen@nhbs.co.uk

Everything for wildlife, science and environment: books, DVDs and wildlife equipment. We act as the distributor, agent or main stockist for over 160 wildlife, science and conservation publishers. Our Distribution Service is tailored to the needs of conservation organisations, museums, zoos, botanic gardens, scientific societies and other specialist natural history and environment publishers who want to concentrate on getting their titles to the right market.

a million
voices for
nature

The Royal Society for the Protection of Birds
Address: The Lodge, Sandy, Bedfordshire SG19 2DL, UK
Phone: +44 (0)1767 680 551
Fax: +44 (0)1767 683 262
Email: filmunit@rspb.org.uk
Website: www.rspb.org.uk
Head of RSPB Film Unit: Mark Percival
Assistant Producer: Robin Hill
Cameraperson: Toby Hough

The Royal Society for the Protection of Birds is a conservation organisation with over one million members. Producers of wildlife films since 1953, the RSPB Film Unit continues to create blue-chip wildlife and conservation programming today for event presentation, broadcast, DVD sales, online distribution and clips sales. Our aim is to showcase the RSPB's most important conservation work and to capture the spectacle of the natural world with award-winning clarity, achieved by a commitment to the principles of ethical wildlife filmmaking.
Credits include: *Eagle Odyssey*, (10 awards incl. Wildscreen and Jackson Hole) *Waterlands*, (9 awards incl. Japan Wildlife Film Festival).
The RSPB Film Unit is open to developing co-productions on the themes of saving nature, stopping species extinction, stopping climate change, and landscape restoration/re-

creation. We periodically offer production internships (6-12 months) usually as camera or field assistant. For more information please contact via email.

San Diego Shark Diving Expeditions, Inc.
Address: 6747 Friars Rd Ste 112, San Diego, CA, USA
Phone: +1 619 299 8560 Fax: +1 619 299 6503
Email: info@sdsharkdiving.com
Website: www.sdsharkdiving.com
Owner: Doc Anes

White Shark diving logistics, boat charter, cage rental and chain mail shark-suit rental. Assisted on NatGeo shoots, BBC's *The Blue Planet*, Disney *Oceans* scene.

Save Our Seas Foundation
Headquarters: 6 Rue Bellot, 1206, Geneva, SWITZERLAND
Chief Executive Officers: Peter Verhoog and Georgina Wiersma
SOS Shark Centre SA: 28 Main Rd, Kalk Bay, Cape Town, SOUTH AFRICA
Manager: Meg Ledeboer
Principal Scientist: Alison Kock
SOS Shark Centre USA: Located in the Oceanographic Center of Nova Southeastern University, Fort Lauderdale, Florida, USA
Directors: Richard E. Dodge, Mahmood S. Shivji
Website: www.saveourseas.com

From a small not-for-profit organisation funding just five projects, in less than ten years, the Save Our Seas Foundation (SOSF) has grown to become a major player in the fight to save the world's oceans and the wealth of marine life they contain. During that time the SOSF has provided financial and, equally important, practical assistance to over 150 marine research and conservation projects spread around the world. The SOSF HD Productions footage archive contains underwater and topside high-definition video gathered on numerous expeditions to some of the most pristine marine environments on the planet. The library features a wide variety of species, new behaviour and pioneering scientific research. Our library is an ever-increasing resource that is utilized by many networks and production companies. SOSF footage has featured in natural history feature films and documentaries for the BBC, National Geographic, PBS, Discovery and ZDF amongst many others.

 SUSTENTABLES

SustentableS
Country: IRELAND/Worldwide
Website: www.sustentables.com.mx
Founder, Media Relations: Ciara Backwell – ciara@sustentables.com.mx
Founder, General Manager: Oscar Velazquez – oscar@sustentables.com.mx

So you have a community project in motion, or you want to set one up, but need support and skills? The SustentableS platform is a tool for a transnational community of people that are interested in sharing their knowledge, ideas, projects and experience for the design of high impact actions that reduce the stresses we pose upon our planet. We have highly skilled members from various industries ready to help you. Come join a global online network of people with the interest of sharing knowledge and power to boost innovation and local sustainable development initiatives! We are always on the look out for films and media related to sustainable development. Focus on educational videos that can be shown in English, Spanish. Also great is film without spoken language – pictures and body language are universally understood. Looking for new members, new community projects, sponsors, and partner organisations. Keep an eye on www.sustentables.com.mx for international exchanges to local communities worldwide.

United Conservationists
Address: 71 Barber Greene Road, Toronto Ontario Canada M3C 2A2, CANADA
Phone: +1 416 445 0544 ext:143
Email: info@unitedconservationists.org
Website: www.unitedconservationists.org
UC Team: Rob Stewart, Julie Andersen, Tristan Bayer, Jennifer Zabawa, Paul Wildman and Dustin Titus

We are the next generation of conservationists, reinvigorating and reinventing conservation as we know it. The conservation movement today isn't effective enough. Nearly every nation's emissions have increased since Kyoto, and our consumption and destruction is rising as exponentially as our population. Deforestation, overfishing, habitat loss, and extinctions are all issues we've known of for decades, yet they have all gotten worse. Studies show that individual actions alone can't solve our environmental crisis. Governments and corporations need to do their part but historically only change with public pressure. United Conservationists' mandate is to bring conservation and activism into the living room, theater, classroom, office and local community – making it a part of our every day life. Through media, we are building awareness and creating a community of advocacy. Most importantly, we are inspiring hard-hitting, unified environmental activism all over the world to create real, lasting, scalable change.

The Wildlife Garden Project
Address: Nottingham, UK
Phone: +44 (0)7948 377224
Email: contact@wildlifegardenproject.com
Website: www.wildlifegardenproject.com
Founder and Filmmaker: Laura Turner

One year, one garden, one film and a whole lotta wildlife! Here at The Wildlife Garden Project, we are transforming an ordinary garden into a haven for wildlife. We will show you exactly how we did it through our film, which we are shooting over the course of the transformation, and through our website. On the website you'll find 'how to' videos, tips for your wildlife garden, information on garden species, fun, games and a forum where you can connect with other nature lovers. So get those spades out and enjoy all those creatures that will make your new wildlife garden their new home! We have lots of talented volunteers, each with their own unique skills and specialities. If you think you have something to offer to help us spread our wildlife gardening message, we would love to hear from you!

114

Wildlife Sound Recording Society

Wildlife Sound Recording Society
Country: UK/Worldwide
Email: membership@wildlife-sound.org
Secretary: secretary@wildlife-sound.org
Web Officer: webofficer@wildlife-sound.org
Website: www.wildlife-sound.org

The Society was founded in the UK in 1968 and has a global membership of well over 300. Our aims are to: encourage the recording of wildlife sounds, up-skill recordists and promote bioacoustic study. Annually we organise: Members' Day/AGM, spring and winter field recording meetings plus local meetings. Dedicated residential technical workshop courses are held every 2-3 years. Each year members receive four newsletters, two editions of our magazine *Wildlife Sound*, plus four CDs of members' work. We have strong links with the British Library where many thousands of our members' recordings are deposited. New members are welcome. Always interested to hear from people wishing to use high quality wildlife sound recordings in their projects.
WSRS is a society run by volunteers. As such we are unable to offer work experience/internships.

Wildlife Spain
Address: C. Pozo Amarillo 35, Salamanca 37002, SPAIN
Phone: +34 693514088
Email: info@wildlifespain.com
Website: www.wildlifespain.com
Founder and Directing Manager: Pierre Balsam – pierre@wildlifespain.com

We offer a range of experiences to the public including Big Cat Encounters, Wildlife Digital Photography Days, 'Lost in Birding' educational programmes etc. Our goal is to provide support to film producers on the field, learn from it and start producing our own wildlife films with or without outside financing. Our side contribution to wildlife is to keep advocating for change of traditional environmental practices, preserving fragile ecosystems. We are keen to collaborate with nature and conservation organisations. Wildlife conservation themed films, wildlife films with educational and/or experimental dimension. We are into nature and wildlife film categories. We do consider the co-production of short productions in a short to medium future. Not presently offering work experience placements for lack of financial resources but open to talent proposals in the future.

Wildscreen
Address: Ground Floor, The Rackhay, Queen Charlotte Street, Bristol BS1 4HJ, UK
Phone: +44 (0)117 328 5952
Fax: +44 (0)117 328 5955
Email: info@wildscreen.org.uk
Website: www.wildscreen.org.uk
Chief Executive: Richard Edwards – richard.edwards@wildscreen.org.uk

UK-based charity using the power of wildlife films and photos to promote greater understanding of the natural world and the need for its conservation. Key initiatives: Wildscreen Film Festival and Panda Awards (one of the world's most prestigious, influential wildlife and environmental film festivals held every two years, Bristol, UK – next festival October 2012); WildFilmHistory (online guide to pioneering people and productions behind 100 years of natural history filmmaking), ARKive.org (global online project profiling the world's species, creating a stunning audio-visual record of life on Earth); WildPhotos (exploring the power of nature photography each October); and Wildscreen Outreach (touring programme of award-winning films and masterclasses).

Wildscreen Film Festival Panda Award categories: Animal Behaviour, Campaign, Children's Choice, Cinematography, Earth Sciences, Best Editing, Environment, Innovation, Best Music, New Media, Newcomer, People & Animals, Popular Broadcast Programme, Presenter-led, Best Script, Best Series, Short Film, Sound, Theatrical, Wildscreen's Award to promote filmmakers from developing countries, Jury's Special Prize, Christopher Parson's Award for Outstanding Achievement, and Golden Panda. For sponsorship opportunities please contact the Wildscreen Festival & Events Team. Each Wildscreen Festival, a small dedicated team of volunteers are chosen through an application process - to be considered for such a role please contact the Wildscreen Festival & Events Team.

Wild Work Productions
Email: info@wildworkproductions.com
Website: www.wildworkproductions.com
Contact: Marleen van der Werf

Are you a scientist or NGO looking for a modern way to communicate your knowledge or to generate new ways of funding for your work? Wild Work Productions now offers you the chance to have a professional documentary made about your work. A documentary film is a unique opportunity to share your findings and awareness with a broader audience, to present your project professionally, to enrich your mailings, website or online grant applications and generate more funding possibilities, worldwide.

EQUIPMENT HIRE/SALES

Amphibico Underwater
Email: info@amphibico.com
Website: www.amphibico.com

Amphibico Underwater was founded in 1988 and is renowned in the industry for innovative designs and advancing underwater imaging technologies.

Augur Films Ltd
Address: Valley Farmhouse, Whitwell, Norwich NR104SQ, UK
Email: augurfilms@gmail.com
Phone: +44 1603 872498
Website: www.telinga.co.uk
Contacts: Richard and Julia Kemp – telinga@augurfilms.co.uk

Parabolic microphones designed in Sweden specifically for wildlife recording in the field. Used by many top professional wildlife recordists, documentary makers and scientists, who require high quality recordings; also models for the amateur enthusiast. Telinga with a parabola will pick up a whisper at 100 metres. We will be pleased to answer any queries you may have about recording, and can source other recording equipment for you too.

Canopy Access Limited
Country: UK
Website: www.canopyaccess.co.uk
Directors: James Aldred & Grant Harris

Canopy Access Limited provides safety at height for working on ropes in the rainforest canopy. CAL was set up in 1998 to provide camera assistance and technical rigging solutions for the wildlife TV industry and has been providing access, training and consultancy on a full time basis ever since.

Dave Evans Broadcast Engineering
Address: 17 Peartree Lane, Kingswood, Bristol BS15 4SG, UK
Email: info@debengineering.co.uk
Website: www.debengineering.co.uk

Independent Mechanical broadcast technician, with twenty-five years experience working for BBC Bristol, covering design and manufacture for all branches of broadcasting including sound, filming, and studio equipment. I have worked with the Natural History Unit, local news studios, local radio and radio OBs and have undertaken project work in conjunction with electronic services & in-house program making.

DOER Marine
Address: 1827 Clement Ave, Building 19, Alameda CA 94501, USA
Phone: +1 510 530 9388
Fax: +1 510 749 8377
Email: info@doermarine.com
Website: www.doermarine.com
President/CEO: Liz Taylor

DOER was founded in 1992 by Dr. Sylvia Earle as Deep Ocean Exploration and Research, a marine consulting firm. In 1995 Earle became Explorer in Residence at the National Geographic Society and later established her own non-profit foundation: thesealliance. DOER president, Liz Taylor, along with subsea specialist Ian Griffith, expanded the firm's scope and capabilities to include ROV and submersible support services leading to the demand for full engineering and operations capacity. Tony Lawson, with his extensive experience with underwater systems, joined the company as Director of Engineering.

Flight Logistics Ltd
Address: The Cabair Building, Elstree Aerodrome, Borehamwood, Herts WD6 3AW, UK
Email: operations@flight-logistics.co.uk
Website: www.flight-logistics.com/Portamount.html

Aerial filming equipment, including, of specific interest to wildlife and documentary film makers, the Portamount. This vibration-damping monopod has a surprisingly good performance, and importantly needs no installation, therefore is not a permission or insurance problem when used in the air. The Portamount was used extensively on BBC's *Planet Earth*.

Green Door Films
Address: 38 Glenham Road, Thame, Oxfordshire, OX9 3WD, UK
Phone: +44 (0)1844 217148
Fax: +44 (0)1844 217148
Email: info@greendoorfilms.co.uk
Website: www.greendoorfilms.co.uk
Main contact: John Hadfield

Leading specialists in digital high-speed video. Our current cameras include the Phantom FLEX, up to 2,500fps in full glorious HD. Using two Flex cameras and rigs, 3D high-speed footage can be achieved. Our Emmy award-winning crew can advise on all aspects of your high-speed requirements.

Handykam.com
Address: P O Box 43, Hayle, Cornwall, TR27 5YJ, UK
Email: sales@handykam.com
Website: www.handykam.com
Directors: Mike Nash, S Nash, & L Wincell

First choice for bird box cameras, nest box cameras, wildlife cameras and inspection cameras. Visit Handykam.com for all types of cameras for wildlife and commercial applications. Based in Cornwall UK, we are one of the leading specialist camera companies in the world. Trading for over ten years, our products have been used and trusted by experts in 100+ leading worldwide institutions like BBC, UK Wildlife Trusts, RSPB, WWF, Oxford University, London Zoo, World Parrot Trust to name a few. We have featured throughout the media including BBC, *Daily Mail*, *The Guardian* for our high-quality, value for money products with leading customer service.

Hireacamera.com
Address: Unit 5, Wellbrook Farm, Berkeley Road, Mayfield, East Sussex, TN20 6EH, UK
Phone: +44 (0)1435 873028
Fax: +44 (0)1435 874841
Email: info@hireacamera.com
Website: www.hireacamera.com
General Manager: Jaine Creighton
Senior Sales Advisor: Amy Harcourt – Amy@hireacamera.com

Hire of cameras, camcorders, lenses and accessories. Delivery nationwide with the option of 65 pick-up and drop-off points. All bookings are insured in transit and are delivered the day before the hire period and collected the day after.

Hydra Support
Country: UK
Phone: +44 (0)1273 720510
Email: info@hydrasupport.com
Website: www.hydrasupport.com
Lighting Cameraman: Sean Russell – Sean@srcamera.com

Hydra Support provides rental and sales of a versatile and multi-function camera support rig. For camera support upon and below the waterline, including quick rigging support upon vehicles, single-arm tree pods and camera slider rails. For productions considering multi-location and adventure filming the Hydra Support rig will provide the lightweight multi-function support kit that works across all formats: DSLR, compact 35mm, High Definition and large format 35mm kits.

JrF - Hydrophones, contact microphones & specialist audio products
Address: 4, North Street, Anlaby, East Yorkshire HU10 7DE, UK
Email: tempjez@hotmail.com
Website: www.hydrophones.blogspot.com
Owner/Maker: Jez riley French

As well as my work as a field recordist, specialising in explorative sound, I make and sell a range of acclaimed hydrophones, contact microphones and other specialist audio products. My products are used by location sound crews, artists, composers, aquariums, universities and other organisations around the world. I also lecture and tutor on the subject of field recording.

Pink Noise Systems Ltd
Address: Rose Tree Cottage, The Street, Coaley, Dursley, Glos GL11 5EB, UK
Phone: +44 (0)1453 899 189
Email: sales@pinknoise-systems.co.uk
Website: www.pinknoise-systems.co.uk
Contact: John McCombie

Pink Noise Systems are independent location audio specialists, renowned for their in-depth knowledge and impartial expert advice on all things audio in the video and DSLR markets. We are a leading UK based supplier of Pro-Audio Equipment for Location Sound Recording. We offer expert advice and training based on many years of practical professional experience. We have a superb product range with most items in stock. We can tailor packages and build bespoke kits to suit all budgets.

Proactive UK Ltd
Address: 1 Eastman Way, Hemel Hempstead, Herts HP2 7DU, UK
Phone: +44 (0)1442 292929
Fax: +44 (0)1442 292930
Email: sales@proav.co.uk
Website: www.proav.co.uk

Whether you are a broadcaster or budding amateur videographer, the team at Proactive UK Ltd are on hand to help you choose the right equipment fast and at the right price. With over twenty-five years experience we can help you make informed decisions about what equipment will best suit your needs and budget.

Production Gear Ltd
Address: Studio 2000, 5 Elstree Way, Borehamwood, Hertfordshire WD6 1SF, UK
Phone: +44 (0)20 8236 1212
Fax: +44 (0)20 8236 1414
Email: simon@productiongear.co.uk
Website: www.productiongear.co.uk
Sales Manager: Simon Beer

Production Gear is a leading UK-based reseller and distributor of broadcast, professional and video-DSLR cameras, lenses, tripods, microphones and accessories. We have an extensive website and a stocked 1,000 square foot showroom at our Hertfordshire offices where you can visit us for a demonstration of the latest technology. Our service department can supply spare parts, provide routine services and estimate and repair damaged and faulty equipment. We work with specialist lenders and through them can offer you a range of finance options to facilitate your purchase. Please see our advert at the front of this resource for more information.

Rycote Microphone Windshields Ltd
Address: Libby's Drive, Slad Road, Stroud, Gloucestershire GL5 1RN, UK
Phone: +44 (0)1453 759338
Fax: +44 (01453 764249
Email: info@rycote.com & sales@rycote.com
Website: www.rycote.com

Rycote Microphone Windshields Ltd is a manufacturer of accessories, mic windshields windscreens, suspensions and shock mounts for both professional and consumer broadcast microphones and camcorder-mounted microphones.

SCV London
Address: 40 Chigwell Lane, Oakwood Hill Industrial Estate, Loughton, Essex IG10 3NY, UK
Phone: +44 (0)20 8418 1470
Email: info@scvlondon.co.uk & sales@scvlondon.co.uk
Website: www.scvlondon.co.uk

SCV London is one of the most high profile distributors in the UK recording industry today. Offering a wealth of recording technology products for professionals and hobbyists alike, SCV London can offer over 1,000 products from 17 different manufacturers ranging from computer products to award winning studio monitors. SCV London carefully selects the manufacturers we represent to ensure that we remain the primary supplier of quality recording equipment for all applications.

SeeSense

Address: 55 Manor Close Harpole NN7 4BX, UK
Phone: +44 7967 445829
Fax: +44 1604 833511
Email: nigel@seesense.org
Website: www.seesense.org
MD: Nigel Paine
Technical Director: Paul Rogers – paul@seesense.org

SeeSense specialise in the delivery of high quality HD miniature camera solutions for high-end uses including natural history programme-making. SeeSense are technical specialists in, and an official distributer for, the Toshiba range of HD miniature cameras. SeeSense also offers low light IR sensitive, EM-CCD and thermal-imaging camera solutions as well as compact HD high-speed and high quality sub-miniature cameras. SeeSense create special cameras eg converting to CS-mount, extra HS-SDi outputs and miniature 3D systems. Speak to SeeSense about lenses, recorders, underwater housings and other accessories for these cameras. Offices in the UK and Slovak Republic.

SLOW MO

SlowMo

Address: 84 Thorley Lane, Timperley, Altrincham WA157AN, UK
Phone: +44 (0)7961483137
Email: info@slowmo.co.uk
Website: www.slowmo.co.uk
Director: Mark Johnson
High Speed Cameramen: Jonathan Jones & Ed Edwards

Hire of Photron high-speed cameras, with or without operator. We don't currently offer work experience.

Stratosphere Sound

Address: 7 Sutton Place, Vriende Street, Cape Town 8001, SOUTH AFRICA
Email: info@stratosphere.co.za
Website: www.stratosphere.co.za

Stratosphere Sound, owned and managed by well-known sound specialist Jeff Hodd, has grown from strength to strength since it was established in 2004. Jeff Hodd has been supplying a superior standard of location sound management for over twenty-three years on international and local commercials, documentaries, wildlife/natural history, reality TV, verité, live studio broadcast, multicam wireless, TV drama, feature films and live events.

TShed Ltd

Address: 5a Great George Street, Bristol BS1 5RR, UK
Email: hire@tshed.co.uk
Website: www.tshed.co.uk

TShed is where film-makers come to find or commission the clever kit and expertise that lets them get the pictures which make their TV programmes, features or promos memorable. Engineers of highly specialised camera equipment including HD Nightvision and HD Infrared cameras.

Visual Impact Group
Countries: UK, IRELAND, FRANCE, SWITZERLAND, CROATIA, SERBIA, SOUTH AFRICA
Phone: +44 (0)20 8977 1222
Email: sales@visuals.co.uk
Website: www.visuals.co.uk

Sales, rental and service for the broadcast Industry.

Wide Eye Productions
Address: PO Box 222, Quinns Rocks, Perth, WA 6030, AUSTRALIA
Telephone: +61 8 93052437
Email: info@WideEyeProductions.com.au
Website: www.WideEyeProductions.com.au
Contact: Terry Delahunt

A Perth, Western Australia, based production company. As well as working on our own projects, we also provide production services, crew and equipment to local or visiting production companies.

Wild Images
Address: Suite 255, Private Bag X16, Constantia 7848, SOUTH AFRICA
Phone: +27217940804 & +27217946618 Fax: +27217946618
Email: info@wildimages.tv
Website: www.wildimages.tv
Cameraman: Richard Matthews
Technical: Rob Cowling

Wild Images is an independent media organisation specialising in aerial filming, wildlife sequence work and still image acquisition. Our main focus is in stabilised and inexpensive aerial filming from helicopters and light aircraft and we are building a stock library of superlative aerial images. Wild Images won an EMMY (2011) in Best Cinematography for work on National Geographic's *Great Migrations*. We have a range of specialist filming equipment available for hire.

Wildlife Watching Supplies
Address: Tiverton Way, Tiverton Business Park, Tiverton, Devon EX16 6TG, UK
Phone: +44 (0)1884 254191 Fax: +44 (0)1884 250460
Email: enquiries@wildlifewatchingsupplies.co.uk
Website: www.wildlifewatchingsupplies.co.uk
Contact: Kevin Keatley

All you need to get closer to the wildlife. Designed and developed by wildlife photographer Kevin Keatley. Our designs are made in our workshop in Devon but a lot of our products are exported around the world. We also have dealers throughout Europe. The most popular products that we make are our dome hides, bag hides, lens and camera covers and double bean-bags. We sell to wildlife filmmakers and film production companies, the BBC, RSPB, universities, police units, security companies and British Forces. Wildlife Watching Supplies have supplied the UK Special Forces and NATO with camouflage kit for over fifteen years. Our products have been tried and tested in some of the harshest climates around the world.

PUBLICATIONS/RESOURCES

72&Rising Magazine
HAWNT Media
Address: P.O. Box 1872, Byron Bay, NSW 2480, AUSTRALIA
Phone: +61 421573262
Email: info@hawntmedia.com
Website: www.hawntmedia.com
Director: Rowena Mynott

HAWNT Media produces natural history and science writing and photography as well as magazine publishing. *72&Rising Magazine*: The only aquatic science magazine of its kind! An aquatic publication dedicated to science and research, wildlife and conservation, adventure and the arts. We have a large wildlife film readership and accept articles about wildlife film projects. Water covers 72% of our planet ... and it's rising. Water is essential to all aspects of our lives. We swim in it, we bathe in it, it sustains us. When it freezes we play on it, and we build vessels to sail through it. We travel far and wide to see the creatures that live beneath it and we fight hard to save the beauty that is within it. *72&Rising Magazine* covers all things water-related. Whether you are interested in conservation, science, art, photography, water activities, travel and adventure, you will find something that piques your interest within these pages. Each quarterly issue will bring to you the latest in marine and aquatic research, inform and involve you in critical conservation issues, showcase inspiring photographers and take you on a journey around the globe with our roving contributors. We invite communication from sponsors and are open to collaborations. We are always interested in hearing from people that might like to contribute. CVs and publication content can be sent via email or post. We would prefer contributors to be experienced writers, photographers and/or scientists but are happy to hear from anyone interested in being part of our publication. We would also consider work experience placements.

Animal Jobs Direct Ltd
Address: 27 Old Gloucester Street, London, WC1N 3AX, UK
Email: admin@animaljobsdirect.com
Website: www.animal-job.co.uk

Animal Jobs Direct is the site with the latest worldwide animal jobs, career advice, training courses and volunteer opportunities. Visit us for jobs with dogs, jobs with horses, wildlife jobs, jobs with cats, animal charity jobs, veterinary jobs and more. Your dream job working with animals could be just a click away.

ARKive
Addresses: Wildscreen, Ground Floor, The Rackhay, Queen Charlotte Street, Bristol BS1 4HJ, UK
Phone: +44 (0)117 328 5950
Fax: +44 (0)117 328 5955
Email: archive@wildscreen.org.uk
Wildscreen USA, 10 G St NE, Suite 710, Washington DC 20002, USA
Phone: +1 202 248 5066
Fax: +1 202 315 3750
Email info@wildscreenusa.org
Website: www.arkive.org

ARKive is an initiative of the UK-based charity Wildscreen which uses the power of wildlife films and photos to promote a greater understanding of the natural world and the need for its conservation. To find out more about Wildscreen's key international initiatives please visit www.wildscreen.org.uk or the 'Organisations' section within this directory.

Aspen Valley Film Production Guide
Address: Aspen, Colorado, USA
Email: info@aspenvalleyfilm.com
Website: www.aspenvalleyfilm.com

Adventure 411 online film production guide for adventure, extreme sports and wildlife film professionals.

BBC Wildlife Magazine
Address: 4th Floor, Tower House, Fairfax St, Bristol BS1 3BN, UK
Phone: +44 (0)117 314 7366
Email: wildlifemagazine@bbcmagazines.com
Website: www.discoverwildlife.com
Editor: Sophie Stafford – sophiestafford@bbcmagazines.com

Your essential guide to the natural world, showcasing the wonder and beauty of wildlife and helping you to experience and enjoy nature more. Packed full of breathtaking images, informative features, British wildlife, practical advice and much more. This is a must-have read for everyone with a passion for the natural world. If you like feeding the birds in your garden, spotting wildlife in the British countryside or going on safari, then it's the magazine for you! Experience the wonder and beauty of nature through the inspirational images of the world's finest wildlife photographers and enjoy fascinating features on the animals and the world around us. Plus, all of our practical advice, expert tips and ideas for great days out will help you to understand, experience and enjoy nature more.

itvWILD
Address: ITV Studios Limited, Anglia House, Norwich NR1 3JG, UK
Email: contact@itvwild.com
Website: www.itvwild.com

Search thousands of wildlife videos from one of the largest collections in the world and enjoy exclusive features from ITV wildlife programmes. With thousands of animal videos available and hundreds of thousands of keywords and search terms, you'll be amazed at the videos we have available to watch!

Natural History Network
Address: 14 Canynge Square, Clifton, Bristol BS8 3LA, UK
Email: info@naturalhistorynetwork.co.uk
Website: www.naturalhistorynetwork.co.uk
Owners/Directors: Lizzie Green & Vicky Halliwell

Natural History Network is an online focal hub for those working in the international wildlife film business. We aim to help the best people find the best jobs and the best production companies find the best talent. We offer an environment that is easy to navigate, personal, and trusted. Whether you are a freelancer looking for work, or a production company in need of a highly skilled team, NHN is the place to come. At its very core Natural History Network will be a place to find out what's going on, who is doing what and where the best opportunities lie. We do offer work experience – contact us by email.

NHBS - Environment Bookstore
Address: 2-3 Wills Road, Totnes, Devon TQ9 5XN, UK
Phone: +44 (0)1803 865913
Fax: +44 (0)1803 865280
Email: customer.services@nhbs.co.uk
Website: www.nhbs.com
Managing Director: Nigel Massen – nmassen@nhbs.co.uk

Everything for wildlife, science and environment ... Books, DVDs and wildlife equipment. We act as the distributor, agent or main stockist for over 160 wildlife, science and conservation publishers. Our Distribution Service is tailored to the needs of conservation organisations, museums, zoos, botanic gardens, scientific societies and other specialist natural history and environment publishers who want to concentrate on getting their titles to the right market.

Reelscreen
Address: Suite 100, 366 Adelaide St. W, Toronto, Ontario M5V 1R9, CANADA
Phone: +1 416 408 2300 & +1 888 988 7325 Fax: +1 416 408 0870
Email: bwalsh@brunico.com
Website: www.realscreen.com
Editor: Barry Walsh
Realscreen is the only international magazine devoted exclusively to the non-fiction film and television industries. *Realscreen* aims to bring diverse communities together for dialog, debate and discussion about the global business of factual entertainment.

Wildeye Publishing
Address: Wildeye, Heather Lodge, The Moor, Reepham, NORWICH NR10 4NL, UK
Phone: +44 (0)1603 871141
Email: info@wildeye.co.uk
Website: www.wildeye.co.uk/publishing

Wildeye Publishing specialises in publications for wildlife film-makers worldwide. See some of our publications in the Further Reading section of this book. We started with the guide *Careers in Wildlife Film-making*, which became essential reading for anyone wishing to get into the industry, and now have a growing list of useful books such as this guide! We have also been publishing the monthly emailed newsletter *Wildlife Film News* – part of the www.wildlife-film.com project – since the late 90s.

WildFilmHistory
Address: Ground Floor, The Rackhay, Queen Charlotte Street, Bristol BS1 4HJ, UK
Phone: +44 (0)117 328 5952
Email: info@wildscreen.org.uk
Website: www.wildscreen.org.uk/initiatives-wildfilmhistory
Chief Executive: Richard Edwards
WildFilmHistory is an initiative of the UK-based charity Wildscreen which uses the power of wildlife films and photos to promote a greater understanding of the natural world and the need for its conservation. To find out more about Wildscreen's key international initiatives please visit www.wildscreen.org.uk or the 'Organisations' section within this directory.

Wildlife Extra
Address: Mill House, Brinsop, Hereford HR4 7AX, UK
Email: editor@wildlifeextra.com
Website: www.wildlifeextra.com
Editor: Powell Ettinger

Wildlife Extra is for people who like wildlife, who like watching wildlife, who like conserving wildlife, who like photographing wildlife and who like hearing the latest wildlife news. We bring you the latest news, a guide to UK nature reserves & National Parks and wildlife hotspots, a selection of wildlife and conservation jobs and let you know the best places to watch whales or go on a safari holiday.

Wildlife-Film.com
Country: UK/WORLDWIDE
Email: info@wildlife-film.com
Website: www.wildlife-film.com
Editor/Producer: Jason Peters
Executive Producer: Piers Warren

THE international website for wildlife film-makers · All the latest news about wildlife film festivals, personnel wanted, equipment for sale, courses, footage wanted, new productions, competitions and more. Specialist directories of companies, organisations and people connected with the wildlife film and TV industry. Incorporating the acclaimed free e-zine *Wildlife Film News* emailed monthly to subscribers.

FREELANCERS

DIRECTOR OF PHOTOGRAPHY/CAMERA OPERATORS

(LIGHTING CAMERA/DIRECTOR CAMERA/CINEMATOGRAPHER)

Joaquín Gutiérrez Acha – Director/Cameraman
Country: SPAIN
Phone: +34 956 873475 & +34 699 942868
Email: joaquingacha@bitisdocumentales.com
Website: www.bitisdocumentales.com

Doug Allan – Topside and Underwater Cameraman
Tartan Dragon Ltd
Address: 13 Rockleaze Court, Rockleaze Avenue, Sneyd Park, Bristol BS9 1NN, UK
Phone: +44 (0) 117 973 7579 & +44 (0)787 6032608
Fax: +44 (0) 117 973 5771
Email: dougallancamera@mac.com
Website: www.dougallan.com
Cameraman: Doug Allan
Stills: Sue Flood

Filming for wildlife, scientific and expedition documentaries, underwater and topside; stock footage and stills library; multiple award-winning team with 4 BAFTA's, 4 Emmy's, 4 Wildscreen Pandas. We are open to any new film proposals that need top quality filming.

Paul Atkins – Director/DOP/Cinematographer
Address: USA
Website: www.paulatkins.com

Fiona Ayerst – Underwater Camerawoman
Deep Fried Films
Address: P O Box 659, Mossel Bay 6500, SOUTH AFRICA
Phone: +27 44 6903681
Fax: +44 86 7195309
Email: fiona@deepfriedfilms.com
Website: www.deepfriedfilms,com

Fiona, originally from Kenya, is a camerawoman specializing in underwater work, especially with sharks She lives in the beautiful Garden Route area of the Western Cape in RSA and has access to many pristine areas and wild animals. Fiona also runs a photography internship program in South Africa and details are available on www.fionaayerst.com

Jiri Bálek – Cameraman/Editor
Lemuria TV
Address: Tisá 398, 40336, CZECH REPUBLIC
Phone: +420 602410580
Email: jiri.balek@lemuriatv.cz
Website: www.lemuriatv.cz

Cameraman with twenty-five years of experience in animal filming.

Nick Ball – Cameraman/Zoologist
Natural History Media
Address: Sandton, Johannesburg, SOUTH AFRICA
Phone: +27 768409454
Email: n.ball@naturalhistorymedia.com
Website: www.naturalhistorymedia.com

Natural History Media specialises in wildlife, conservation and environmental documentary filmmaking and photography. In addition, we produce regular short ENG segments for international news agencies on environmental, conservation and wildlife current affairs throughout Africa and worldwide. With backgrounds in zoology and eco-tourism we can provide expertise and access to a variety of unique locations and offer professional location management services, facilitating shoots before, during and after filming. Natural History Media has a large HD stock library, with a broad range of footage and photography from around Africa and the UK. We have full HD broadcast cameras, audio and accessories. We are always interested in hearing new ideas and stories and are always happy to provide our expertise and contacts to develop ideas in the wildlife, conservation, adventure and cultural genres. We would be looking for collaborators and sponsors and always consider co-productions. We would consider work experience and internship applicants, but not actively looking. Please send CVs by email.

Tim Balmer – Videographer
Nature Images
Address: 4 Hodges Close, Canford Heath, Poole, Dorset BH178QE, UK
Phone: +44 (0)1202 683886 & +44 (0)7876207328
Email: t.balmer@ntlworld.com
Website: www.uknatureimages.co.uk

Freelance videographer and photographer specializing in all aspects of wildlife and natural history, from invertebrates to mammals, with a special interest in birds. I have a good knowledge of my home county of Dorset and have access to a variety of habitats throughout the county. I also have plenty of long-lens experience in both still and video work and as a freelancer I work in-house on all aspects of the process include writing and producing my own music. As I'm new to film-making I would welcome contacts from like-minded people with complimentary skills, ie scriptwriting, as I often struggle to find the time to do everything myself, and would rather be behind the camera. I would also welcome contacts from collaborators with specific and award winning ideas for future projects.

Christian Baumeister – Cameraman/Cinematographer
Light & Shadow GmbH
Address: GERMANY
Website: www.lightandshadow.tv

Tristan Bayer – Producer/Director/Cinematographer
Earth Native
Address: Los Angeles, USA
Website: www.tristanbayer.com

Raymond Besant – Wildlife Cameraman/Photographer
Raymond Besant Photography & Film
Address: Glenburn, 41 Forest Road, Kintore, Aberdeenshire AB51 OXG, Scotland, UK
Phone: +44 (0)1467 632513 & +44 (0)7713328493
Email: raybesant@gmail.com
Website: www.raymondbesant.com

I am a freelance wildlife cameraman with a passion for birds and remote islands! I am based in Scotland and happy to travel. I have experience of using the Sony EX-3 system and Panasonic Varicam with HJ40. I'm comfortable using file-based media and edit using FCP. I'm happy to consider any filming project and particularly like those with an environmental story. My first film was called *The Flying Dustbin* which I produced, filmed and narrated on a small budget. It won Best of Category – Amateur and a Merit Award for Scientific Content at the 31st IWFF in Montana in 2008 and was shortlisted in the Best Film on a Limited Budget Category at Wild Talk Africa in Durban 2009. I have additional photography credits on BBC *Panorama* and *Natural World* films and have most recently been filming for the 2020v multimedia conservation project. I am also an award-winning stills photographer and have fourteen years press photography experience travelling extensively in Africa and Europe. I love to dive when I get a chance and have PADI and Nitrox qualifications. I have excellent identification skills, particularly birds and have experience of spending extended periods in the field.

Ralf Bower – Documentary and Wildlife Cameraman
Address: Bristol, UK
Website: www.ralphbower.com

Herbert Brauer
Address: Postnet Suite 1327, Private Bag 153, Johannesburg 2021, SOUTH AFRICA
Phone: +27 83 457 7270
Email: brauer.herb@gmail.com

Credits: *The Last Lioness* (2X Awards – Japanese Wildlife Film Festival & 1 Roscar), *Bonecrusher Queens, Cheetah Blood Bothers* (Award - SAFTA), P*redator Battleground, Lions of Crocodile River, Return of the White Lion, Deadly Summer*, with Aquavision TV Productions for Nat Geo Channel. Experienced to lead crews and to film in remote wilderness areas with little/no infrastructure. Regards sensitivity to environment as required priority. Based in Johannesburg but looking to film internationally. Lately been offering talks and workshops on human · environment interaction and relationship. Planning to offer training in filming wildlife/environmental productions in future. Searching to co-develop and/or film productions, which document and/or promote a deeper knowing and respect for Earth, especially where assignments include shoots in remote wilderness areas. Pursues high level of documentary integrity.

John Brown – Wildlife Cameraman/Director
Address: Oxford, UK
Website: www.johnbrownimages.co.uk

Éamon de Buitléar – Director/Cameraman/Producer
Address: IRELAND
Website: www.eamondebuitlear.com

Dean Burman – Filmmaker
Address: Staffordshire Moorlands, UK
Phone: +44 (0)1782 505 271 & +44 (0)7966 250 834
Email: dean.films@hotmail.co.uk
Website: www.waterwolf-productions.co.uk

Dean is a passionate wildlife and specialist underwater filmmaker with experience in tropical to temperate waters Filming in DVCAM, HDV, HDCAMEX AND HDCAM. His ground-breaking film about Pike won numerous awards and footage has been featured on various programmes including the BBC blue-chip series *The Nature of Britain*. He has written articles for mainstream magazines including *BBC Wildlife*, held TV and radio interviews and has worked as a freelance cameraman for the BBC NHU, Japans NHK Europe channel and CBBC's popular *Deadly 60* programme. The natural world is his true passion.

Tom Burn
Photography

Tom Burn - Videographer/Photographer
Tom Burn Photography
Address: Dorset, UK
Website: www.tomburnphotography.net
Email: t.burn24@gmail.com

Wildlife photographer and videographer based in Dorset, UK. Available for hire to work in many different production roles, with the main focus being camera operator. Completed Wildeye Introduction to Wildlife Filmmaking and the Wildlife Film Academy Course. I am eager to support or co-produce Wildlife Films in the UK or abroad.

Adrian Cale – Cameraman
Address: London, UK
Phone: +44 (0)77 8920 5211
Email: ade.cale@gmail.com
Website: www.adriancale.co.uk

I am a cameraman who has filmed a wide variety of natural history content for various international broadcast and production partners. Also operating as a self-shooting producer director, I am often entrusted to go out into the field alone with only programme notes and a camera kit to bring back the required images and sequences. I am also a camera operator tutor for Wildeye (The International School of Wildlife Film-making), teaching a creative camera technique module on weekend Wildeye courses.
Credits include: *Tarsier Towers*: 25 x 30'series – Channel 5. *Panorama: Palm Oil – Dying for a Biscuit* – BBC. *Baboon Boot Camp*: Parthenon Entertainment. *Gibbons: Back in the Swing*: 5 x 30' – Animal Planet/Discovery Networks. *Woolly Jumpers: Made in Peru*: Animal Planet/Discovery Networks.
Winner BEST NEWCOMER AWARD at the International Wildlife Film Festival (IWFF) 2006. My combination of skill sets can compliment a number of crewing options and allow me to accommodate flexible and demanding budgets. I also develop my own independent film projects which affords me a clear understanding of what it takes to carry a good program idea through from concept to completion.

Andy Casagrande IV – Camera Operator/Presenter
Address: Naples, Florida, USA
Phone: +1 202 4154472
Email: andycasagrande@yahoo.com & abc4explore@yahoo.com
Website: www.abc4explore.com

A veteran field producer and cinematographer, Andy B. Casagrande's passion for wildlife, as well as his experience as a naturalist and documentary filmmaker, have taken him around the world to capture the behavior of some of the planet's most fascinating creatures and fiercest predators. Andy risks everything to get the shot, including swimming uncaged with Great White Sharks, on foot with lions, face to face with king cobras, and jumping out of helicopters to film Polar Bears.

Carles Castillo
Nature Productions
Address: Nor C/Farigola, 5 "El Temple", Santa Mª de Palautordera 08460 (Barcelona) SPAIN
Phone: +34 670898490
Email: info@carlescastillo.com
Website: www.carlescastillo.com

Thematic documentaries production company specialists in hunting, fishing, underwater and nature documentaries for thematical channels or other clients. We work for the main TV channels of different countries and we sell the documentaries in DVDs (home video). We are looking for camera work in nature documentaries as well as making our own productions. Our categories in the festivals are: wildlife, hunting, fishing. We are looking for sponsors and collaborators and we consider co-productions. At this moment we don't accept CVs.

Amol Chaugule – Cameraman
Ambi Creations
Address: 10, Geetanjali apartments, N.Tanajiwadi, Shivajinagar, Pune 411005, INDIA
Phone: +91-9822522134 & +91-2025813034
Fax: +91-2025813034
Email: ambicreations@gmail.com
Website: www.ambicreations.com
Proprietor, Producer, Cameraman: Amol Chaugule

We are a production house in India providing various categories of services like video camera crews, production assistance, location scouting

Richard Claxton – Camera operator
CN Images
Address: Addison Road, Brierley Hill, Dudley DY5, West Midlands, UK
Phone: +44 (0)7949 938318
Email: cnimages1@yahoo.co.uk
Website: www.cn-images.co.uk

With over ten years of video experience and thirty years of wildlife, tracking nesting birds and animals within the UK, I have started to produce a select collection of DVDs. Plus videoing some known local bands, I have a current CRB. I am currently seeking opportunities within the conservation/wildlife field, but open to all offers, working as team or solo.

133

Jonathan Clay – Director/Cameraman
Melting Penguin
Address: 32 Rudgleigh Rd, Pill, Bristol BS20 0DS, UK
Phone: +44 (0)7973 293339
Email: jon@meltingpenguin.com
Website: www.meltingpenguin.com

Melting Penguin is the company of filmmaker and photographer Jonathan Clay, a freelance producer, director and cameraman specialising in natural history, environmental and adventure documentaries for television.

Richard Clutterbuck – Freelance Cameraman
Address: Bristol, UK
Website: www.richardclutterbuck.co.uk

Nick Coburn Phillips – Cameraman
Countries: Brunei (End 2012) & UK
Phone: +673 2391852 & +673 8201852
Skype: diverseasia
Email: diverseasia@yahoo.com
Website: http://web.me.com/dumbodancer/NICKCOBURNPHILLIPS/BIOGRAPHY.html
Marine Scientist/Cameraman/Emerging Explorer: Nick Coburn Phillips

Topside and underwater photographer and marine environmental film-maker. Director and producer. Creator of Borneo Sharkarma. Films submitted to this years Wildlife Conservation Film Festival ~ Sag Harbour ~ NEW YORK State. Specialty in diving and underwater technology, underwater imaging; deep diving, rebreather and wreck environments. Looking for marine wildlife conservation co-productions.

Karla Munguia Colmenero – Wildlife Camerawoman/Presenter
Address: Jesus del Monte, MEXICO
Phone: +52 5516679565
Email: karla.munguia@gmail.com
Website: www.karlamunguia.tv

Beating 34,000 applications worldwide, I was one of the six participants on Animal Planet's 'docu-reality' show *Unearthed, Film School Wild*. After that I spent three years in South Africa working as camera operator and off line editor for Animal Planet's Series *Shamwari: A Wild Life* and *Wild and Woolly*, as well as *Ocean Rescu'*, filmed at the Gold Coast, Australia. I am now keen on presenting my concerns and passion for wildlife, as well as working as production assistant or camera assistant. I have a level 5 SSI Scuba diving expertise, including Night Limited Visibility. I am currently looking for presenter-led films with a high conservation content. I am not looking for a production based on misleading audiences. For example shows based on animal attacks. What we need is people looking after the survival of our species, not people terrified of them.

Georgia Court – Camera Woman
Address: Table View, Cape Town 7441, SOUTH AFRICA
Phone: +27 (0)82 619 0506
Email: georgiacourt@gmail.com
Website: www.georgiacourt.co.za

Georgia Court has worked across drama, documentary, wildlife and film. Her passion is camera operating and lighting, although she has also produced, directed and edited documentaries and television inserts.

Steve Cummings – Cameraman
Address: 5 Bracewell Grove, Halifax, West Yorkshire, HX3 5HP, UK
Phone: +44 (0)1422 360 548
Email: steve_cummings@btinternet.com
Website: www.stephencummings.co.uk

Freelance cameraman, Avid/FCP editor. Stock Images available. Material may be viewed on thebaldibis You Tube Channel: www.youtube.com/TheBaldIbis
Awards: Sonderpreis des Tierschutbeirates von Rheinland-Pfalz in Naturale 2004/2005 International Nature Film Festival for *Return of the Waldrapp*. Honorable Mention For Conservation Message for *Birds, Bins and Bullets* in IWFF 2009. Honorable Mention for Portrayal of a Critical Issue in IWFF 2008 for *The Honey Buzzard*. Have had material broadcast on PBS Malta and webcast by Birdlife Malta. Aside from regular corporate shoots, wildlife clients include RSPB and Natural England.

Sue Daly - Film-maker
Address: La Retraite, Sark GY10 1SF, BRITISH CHANNEL ISLANDS
Phone: +44 1481 832175
Email: sue@suedalyproductions.com
Website: www.sudedalyproductions.com

Underwater photographer and film-maker, writer and editor. I also run underwater photography workshops in the Channel Island of Sark.

Sophie Darlington – Wildlife Cinematographer
Address: London, UK
Website: www.sophiedarlington.com

Shekar Dattatri – Director Camera
Country: INDIA
Website: www.skardattatri.com

Michael Dillon – Cameraman/Producer/Director
Michael Dillon Film Enterprises
Address: 91 Barker Rd, Strathfield, NSW 2135, AUSTRALIA
Phone: +61 297469554 & +61 419249582
Email: mcdillon@ozemail.com.au
Website: www.michaeldillonfilms.com.au

Specialise in adventure and wildlife documentaries. Many Australian Cinematography awards, plus Emmy nominations for Survivor and National Geographic Special *Those Wonderful Dogs*. For full CV see website. Cameras include Aaton XTR Prod plus various HD video cameras and lenses ranging from wide to 800mm plus macro probe and snorkel lenses. Looking for any projects that involve adventure, wildlife, conservation. Mostly enter into International Adventure Film Festivals. Accept CVs by email for work experience placements.

Cristian Dimitrius – Director/Filmmaker/Photographer
Cristian Dimitrius Productions
Address: Rua das Tabocas 170, São Paulo 05445020, BRAZIL
Phone: +55 11 8906 7626 & +55 11 2892-6683
Email: cristian@diveadventures.com.br
Website: www.cristiandimitrius.com
Director: Cristian Dimitrius · cdimitrius@yahoo.com

Biologist, wildlife filmmaker, photographer, expedition leader and dive instructor. One of the few Brazilians who dedicates his full time to document the natural history of our planet both topside and underwater, having more than 3,000 dives in the most diverse environments. Has been exploring places like Galapagos, Patagonia, Canada, Australia, Thailand, India, Africa, Antarctic and Bahamas. In Brazil, he has a lot of knowledge about the Brazilian Pantanal, Amazon, Coastal and Oceanic Islands. I work specially with pure wildlife films, wildlife photography and conservation-themed documentaries. He has also several articles published in diving and nature magazines.

Paul Dimmock – Camera Operator/Underwater Videographer
Address: The Barn, Warren Farm, High Street, Ridgmont, Beds MK43 0TS, UK
Phone: +44 (0)7921848447
Email: pjdimmock@hotmail.com
Website: www.about.me/pjdimmock

I am a researcher, camera operator, photographer, self-shooting assistant producer, underwater photographer/videographer, production coordinator ... I create and research factual content with strong character-led stories involving wildlife. I photograph and film above and below the water, focusing on achieving captivating images and composition, which refreshes the viewers understanding. My determination and grit has enabled me to source valuable locations and professional cast on several productions and my creative ability means I always have ideas and can see how to pitch them. Experienced in directing crew and productions, producing drama and documentary, shooting DSLR and professional camera equipment. I am always on the look out for intriguing content and projects to work on as well as interesting people to work with. I am diverse in my outlook and like working on a variety of productions. I would consider working alongside or for any productions that have wildlife at their heart and which have a positive message that they are trying to achieve.

Mark Dodd – Director/Cameraman.
1080 Film and Television
Address: 26 Blackthorn Way, Poringland, NR14 7WD, UK
Phone: +448484181338 & +447973521409
Email: contact@markdodddp.com & info@1080films.co.uk
Websites: www.markdodddp.com & www.1080films.co.uk

Multi award-winning director specialising in production of human interest environmental films. Very high production values. Able to offer cost-effective director/cameraman services to other production companies.

Martin Dohrn – Cameraman/Producer
Ammonite Ltd
Address: UK
Website: www.ammonite.co.uk

Steve Downer - Lighting Cameraman & DOP
Address: Birmingham, UK
Phone: +44 (0)7706 014301 & +44 (0)7827 411329
Email: stevedownerfilms@gmail.com
Website: www.wildlife-cinematography.co.uk

Specialist freelance wildlife/nature lighting cameraman, DOP & camera operator, with credits on over 100 international television programmes including Pla*net Earth, The Blue Planet* and *National Geographic Explorer.* Winner of numerous awards for cinematography, including two Emmys. Specialist skills include macro, time-lapse, and blue/green screen filming, shooting on 16/35mm film or HD video. Exceptional experience of filming small creatures – insects, amphibians and small mammals – and dangerous reptiles, on location or in studio.

Rob Drewett – Cameraman
Address: 1 Newington Studios, Newington Farn, Near Tetbury,
Gloucestershire GL88UE, UK
Phone: +441666890358 & +447595371144
Email: robthecameraman@gmail.com
Website: www.iawf.org.uk/profiles/member.asp?membersid=1209

Rob Drewett is a natural history and documentary cameraman, with a specialty in underwater filming & 3D stereography. Before he found his enthusiasm for filmmaking, Rob was an arboriculturalist and spent many years climbing trees for a living. Whilst traveling Rob found his zeal for Scuba diving where he first picked up a camera underwater. Since then he has worked on many productions taking him to many walks of the world and on one job he actually beat the Guinness world record for a complete circumnavigate of the globe in the fastest time by powerboat. With his skills he feels as comfortable shooting sync, making wildlife behavior sequences, being underwater or on an adventure, with adapting well to each task at hand. He can also edit with Final Cut Pro and is very technical minded, Rob keeps an active interest in all the latest equipment and has a wide knowledge of formats and filming techniques including Infrared and 3D.

David Elkins – Cinematographer
Elkins Eye Visuals
Address: Northern California, USA
Phone: 011-408-266-1270 & 011-707-280-1648
Email: david@elkinseye.com
Website: www.elkinseye.com

David is highly creative and award-winning director of photography and camera operator with a wide range of experience on a variety of documentary, broadcast and commercial productions.

John Evans – Wildlife Cameraman/Photographer
JSE Film Productions
Address: Isle of Anglesey, Wales, UK
Website: www.johnevanswildlifefilms.co.uk

Justine Evans – Director/Lighting Camera
Address: London, UK
Website: www.justineevans.com

James Ewen – Director/Cinematographer
Earthmedia
Address: Oslo, Norway
Website: www.earthmedia.co.uk
Email: james@earthmedia.co.uk

Earthmedia is an award winning media production company run by James Ewen. James is a UK native with a wide-ranging experience of high-end documentary production. He turns his lens on many subjects but keeps natural history as the main focus of his work. James has worked in many countries and has extensive experience of filming in Africa.

Floyd Fernandez – Caving Cameraman
MadRat Productions
Address: 2517 Leoti Dr, Colorado Springs, CO 80907, USA
Phone: +1 719 200 2590
Email: cavingincolorado@yahoo.com
Website: www.cavingincolorado.tv

MadRat Productions is a video-capturing service and production service company. Dealing with 'cave location shooting', as well as other extreme environment, We specialize in video-capturing including but not limited to underwater, ice caves, dust-filed, high altitude environments. I graduated from Rocky Mountain College of Art and Design with a Bachelors in Fine Art. I spent six years creating and video taping Installation Art. Installation Art is the reconstruction of an interior space. I've spent four years creating internet video on the activities of the Nation Speleological Society, and activities of its local grotto, the Southern Colorado Mountain Grotto. These activities have ranged from dust filled rooms, to water-soaked passageways, to overnight excursions underground. This helped me gain the knowledge and experience to handle extreme weather situations. I have now turned professional for two years. My projects include making organization DVDs for the Williams Canyon Project, Restoration Church in Fountain, and The Abundant Harvest community Garden Project. I also created the Glenwood Springs hosting Video for the 2011 convention for the National Speleological Society.
Equipment: HDR-FX1 Sony Camera, CamRade DS-HDR Z1 Desertsuit for the HDR-FX1, CowboyStudioShoulder SupportPad for VideoCamcorder, CameraDV/DC, Lastolite Professional EzyBalance Grey/White card 20", Sony MDR-7502 headphones, Zoom H2 Portable Recorder, Audio Technica Shotgun Microphone, Sunpak Platinum plus mono pod, Sony VCT-870RM Tripod, Nite Rider Moab Light, Sima SL-20LX universal LED On Camera light, Dell Studio 1555 Laptop, Adobe Master CS3

Richard Fitzpatrick – Director of Photography
Address: C/James Cook University, Marine & Tropical Biology, Cairns 4878, AUSTRALIA
Phone: +61 418183024 AUS & +44 7763685191 UK
Email: sharktraker.fitzpatrick@gmail.com
Website: www.Fitzpatrick-hd.com

An Emmy nominated cinematographer specialising in high definition and 3D video systems as well as being a qualified marine biologist specialising in sharks. He has shot more than fifty films for clients such as the BBC, National Geographic and Discovery Channel and is renowned for filming complex behavioural sequences (including high speed, time lapse, motion control and underwater) many never seen before. Richard has also shot many presenter-led programs – being able to switch quickly between topside and underwater filming. Richard also has a large biological studio facility based at JCU Cairns. Looking at all proposals: blue-chip, presenter-led. Looking for co-production partners to take advantage of Australian government incentives.

Kevin Flay – Lighting Cameraman
Address: Bristol, UK
Website: www.flayphotography.com

Marc van Fucht – Cameraman/Director
Morbid Eye Pictures
Address: NETHERLANDS
Website: www.morbideye.nl

Simon de Glanville – Cameraman/Photographer
Address: London, UK
Website: www.simondeglanville.co.uk

Jeff Goodman – Cameraman/Director
Address: The High Barn, Sancreed, Penzance, Cornwall TR20 8QY, UK
Phone: +44 (0)1736 788705
Email: jeffgoodman@supanet.com
Website: www.jeffgoodman.co.uk

Jeff Goodman is an award winning TV freelance cameraman. Based in Bristol and Cornwall (UK) and working globally, with over thirty years experience in wildlife, underwater, presenter-led programming, Aerial and sound sync lighting camera work. Jeff also holds underwater wildlife Video and editing workshops for beginners and semi-professionals.

Julio Recio González – Director of Photography/Cameraman
Address: C/Lagasca 21·5°·2, Madrid 28001, SPAIN
Phone: +34 696377255 & +34 915771205
Email: ambaamba57@gmail.com

Director of Photography and cameraman specialist in the filming of documentaries about wildlife, ethnic communities, adventure sports and 4x4 journeys. During the last twenty years I have been working (freelance) for Transglobe Films and Argonauta Productions in co-production with several Spanish and foreign TV channels: TVE, TM, C+, A3TV, National Geographic & Discovery Channels, La Cinquienne. I have worked in more than fifty countries throughout Africa, Asia, America and Oceania. Also have experience in aerial, cave, mountain and underwater photography.

Ricardo Guerreiro – Wildlife Photographer/Cameraman
Country: PORTUGAL
Phone: +351 910732177 & +351 969336964
Email: zevimetal@gmail.com
Website: www.zevi.cabine.org/rgfoto/

Freelance natural history photographer and cameraman working in Portugal. May also work as assistant to foreign production teams coming to Portugal. Main interests: NH filmmaking and stills photography, including the rural traditional practices of agriculture and their interaction with wildlife. Some experience in film editing also.

Samuel Guiton – Time-lapse Camera Operator
Address: 9 rue mélusine, 79310 Verruyes, FRANCE
Phone: +33 664319816 & +33 549644360
Email: s.guiton@gmail.com
Website: www.dailly-guiton.jimdo.com

I'm a French freelance camera operator specialising in wildlife and time-lapse shots. I have been involved in shooting for several series as *Wild France* (Gédéon Programmes) and *Life in Fire* (Saint Thomas Productions). You can have a look at my showreel here: http://vimeo.com/24957539

Dominique Gusset – Cinematographer/Videographer
Address: 317 Duncans Cove Rd., Duncans Cove, Nova Scotia B3V 1K4, CANADA
Phone: +1 1 902 440 7580
Email: dominiquegusset@gmail.com

Documentary cinematographer/videographer/camera operator (35mm, 16mm film, digital, HD) for television broadcast (CBC-RC, NFB, Bravo, etc).

Dick Harrewijn – Freelance Cameraman
Address: Utrecht, NETHERLANDS
Phone: +31 618182655
Email: ik@dickharrewijn.com
Website: www.dickharrewijn.com

From the start of my first days in film-making I've gained much experience from pre- to post-production. I'm best described as a young cameraman with good knowledge of (digital) post-production workflows and a huge passion for wildlife. Besides being a cameraman I'm working as a colorist and on location sound recordist. Skills: adventure, animal behaviour, blue/green screen, camera loading and assistant work. Data workflow, DVD authoring, editing, field audio gathering equipment, Final Cut Pro, HD, Open Water Dive Licence, RED ONE, sound recording, stills photography, time-lapse.

Graham Hatherley – Natural History Cameraman
Address: Dorset, UK
Phone: +44 1202 811320 & +44 7775783156
Email: gh@grahamhatherley.com
Website: www.grahamhatherley.com

A specialist long lens and macro naturalist cameraman with eighteen years experience in wildlife films. Principal cameraman on several *Natural World* films for BBC2 (also for WNET's *Nature* series) and wildlife cameraman for programmes such as *Autumnwatch*, *Springwatch*, *Life In The Undergrowth*, *Nature's Calendar*, *The One Show* and *Coast*. South region Royal Television Society award winner for camerawork. Sole trader not looking for talent and not normally offering work experience.

Nick Hayward – Cinematographer
Address: 13 Spring St, Melbourne 3181, AUSTRALIA
Phone: +61 428104313 & +61 398203103
Email: info@nickhayward.com.au
Website: www.nickhayward.com.au

Experienced wildlife cinematographer. Credits with BBC, ABC, Tigress, Green Umbrella etc. Have shot in locations as diverse as the Sub Antarctic to the Arabian Peninsula. Currently filming wildlife stories around Australia and a film on Lyrebirds.

Skip Hobbie – DP/2nd Camera/AC/Field Producer
Address: Austin, Texas, USA
Phone: +1 512 293 7547
Email: skizip@gmail.com
Website: www.skipswildlife.com

Freelance wildlife cameraman, AC, field producer, and all around field production specialist. Experienced with long lens, macro, set work, rope access, and high speed. Emmy nominated in 2010 for work on National Geographic's 'Climbing Redwood Giants.'

Steve Hudson – Underwater Camera operator
Pelagic Productions Ltd
Address: NEW ZEALAND
Website: www.pelagicproductions.com

141

Pieter Huisman – DOP/Lighting Cameraman/Camera Operator
EYESEALAND Visual Media
Address: Amsterdam, NETHERLANDS & Auckland, NEW ZEALAND
Phone: +64 9 5513603 & +64 (0)21 02418216
Email: pieterhuisman@eyesealand.com
Website: www.eyesealand.com

Pieter Huisman has a background in documentaries, having filmed in over thirty countries since 1998. He enjoys working as part of team, as well as on projects that require self-motivation and an independent mindset. Pieter's love for nature, determination and patience are endless. Skills include using extreme telephoto lenses, macro, underwater, infrared nocturnal and remote controlled cameras. He is also proficient as an editor and colourist. References include Channel 4, Animal Planet and National Geographic. As of 2010, Pieter uses both the Netherlands and New Zealand as base camps.

Lourens Human – Camera Owner/Operator
Human Being Pictures
Address: Gordon's Bay, Cape Town 7151, SOUTH AFRICA
Phone: +2721 8561046 & +27 836263017
Fax: +27 21 8561046
Email: humanbeingpictures@gmail.com
Website: humanbeingpictures.tv

A freelance cameraman for twenty-three years. Have completed six cross-Africa documentaries, each taking three months and travelling 23000km at a time. Climbed Mount Kilimanjaro whilst doing a documentary for Discovery! DOP on cooking/magazine/wildlife and drama shows. Have P2 500 Panasonic camera, GoPro mountable/underwater camera (kit complete with sound and lighting equipment.) plus FCP editing facilities. Looking to do wildlife/travel programs. Have got lots of contacts in Botswana. Would definitely consider co-productions.

Mike Hutchinson – Lighting cameraman
Address: Bristol, UK
Website: www.mikehutchinson.com

Gail Jenkinson – Camera Operator
Address: Bristol, UK
Phone: +447986711956
Email: gailjenkinson1@me.com
Website: www.web.me.com/gailjenkinson1

Freelance camera operator working in natural history, adventure and documentary film-making. Qualified HSE part 4 Scuba. Advance bush craft and survival training. First Aider.

Mick and Pat Jenner – Film Makers
M&PP (Wildlife) Videos
Address: "Highdown", Dappers Lane, Angmering, Littlehampton, West Sussex, BN16 4EN, UK
Phone: +44 (0)1903 771912 & +44 (0)7906357860
Email: info@mppvideos.co.uk
Website: www.mppvideos.co.uk

Husband and wife wildlife film makers Mick & Pat Jenner specialise in wildlife and travel films. We have an extensive library of stock footage from all over the world including Africa, India, Australia, Sri Lanka, Borneo, Bali, Costa Rica, Peru, Mexico, Tobago, Dominican Republic, Mauritius as well as the UK.

Jonathan Jones – Lighting Cameraman
Address: Bristol/Norfolk, UK
Website: www.jipjones.co.uk
Email: jonathan@emberfilms.co.uk

Richard Jones - Cameraman
Address: Bristol, BS8 4HH, UK
Phone: +441179734051 & +447905803997
Email: richard@rmjfilming.com
Website: www.rmjfilming.com

I am a versatile wildlife and documentary cameraman who has largely concentrated on high-end natural history filming for the past twenty years. Specialising in blue-chip programmes, I have shot sequences for some of the most successful natural history programmes such as *Life, Natures Great Events, Swarm* and the BBC's *Natural World* strand. I have been nominated for Cinematography awards at some of the most prestigious Wildlife Film Festivals, such as Wildscreen and Jackson Hole. Credits include Principal Cameraman on the Large Format Film (Imax) *Roar Lions of the Kalahari*, which was nominated for three Cinematography Awards.

Sandesh Kadur – Camera Operator
Felis Creations
Address: #295 39th 'C' Cross 10th Main 5th Block, Jayanagar, Bangalore 560041, INDIA
Phone: +91 9448059209
Email: sandesh@sandeshkadur.com
Website: www.sandeshkadur.com

Experienced freelance natural history camera-operator having captured rare sequences of King Cobras to Tigers in the jungles of India. Filmed on various shoots for BBC *Natural World*, National Geographic, Discovery and Animal Planet. Specialize in natural history and crave to film new behaviour of rarely-seen species. Experience with camera-traps and have worked extensively with various configurations.

Richard Kemp – Producer/Director/Cameraman
Address: Valley Farmhouse, Whitwell, Norwich NR104SQ, UK
Phone: +44 (0)1603 872498
Email: augurfilms@gmail.com

Veteran field producer and cinematographer of many years experience in difficult locations worldwide. Specialities: Spain, SW America, Russia, East & SW Africa. Experienced with HD, long-lens, sync etc. Available: Canon 33:1 f4.5 with HD x2converter & microforce zoom controller; also Arri SR if required. No project too large or too small: at home in Norfolk or abroad. Also complete production of DVDs for charities/similar organisations. Made many Survival series documentaries 1973-2000, including *The Land of The White Fox*, "outstanding animal behaviour film" award at 1993 ABS Film Festival. Principal cameraman for Discovery's *Polar Bears: Hunters on Ice*, awarded Wildscreen Panda For Animal Behaviour 1998 and nominated for Best Photography Royal Television Society 1999.

Pawel Kot – Camera Operator/Still Photographer
Address: SOUTH AFRICA
Website: www.pawelkotphotography.com
Email: mail@pawelkot.com

Hairy Frog
Productions

Mike Linley – Director Cameraman
Hairy Frog Productions Ltd
Address: 4 The Paddock, White Horse Lane, Trowse, Norwich, Norfolk NR14 8TD, UK
Phone: +44 (0)7885964790
Email: hairyfrog@lineone.net
Website: www.hairy-frog.co.uk
Director/Producer/Cameraman: Mike Linley – mike_linley@yahoo.co.uk

Wildlife production company with full HD kit (BBC specs) + GoPro hero in flat optic housing + video-microscope and endoscopes + Canon 7D time-lapse kit. Over 400 credits mainly as a Producer for Survival/Anglia Television. Now also producing Wildlife Interactive Touch-screens. Over forty International awards to date. Specialist in herpetology, entomology and UK wildlife. Large video, sound and stills library. Always happy to co-produce. Limited work experience opportunities, depending on current projects.

Alastair MacEwen – Cameraman/Director
Website: www.macewen.co.uk

Justin Maguire – Wildlife Cameraman
Address: 1556 Dempsey Road, North Vancouver V7K 1T1, CANADA
Phone: +1 7789681517
Email: jm@justinmaguire.co.uk

Multi award-winning wildlife cameraman.

Feisal Malik – Camera Operator
Address: PO Box 25253 · 00603, Nairobi 00603, KENYA
Phone: +254 (0)733 722818 & +254 (0)721 431432
Email: fmalik25@yahoo.com

I am a camera operator, specialising in wildlife. I also photograph wildlife and have guided safaris around Kenya from the 90s. An eye for photography and knowledge on animal behaviour enables me to understanding animal instinct. I am able to prejudge my subjects movements, getting those spectacular shots. I spent a month filming elephants in the Kruger. I have good relations with the tribesmen around Kenya who live in the vicinity of the National Parks. I was selected for the Durban International Film Festival and identified by filmaka.com as one of the upcoming film-makers in Africa. I am looking for collaborators/sponsors and would consider co-productions. I do have projects that I am looking to get funding for.

Richard Matthews – Aerial Cameraman/Director
Wild Images
Address: Suite 255, Private Bag X16, Constantia 7848, SOUTH AFRICA
Phone: +27217940804 & +27217946618
Fax: +27217946618
Email: richard@wildimages.tv
Website: www.wildimages.tv

Wild Images is an independent media organisation specialising in aerial filming, wildlife sequence work and still image acquisition. Our main focus is in stabilised and inexpensive aerial filming from helicopters and light aircraft and we are building a stock library of superlative aerial images. Wild Images won an EMMY (2011) in Best Cinematography for work on National Geographic's *Great Migrations*. We have a range of specialist filming equipment available for hire. We are always open to new ideas for natural history or documentary films but now make these through our sister company Table Mountain Films. We regularly approach broadcasters to fund own programs and the programs from our collaborators. We offer some work experience positions. CVs should be emailed to us for consideration.

Christiaan May – Director/Cameraman
Country: UK
Website: www.christiaan-may.com

Paul Mills – Cameraman/Editor
Address: 1 Constitution St, Grahamstown 6139, SOUTH AFRICA
Phone: +27828509810
Email: rpmills@telkomsa.net

Shoot P2 HD, produced wildlife documentaries in the past. World's first African Wild-dog birth ever observed and recorded, have wide stock of wildlife and scenery available in 576 and HD and stills. I am passionate about production, and I have done a lot of art and social commentary documentary. I used to shoot hard news.

Robin Moore – Wildlife/Nature/Conservation Videographer
Address: 3155 Mt Pleasant St NW, Apt 302, Washington 20010, DC, USA
Phone: +1 2023605339 & +1 57123163455
Email: robin@robindmoore.com
Website: www.robindmoore.com

I am an award-winning wildlife photographer who specialized in stills and motion of conservation issues globally. An Associate of the International League of Conservation Photographers, I employ striking visuals and powerful storytelling to effect change. Robin is currently working on a film on the decline and extinction of amphibians in addition to several projects in Haiti. I am always looking for ideas for conservation-themed stories. I am looking for collaborators/sponsors and do consider co-productions. Not currently offering work experience.

Rolando Menardi – Filmmaker
Address: Via Castello, 3 Cortina d'Ampezzo 32043, ITALY
Phone: +39 3477004254
Fax: +39 04362716
Email: rolando.menardi@tin.it

Wildlife camera director, Director of Photography. Rolando Menardi is a specialized wildlife cameraman with broad experience from deserts to high mountains, from tropical to arrid high altitude climates and underwater. He is working mainly for BBC, NatGeo, ORF, NDR, Arte, Canal Plus, etc.

Rick Morris – Underwater Camera/Director/Editor
R.E.M Films
Address: 100 Huguenot Ave, Apt 6A, Englewood, NJ 07631, US
Phone: +1 1 508-237-4830
Website: www.vimeo.com/user1319269
Email: envirodiver@yahoo.com

I am a nature and marine science director/producer, cameraman and editor. I focus on underwater films but shoot all nature and wildlife as well as news and studio work. Won several film festivals with my work on the Census of Marine Life and now work as a studio cameraman in NYC on *Countdown with Keit Olbermann*. I have several series ideas and don't need more ideas to develop just films to work on and funding. My festival categories are nature & wildlife, science, exploration, sustainability and oceans. I only look for experienced filmmakers and have no internships. Seldom look at resumes.

Arne Naevra – Wildlife Cameraperson/Producer
Naturbilder
Address: NORWAY
Website: www.naturbilder.no

Simon Normanton – Director/Cameraman/Sound Recordist
Lighthouse Films
Address: UK
Website: www.lighthouse-films.co.uk

Peter Nearhos – Cinematographer
Fireflyfilms
Address: AUSTRALIA
Website: www.nearhos.com/peter

Pim Niesten – Cameraman/Zoologist/Wildlife Filmmaker
Address: Mechelen, BELGIUM
Phone: +32 (0)485 593049
Email: pimniesten@hotmail.com
Website: pimniesten.skynetblogs.be

After getting a masters degree in Zoology, Marine Biology and a Bachelor in Cinematography I've been working as a camera operator, camera and field assistant and sound operator for wildlife film projects since 2006, mainly in Europe and Africa. During my first experiences in the professional world of wildlife filmmaking I was involved in pre- and postproduction: doing research, logging footage and editing trailers for wildlife documentaries. With the ever-present aspiration to become a wildlife camera operator and in order to get more hands-on experience in the field I became a camera assistant, sound recordist and second camera operator for various wildlife film productions. Besides assisting jobs, I'm also gaining experience as a wildlife cameraman for various productions. Currently filming nature and wildlife in the Durmitor Mountains and Tara River Canyon in Montenegro (2010-11).

Ivo Nörenberg – Cameraman
Gulo Film Productions
Address: Bornholdts Treppe 3, Hamburg 22587, GERMANY
Phone: +49 40823036 & +49 1793996264
Email: ivo@gmx.com

Long-lens cameraman. Experience all over the world.

Rubén Casas Oché – Director/Lighting Cameraman
Address: C/Silfide 6A Bajo A, 28022 Madrid, SPAIN
Phone: +34 622 299 640
Email: info@rubencasas.com
Website: www.rubencasas.com

I'm a dedicated and effective Spanish documentary filmmaker, and multi-skilled camera operator specialized in natural history, social anthropology, narrative, travel and marine environments, with ten years experience of filming in numerous challenging environments around the globe; from third-world countries, jungles, deserts, mountains, oceans or tribal communities. Looking for natural history, science, history and travel proposals and happy co-produce.

Mark Payne-Gill – Natural History Cameraman/DOP
MPG Films Ltd
Address: Rock Farm, Bristol Road,Wraxall,North Somerset, BS48IQ, UK
Phone: +44 7768692166
Email: mpg66@tiscali.co.uk
Website: www.mpgfilms.co.uk

With an incredibly versatile career spanning more than twenty years, Mark has worked on natural history films with the BBC and independents in more than forty countries. As lighting cameraman he has gained a unique range of skills in film and digital video styles/techniques. Mark's experience includes shooting for 35mm feature films, TV drama productions, commercials, 3D, special FX, presenter and actuality sync shooting, interior and exterior lighting, drama reconstructions and, of course, as a specialist natural history cameraman.

Daniel Pinheiro – Camera Operator
Country: UK and PORTUGAL
Phone: +351 964376768 & +44 (0)7519945823
Email: dpinheiro80@gmail.com

Freelance assistant camera operator and sound recordist. Graduated in Audiovisuals. Post-graduated with an MA in Wildlife Documentary Production from University of Salford. Eight years experience as sound operator and editor for radio and in live recordings of orchestras. Member of the Wildlife Sound Recording Society. Skills: Final Cut Pro, Pro Tools, animal behaviour, tracking wildlife, editing. Field audio gathering equipment, Sound recording, stills photography, time-lapse. In 2011 I produced a film about the wildlife of the Mondego River in Portugal and also worked as sound recordist and camera assistant in a film about Macaws in Tambopata Peru.

Matthias Popp – Cameraman/Producer
Popular Pictures
Address: C/Tallers 77, Barcelona 08001, SPAIN
Phone: +34 644263856
Email: info@popular-pictures.com
Website: www.popular-pictures.com

Bilingual camera crews in Spain. We are reliable production partner for international broadcasters and AV productions in Spain. Well-trained professionals, bilingual crews and top of the range professional equipment are some of our (many) strengths.

Michael Potts – Cameraman/Photographer
Address: UK
Website: www.michaelpottsphotography.com

Olivia Prutz
Country: UK
Phone: +44 (0) 7886 860 051
Email: info@twohorseshoe.co.uk
Website: www.twohorseshoe.co.uk

I am a freelance camera operator available for daily work or long-term projects. I am also interested in collaborations and co-productions. I have a wide range of experience but specialise in conservation filmmaking and educational documentaries. My most recent project is an educational documentary on Conservation Agriculture in Malawi. Currently in post-production, it is to be broadcast on national Malawian television in 2012 and distributed regionally on DVD. I am based in the Midlands but willing to travel. I have worked in Africa, Europe and around the UK. I am interested in all proposals and film subjects, but particularly in conservation, human interest and adventure. I work for all outputs including broadcast, DVD and online. I have a flexible fee, from a variable daily rate to a percentage of profit. I am also keen to work with non-profit organisations at reduced rates/expenses only. I am looking for collaborations, co-productions and sponsors.

Lynne Richardson – Director/Lighting Camera
Africa Wildlife Films
Address: SOUTH AFRICA
Website: www.africawildlifefilms.co.za

Philip Richardson – Director/Lighting Camera/Producer
Africa Wildlife Films
Address: SOUTH AFRICA
Website: www.africawildlifefilms.co.za

Alberto Saiz – Director/Cameraman
NaturaHD
Address: Atenas, 41· Alicante 03009, SPAIN
Phone: + 34 696791657
Email: info@naturahd.com
Website: www.naturahd.com

More than eight years working in documentary and natural history films. I have experience in all SD and HD formats, including RED One and 3D parallel rigs and in techniques including time-lapse, time-study, motion control, cable dolly, jimmy jib, tracks, mini cams, lighting and sound. Speak Spanish and English. I'm based in Europe and Kenya (Masai Mara).

Alessandro Sangiorgi – Filmmaker/Cinematographer
Mohegan Filmmaking
Address: Via Cerchia n.219, 47121 Forli, ITALY
Phone: +39 347 0547587
Email: sangiorgialessandro@libero.it & alex.africa@libero.it
Website: www.moheganfilmmaking.com

As a cameraman, I am absolutely passionate about wildlife, adventure and observational filmmaking. I graduated in Natural History with a two years thesis work about the wildlife film industry. I am used to working in the hard environments of the African bush (as a professional field guide too) and jungles, and I am accustomed to being away from home for long periods at a time. I will always bring a professional attitude and sense of humour to the job, whatever it may be. Able to work with Betacam SP, Digital Betacam, Dv, Dvcam, HDV. Working on documentary film, wildlife film, environmental and traditional TV programmes, nature and science TV programmes. I am very interested to work, or be part of a team making wildlife docs or TV nature programmes and I am actively looking for adventure, pure wildlife and human-interest ideas.

Majid Sarhaddi – DOP/Cameraman/Producer
Wild Planet Productions
Address: UAE
Website: www.wildplanetfilms.org

Phil Savoie – Director/Camera
Frog Films
Country: Montana, USA & UK
Email: phil@philsavoie.com & philshoots@gmail.com
Website: www.philsavoie.com

Werner Schuessler – Director, Director of Photography
Are U Happy? Films
Address: Gerda-Weiler-Str. 1, 79100 Freiburg, GERMANY
Phone: +49-177-761 6263
Email: info@areuhappyfilms.com
Website: www.areuhappyfilms.com

Currently in Production: *Passion and Patience – Up Close with the World's Leading Wildlife Filmmakers*. We offer the following production services: experienced camera operator (Werner Schuessler) to hire and co-Productions.

Mark Sharman – Cameraman
Address: 6 Chatsworth Road, Arnos Vale, Bristol BS4 3EY, UK
Phone: +44 (0)7779 227307
Email: mark@sharmancam.co.uk
Website: www.marksharman.co.uk

Adventure, people, wildlife, underwater, live action. Mark is a freelance cameraman working across all aspects of documentary and factual programming, with recent work focusing on adventure, people and wildlife content for the likes of Animal Planet, BBC, Channel Five and Nat Geo Wild. Recent credits and experience include BBC's *The One Show*, *Gorilla School* for Animal Planet, *Night Stalkers: Leopards and Crocodiles* for Nat Geo Wild and *Tarsier Towers* for Channel Five (UK). Mark is a full HSE qualified SCUBA diver and with people and wildlife topside work, brings underwater camera, creative lighting and sequence building skills to the table.

Andy Shillabeer – Director of Photography
Lost World Films Ltd
Address: Plymouth, UK & San Francisco, USA
Website: www.lostworldfilms.com

Steven Siegel – Videographer
Raven On The Mountain Video Productions
Address: 1160 Kane Concourse, Suite 402, Bay Harbor Islands, Florida 33154, USA
Phone: +1 305 343 2179 (cell) & +1 305 865 9861 (office)
Fax: +1 305 866 8639
Email: RM4BIRDS@yahoo.com
Website: www.ravenonthemountain.com
Videography and post-production: Steven Siegel
Administrator: Wendy Siegel

I specialize in wild birds, and the techniques needed for small bird close-ups and flight shots. I shoot in HD with a Sony EX3/Nikon 80-400 combination, with Nanoflash for high bitrates in 4/2/2 color space. My films have won several awards, including 1st place in the UWOL Challenge #20 (2011). I filmed for the 2011 motion picture *The Big Year* (20th Century Fox). Being a birder, I know birds, their behavior and how to get close. Specialties include hummingbirds, songbirds (singing), and ducks in flight. Current project is a documentary on the growth of birding in the United States.

Mark Slemmings – Underwater/Topside Cameraman/Photographer
Country: UK
Website: www.slemmings.com

Robin Smith – Director Of Photography
Country: Bristol, UK
Phone: +44 (0)7970283720
Email: robin@robinsmith.tv
Website: www.robinsmith.tv

Robin is an award winning DOP and director, with a background in mainly natural history, adventure and science/history based documentaries. His work has taken him to over sixty countries, filming in locations ranging from the Siberian Arctic to the Kalahari Desert. To date Robin has worked on productions for a number of broadcasters including the BBC, Discovery, Animal Planet, Channel 5, Channel 4 and National Geographic, both directly, and through independent production companies.

Yann Sochaczewski – Camera/Producer
Altayfilm GmbH
Address: Erknerstraße 46, Gruenheide 15537, Berlin, GERMANY
Phone: +49 3343473987
Email: mail@altayfilm.com
Website: www.altayfilm.com

Altayfilm is a natural-history film production company based in Berlin (Germany) specialized in producing blue-chip wildlife documentaries with a focus on Russia and the Far East.

Juan Solera – Camera Operator/Editor
Scorpion TV
Address: 38 Thornaby House, Canrobert St. London E2 0BE, UK
Phone: +44 (0)7804077624
Email: juanantonio.solera@gmail.com
Website: www.scorpiontv.com

We are a distribution company based in UK for over ten years and distributing documentaries internationally. We have BBC, Channel 4 and other award-winning documentaries. Also, we would love to co-produce in wildlife projects. We are already in touch with some producers looking for film ideas. We would love to make adventure, human interest and current affairs documentaries, as they are the main subject in the titles that we distribute. We are looking for collaborators and we definitly consider co-productions as we say above. We accept CV by post for work experience and/or internships.

David Spears – Director/Specialist Macro Cameraman
Clouds Hill Imaging Ltd
Address: Rock House, Curland, Taunton TA3 5SB, UK
Email: david@cloudshillimaging.com
Website: www.cloudshillimaging.com
Contact: David Spears BSc. FRPS FRMS

David Spears is an award winning scientific programme maker, a graduate zoologist, fellow of the Royal Photographic Society and the Royal Microscopical Society. He has been filming sequences for major broadcasters worldwide for over thirty years. His company, Clouds Hill Imaging Ltd. produces video and stills photography to broadcast and publication standard, specialising in scientific, medical and natural history subject areas. Microscopy, macro, time-lapse, endoscopy and schlieren imaging. Library of movie and still images related to natural history, science, medicine and technology. Royal TV Society, British Medical Association, Royal Photographic society major awards. Looking for commissions for specialist programme inserts and sequences.

Sinclair Stammers – Cameraman/Scientific Photographer
MicroMacro Cinematography
Address: Carmarthen, UK
Website: www.micromacro.co.uk

Darryl Sweetland – Cameraman/Biologist/Writer
Asian Wildlife Films
Country: THAILAND
Phone: +66 56 614 963 & +66 81 532 0303
Email: darrylsweetland@yahoo.com
Website: www.asianwildlifefilms.com

Biologist, writer, and cameraman, Darryl has lived and worked in Thailand since 1996. He speaks, reads, and writes Thai. Darryl has extensive experience of looking for and filming Thai wildlife and most often this involves spending long periods in hides and camping in the forest, which is something he loves. From Oct 2007 to March 2010 Darryl was a regular contributor to www.earth-touch.com (Wild Touch – SABC2), and some of his work can be viewed in the Thailand section of their website. Darryl offers a wide range of services to film crews wishing to work in Thailand.

Humphrey Tauro – Camera Operator
Address: 61 Marlborough Avenue, Glasgow G11 7BS, SCOTLAND, UK
Phone: +44 (0)7776107126 & +44 (0)1413576544
Email: humphrey.tauro@gmail.com

Experienced HD camera operator, having worked in extreme conditions and locations.

Gavin Thurston – Cameraman/Director/Presenter
Country: UK
Website: www.gavinthurston.com

153

Gareth Trezise – Cameraman
Address: The Hipped Barn, Cholwell Farm, Stowey Road, Clutton, Bristol BS39 5TG, UK
Phone: +44 (0)7921 517420
Email: garethtrezise@wildlifeinmotion.com
Website: www.wildlifeinmotion.com

Independent wildlife film-maker. Freelance cameraman. Stock footage. Promos. Specialist areas: long lens, macro/studio, animal behaviour, wild dangerous animals, butterflies. Some previous projects include working with Richard Brock – Living Planet Productions & Martin Warren – Butterfly Conservation. Principal cameraman for butterfly sequences & Sir David Attenborough on *Better Butterflies*. Principal cameraman on *Big Cat Safari with Jonathan Scott*. Additional camera work for *The Egret Has Landed* produced by Richard Brock, narrated by Tony Soper.

Nick Turner – Cameraman/Photographer
Address: Stroud, Gloucestershire, UK
Website: www.nickturnerphoto.com
Email: nickturnerphoto@btinternet.com

Claudio Valerio – Underwater Cameraman/Lighting Cameraman/DOP
Va.Le.Cinematografica 78
98 Lungotevere Thaon di Revel, 00196 Rome, ITALY
Phone: +39 063231665
Fax: +39 063231665
Email: cv.valefilm@gmail.com
Website: www.claudio-valerio.com

Freelance underwater cameraman, lighting cameraman, DOP and filmmaker with more than twenty-five years experience in the cinematography and television industry. Underwater/topside crew for documentaries.

Kalyan Varma – Cameraman
Address: #1288, 17th Cross, 7th Sector, HSR layout, Bangalore 560034, INDIA
Phone: +91 9845132740
Email: mail@kalyanvarma.net
Website: www.kalyanvarma.net

I have been working on natural history films for the last five years. Have worked with three BBC *Natural Worlds* and two productions with National Geographic. Have worked in various roles as sound recorder, fixer, research, cameraman (both 5Dm2 and Panasonic as well as experience in time-lapse and high-speed photography). I have very good knowledge and access to natural history in India and a close relationship with the scientific community.

Reece de Ville
Country: UK
Phone: +44 770943532
Email: reeceadeville@gmail.com
Website: www.reecedeville.com

I am a freelance filmmaker who has worked with the BBC, Absolute Radio, Mark Kermode, Thea Gilmore, Middlesex and Bournemouth Universities and many more. I shoot/edit exciting pieces for broadcast, online, advertising, wildlife studies and promos. Previous work includes advertisements for Apple Europe, broadcast packages for the BBC and promos for various digital companies. I'm exceptionally patient, which comes in handy when awaiting the perfect wildlife shot! I'm looking for wildlife projects that tell unique and vital stories · whether that's species conservation across the globe to individual animal study through to macro shot insects and creatures rarely seen on film. Also, if you're looking to create documentaries such as *Project Nim*, for example, with previously shot footage, I can be your editor and help pull together a stunning film. I'm looking to collaborate on projects that have the potential to be fascinating – from company promos to wildlife documentaries, day in the life pieces and features. I've a keen interest in working across the wildlife genre and have worked on projects for the National Trust in England and have shot various local wildlife pieces across the country. I love creating interesting and vibrant work and can offer my clients a cost-effective one-man shoot/edit package with HD cams, rapid editing and an open mind! I am open to projects large or small – lets chat! I'm happy to work with all collaborators and sponsors who are interested in creating rewarding pieces. You can hire me as a one-man shoot/edit or as part of a larger crew – happy to discuss your project and talk about what I can offer. I don't currently offer work experience placements or internships, but I'm happy to chat to anyone who'd like advice or has questions about the industry. I believe it's vital to share knowledge and even more vital to be approachable! I'm always looking to build up a contacts list of sound designers, cameramen, musicians etc, so drop me a line.

John Waters – Wildlife & Documentary Cameraman
Address: Wells, UK
Website: www.johnwaters.tv

Marleen van der Werf - Filmmaker
Wild Work Productions
Email: info@wildworkproductions.com
Website: www.wildworkproductions.com

Filmmaker, Marleen van der Werf, has an Msc in Biology and MA in Wildlife Documentary. Her combined background in biology and filmmaking enables her to understand and capture the beauty of the natural world and sciences at all levels. As a wildlife filmmaker she is specialised in using camera techniques such as macro, underwater, infra red, high speed and aerial filming as well as time-lapse and animation. Furthermore she is a skilled researcher, scriptwriter, director, sound recordist and editor that works worldwide. Marleen van der Werf is also founder of Wild Work Productions.

Simon Werry – Aerial Cameraman
Flying Cameras Ltd
Address: South View Trehunist, Quethiock, Liskeard PL14 3SD, UK
Phone: +44 (0)1579344087 & +44 (0)7971020088
Email: simon@flying-cameras.co.uk
Website: www.flying-cameras.co.uk

Headed by award-winning aerial cameraman Simon Werry, Flying Cameras is able to offer aerial filming services across the globe using both Cineflex and Shotover camera systems. In addition we are able to offer off-road stabilised tracking solutions and complete helicopter and fixed-wing services. Credits include: *Great Migrations, African Cats, Human Planet, Life, Natures' Great Events* and *Yellowstone*.

Mateo Willis – Cameraman
Address: Cranleigh, Surrey, UK
Website: www.mateowillis.com

Kim Wolhuter – Producer/Cameraman
Mavela Media
Address: SOUTH AFRICA
Website: www.wildcast.net

David Wright – Cinematographer/Director
LunaSea Films
Address: Appleton, Maine, USA
Website: www.lunaseafilms.com

Joe Yaggi – DOP
Jungle Run Productions
Address: Jalan Raya Sanggingan #1. Ubud 80571, Bali Indonesia 80571, INDONESIA
Phone: +62 8123813887 & +62 361979109
Fax: +62 361975378
Email: joe@jungle-run.com & joeyaggi@yahoo.com
Website: www.jungle-run.com

I'm a freelance director and cameraman based in Indonesia. I've worked across the Indonesian archipelago and right across the region. Projects I've worked on range from wildlife to social issues, conservation to education. I've contributed to feature docs, factual programs and educational productions as well. Some of my recent credits include: *History of the World*, BBC1 – Indonesia camera unit. *Trashed*, Blenheim Films: A feature documentary presented by Jeremy Irons – Indonesia camera unit. *Alien from Earth*, PBS Nova & ABC Australia – 2nd unit camera. *Heads Above Water*, BBC World – DOP, Co-Director Indonesia. *Age of Stupid*, Feature Documentary Launch USA – Greenpeace Director/DOP. Indigenous rights activist in a burned-out forest beamed live to 600 screens across America. For more please see our website and IMDB.

SOUND OPERATORS

Alien Sound Inc.
Address: 5610 Barton Rd, North Olmsted, OH 44070, USA
Phone: +1 (440) 777 4754 & +1 (216) 789 2337
Email: aliensound@mac.com
Website: www.aliensound.net
Contact: Jonathan D. Andrews – CAS, Mixer

At Alien Sound we specialize in sound recording for wildlife and expedition shoots. Whether you're looking for one sound mixer or a fully equipped sound crew we are the people to talk to. Recent projects include *Expedition Impossible* (ABC), *Out of the Wild: Alaska* and *OTW: Venezuela* (Discovery), *Hillbilly Hand Fishin'*, (Animal Planet), *Expedition Alaska*.

Mike Brink – Sound Recordist/Camera Operator
Address: P.O.Box 2599, Northcliff, Johannesburg, SOUTH AFRICA
Phone: +27 82 892 0183
Email: mikebrink@lantic.net

30+ years experience in film and TV industry. Camera operator and sound recordist with wildlife and nature experience.

Carlo Comazzi – Sound Engineer
Address: Via Fiuggi, 32 Milan 20159, ITALY
Phone: +39-348-5504006
Email: carlo.comazzi@gmail.com
Website: www.carlocomazzi.net

Sound engineering, post-production sound, location, field and studio recording.

Jez riley French – Field Recordist/Composer
Address: 4, North Street, Anlaby, East Yorkshire HU10 7DE, UK
Email: tempjez@hotmail.com
Website: www.JezrileyFrench.blogspot.com

Composer/field recordist and artist with over thirty years experience of working with and developing extended field recording methods. In collaboration with film-makers, my input has been to highlight the often hidden or overlooked sounds around us. I am known in particular for my work with surface vibrations and underwater sounds. I also tutor on workshops about the art of field recording.

Joe Knauer – Sound Recordist
Joe's Location Sounds
Address: Vienna, AUSTRIA
Website: www.location-sounds.com

Sam Nightingale – Sound Recordist
Organic Sounds Ltd.
Address: UK
Phone: +44 (0)7788 973 968
Email: info@organicsounds.co.uk
Website: www.organicsounds.co.uk

Freelance sound recordist, specialising in documentary film, wildlife and environment recording. Experienced in many genres, passionate about the natural world.
Credits: Grey Wolves recordings – Zoological Society of London, Sound Recordist; *Greatest Movie Ever Sold* – Warrior Poets/Morgan Spurlock, Sound Mixer (Feature Documentary); *Famous & Fearless* – CH4/Princess, Sound Supervisor (Entertainment). Training – Wildlife Basic and Advanced Wildlife Sound Recording for Film 2004 & 2009.

Simon Normanton – Sound Recordist/Cameraman
Lighthouse Films
Address: Lincolnshire, UK
Website: www.lighthouse-films.co.uk

Daniel Pinheiro – Sound Recordist
Country: UK and PORTUAL
Phone: +351 964376768 & +44 (0)7519945823
Email: dpinheiro80@gmail.com

Freelance assistant camera operator and sound recordist. Graduated in Audiovisuals. Post-graduated with an MA in Wildlife Documentary Production from University of Salford. Eight years experience as sound operator and editor for radio and in live recordings of orchestras. Member of the Wildlife Sound Recording Society. Skills: Final Cut Pro, Pro Tools, animal behaviour, tracking wildlife, editing. Field audio gathering equipment, Sound recording, stills photography, time-lapse. In 2011 I produced a film about the wildlife of the Mondego River in Portugal and also worked as sound recordist and camera assistant in a film about Macaws in Tambopata Peru.

Mark Slemmings – Cameraman/Sound Recordist
Country: UK
Website: www.slemmings.com

Lee Thompson – Sound Recordist
Address: Cumbria, UK
(Available nationwide and overseas. All inoculations up to date)
Email: Lee@grimnorthmedia.co.uk
Website: www.grimnorthmedia.co.uk

Wildlife sound recording, ENG sound in remote locations and harsh environments. Experience working on conservation, humanitarian and science communication films in Central Africa, Asia and Europe. Boom op on film and TV drama. Experience working in production, editing, wildlife video and stills. PADI Divemaster. Please see website for CV and media. Associate member of the Institute of Broadcast Sound.

Jobina Tinnemans – Wildlife Sound Recordist/Sound Production
Country: Pembrokeshire, UK
Phone: +44 (0)7779235442
Email: mail@jobinatinnemans.com
Website: www.jobinatinnemans.com

If you are looking for music compositions with an edge, get in touch for some quick suggestions to see how my work would compliment your film to help it stand out. Preferred way of working is recording on location to incorporate situational sounds into the soundtrack. Independent production company for BBC3 Radio, first radio work was broadcast by ABC Australia and selected for the ISCM World New Music Festival 2010. Sound recordings are in Griff Rhys Jones' *Pembrokeshire Farm* TV programmes. Currently in collaboration with Peter Zinovieff. Since 2002 I'm working in all facets of sound production. Media concepts which are keen on the vivid use of wildlife sound, next to commentating, to bring the message across would have my special interest.

Chris Watson – Sound Recordist
Country: UK
Website: www.chriswatson.net

Chris Watson is one of the world's leading recorders of wildlife and natural phenomena. He is passionate about recording the wildlife sounds of animals, habitats and atmospheres from around the world. As a freelance recordist for film, TV & radio, Chris Watson specialises in natural history and documentary location sound together with track assembly and sound design in post-production.

PRODUCERS/DIRECTORS

Joaquín Gutiérrez Acha – Producer/Director
Bitis Documentales
Address: Polígono Industrial Las Salinas, C/ Aluvión, naves 4 y 5 El Puerto de Santa María (CÁDIZ) 11500, ESPAÑA
Phone: +34 699 942 868 & +34 956 873 475
Email: joaquingacha@bitisdocumentales.com & joaquin.guti.acha@gmail.com
Website: www.bitisdocumentales.com

Bitis Documentales/Joaquín Gutiérrez Acha is a company specialized in the production of natural history documentaries for film and television. He has worked for companies such as National Geographic Television and Film, National Geographic Channel, National Geographic Digital Motion, BBC (NHU), Canal + France, Canal + España, Parthenon Entertainment, Wanda Vision, Terra Mater Factual Studio, Government of Spain and the Government of Andalusia. We have teams of production, postproduction, studies and our own vehicles. We are interested in producing nature documentaries for television and film. We are not interested in fiction, reality etc, only animal behavior and wildlife blue-chips. Usually our projects are funded by several companies. Yes, we are open for co-production. Now we are not looking new collaborators and in any case prefer to receive CVs by email.

Aneeta Akhurst – Producer
Address: 104 8th St, Petaluma 94952, CA, USA
Phone: +01 707 266 2125
Email: aneeta.c@gmail.com
Website: www.linkedin.com/pub/aneeta-akhurst/6/9b7/7b5

Aneeta has helped produce specialist factual/factual documentary projects for the BBC, Animal Planet, The Discovery Channel, PBS and The Reader's Digest. She has an academic background in biology and natural history film and is a strong production all-rounder having worked on numerous projects from pre-production to the online edit throughout my career. Aneeta has screened work at WildSouth, Reel Earth and received an Honorable Mention, at The International Wildlife Film Festival '07. In addition, she has field experience both studying and filming wildlife in the UK, New Zealand and Indonesia. Looking for projects of a human/animal interaction theme.

Gaby Bastyra – Producer/Director/AP
Address: 2, 147 Queens Drive, London N4 2BB, UK
Phone: +44 7941387314
Email: gabybastyra@gmail.com
Website: www.bee-productions.co.uk

161

Producer, director and AP specialising in wildlife documentaries. Have won Best Newcomer at Wildscreen 2008 and nominated at Jackson Hole 2009 in the same category for film *The White Wood*. Nominated in 2011 in the Best Short category for *Gloop*. Have been working on BBC *Natural Worlds* for the past two years at Passion Pictures.

Christian Baumeister – Director/Producer/Cinematographer
Light & Shadow GmbH
Address: GERMANY
Website: www.lightandshadow.tv

Tristan Bayer – Producer/Director/Cinematographer
Earth Native
Address: Los Angeles, USA
Website: www.tristanbayer.com

Caroline Brett – Producer/Director/Writer
Shake The Tree Productions
Address: Hall Farm House, Rectory Road, Suffield, Norfolk NR11 7EW, UK
Phone: +44 (0)1263768203
Email: carolinebrett@mac.com
Website: www.shakethetree.co.uk

Caroline Brett (BSc Hons/Zoology, Bristol Uni) is a highly experienced and award-winning producer/director/writer. She worked for 21 years for the prestigious Survival series including in Arctic Canada, in the rain forests of Sierra Leone and on a remote Vietnamese island. She also produced the highly successful *Predators with Gaby Roslin* and *Wild about Essex with Tony Robinson*. Caroline has recently made films on black caiman in Brazil, the history of the pearl trade in Bahrain, street children in India and ponies in Scotland, the later two she also filmed. She has photographs at the Specialist Stock Library, has numerous articles and seven books published and while working for Save Our Seas, the foundation won many wildlife film festival awards including Jackson Hole and Wildscreen. I consider film proposals mainly on wildlife, animals and conservation for DVD, Internet, TV and cinema. I consider co-productions.

John Brown – Director/Producer/Camera
Address: Oxford, UK
Website: www.johnbrownimages.co.uk

162

Adrian Cale – Producer/Director
Address: London, UK
Phone: +44 (0)77 8920 5211
Email: ade.cale@gmail.com
Website: www.adriancale.co.uk

I am an independent wildlife film-maker who has written a wide variety of natural history content for various international broadcast and production partners. Content includes press releases, programme pitch documents, synopsis, treatments, scripts and script editing.
Credits include: *Baboon Boot Camp*: Parthenon Entertainment, *International Animal Rescue: Orangutan*: IAR, *Gibbons: Back in the Swing*: 5 x 30' · Animal Planet/Discovery Networks, *Woolly Jumpers: Made in Peru*: Animal Planet/Discovery Networks. Winner BEST NEWCOMER AWARD at the International Wildlife Film Festival (IWFF) 2006. *Make me a Monkey*: Electric Sky Distribution.
My combination of skill sets can compliment a number of crewing options and allow me to accommodate flexible and demanding budgets. I also develop my own independent film projects, which affords me a clear understanding of what it takes to carry a good program idea through from concept to completion. As a freelancer, unfortunately I am not in a position to offer work experience to candidates at this time.

Sharmila Choudhury – Producer/Director/Scriptwriter
Address: 2 Cossins Road, Bristol BS6 7LY, UK
Phone: +44 (0)117 9243965 & +44 (0)7780 586591
Email: sharmila@sharmilachoudhury.co.uk

Freelance natural history producer, director, scriptwriter and consultant. Over fifteen years experience at the BBC Natural History Unit working mainly on Attenborough's landmark series (*Life of Birds, Life of Mammals, Planet Earth, Darwin & the Tree of Life*) and live events (*Springwatch, Saving Planet Earth*). Also experience in international reversioning for European broadcasters Not looking for proposals or offering work experience placements.

Alice Clarke – Producer/Director/Editor/Scriptwriter
NHU Africa
Address: PO Box 12317, Mill Street, Gardens, Cape Town 8010, SOUTH AFRICA
Phone: +27 214221054 & +27 729642281
Email: alice@nhuafrica.com
Website: www.nhuafrica.com

Wildlife documentary production unit. Hire of Panasonic HD camera equipment. Wildlife Film Academy for aspiring wildlife filmmakers. Wild Talk Africa, International Wildlife Film Festival. African based stories only. Broad remit of subjects, styles. We co-produce and commission producers. Send CVs by email for work experience placements.

Jonathan Clay – Director/Producer/Cameraman
Melting Penguin
Address: 32 Rudgleigh Rd, Pill, Bristol BS20 0DS, UK
Phone: +44 (0)7973 293339
Email: jon@meltingpenguin.com
Website: www.meltingpenguin.com

Melting Penguin is the company of filmmaker and photographer Jonathan Clay, a freelance producer, director and cameraman specialising in natural history, environmental and adventure documentaries for television.

Jamie Crawford – Producer/Director/Writer
Address: London, UK
Email: info@jamiecrawfordmedia.com
Website: www.jamiecrawfordmedia.com

I work on both sides of the camera as a presenter and as a producer, director and writer. On screen I work mostly on the BBC's *The One Show* fronting stories on wildlife, adventure and photography, previous credits include wildlife adventure shows for Animal Planet, Discovery and Five. We won a BAFTA with one series and I was nominated as Best Presenter at the Wildscen Panda awards with another. Behind the camera I produce and direct docs on everything and anything from tornado outbreaks in the USA to epic survival tales in Borneo for Discovery, National Geographic, BBC, Sky and others. As a freelancer, I'm always on the lookout for interesting new projects to work on, be it as a presenter or producer/director, as scriptwriter or narrator. As long as the content is interesting, I don't mind what I do (well ... to a point)!

Sandy Crichton
Address: 1 Wesley Mews, The Causeway, Mark, Somerset TA9 4QA, UK
Email sandy@karearea.com
Website: www.karearea.com

Award-winning filmmaker with a wide range of interests in factual programming including natural history, social and observational documentary. In 2008 completed the environmental documentary *Karearea: the pine falcon*, which screened at over sixty film festivals worldwide, picking up twenty-seven awards and a host of nominations in the process. Specialties: making highly visual, unique documentaries with compelling narratives; wildlife films worked on tend to have strong central human characters and are often driven by their personal stories. Looking for collaborators/sponsors and would consider co-productions.

Bob Cruz
TerraSoars
Address: 101 Nelson Story Tower, Bozeman MT 59715, USA
Email: nycruise@hotmail.com
Phone: +1 406 600 0368

Specializing in films about earth science, everything from geology to dinosaurs and fossils. Clients include the United States National Park Service and Museum of the Rockies.

Michael Dillon – Producer/Director/Camera
Michael Dillon Film Enterprises
Address: 91 Barker Rd, Strathfield, NSW 2135, AUSTRALIA
Phone: +61 297469554 & +61 419249582
Email: mcdillon@ozemail.com.au
Website: www.michaeldillonfilms.com.au

Specialise in adventure and wildlife documentaries. Many Australian Cinematography awards, plus Emmy nominations for Survivor and National Geographic Special *Those Wonderful Dogs*. For full CV see website. Cameras include Aaton XTR Prod plus various HD video cameras and lenses ranging from wide to 800mm plus macro probe and snorkel lenses. Looking for any projects that involve adventure, wildlife, conservation. Mostly enter into International Adventure Film Festivals. Accept CVs by email for work experience placements.

Martin Dohrn – Director/Producer/Camera
Ammonite Ltd
Address: Bristol UK
Website: www.ammonite.co.uk

Craig and Damon Foster – Producers/Directors/Cameramen/Editors
Foster Brothers Productions
Address: SOUTH AFRICA
Website: www.senseafrica.com

Jen Grace – Producer/Director/Writer
Jen Grace Productions
Address: 501 S 15th Ave #3, Bozeman, Montana 59715, US
Phone: +1 406 249 2153
Email: minisuperjennifer@yahoo.com
Website: www.jengrace.com

Producer, director, writer, multimedia designer Jen Grace has an MFA in Science and Natural History Filmmaking from MSU. Specializing in conservation, sports and dance film and live production. Clients include the Smithsonian Institution, The Jim Henson Company, Patrick Leonard, 4H and the Montana Ballet Company. Winner IWFF, Jackson Hole, Lunafest, College Television Awards, HATCHfest. Collaborators/sponsors/co-productions all welcome on children's, experimental and conservation subjects. I do not offer work experience/internships.

Cathy Henkel – Producer/Director
Virgo Productions
Address: Z1 the Works, 32 Parer Place, Kelvin Grove, QLD 4059, AUSTRALIA
Phone: + 61 7 3175 9995 & +61 404 162 250
Email: cathyhenkel@virgoproductions.com.au
Website: www.virgoproductions.com.au

Virgo Productions is a boutique screen industries company, specialising in feature documentaries that tell inspiring, positive, global stories with cross-platform delivery to engage audiences through cinema, television, online and DVD release. Best known for *The Burning Season*, which won the IF Award for Best Documentary and the Audience Choice Award at the Brisbane International Film festival and was nominated for an EMMY Award (Outstanding Documentary on a Business Topic), two ATOM Awards and a Golden Panda Award. In 2009 Cathy was awarded Documentary Producer of the Year at SPAA for her work on *The Burning Season*. We are not looking for proposals. Virgo's festival categories are Conservation Documentary, and Business Documentary. We are looking for sponsors with an interest in a proactive response to conservation. We consider co-productions. We do not offer work experience.

Jigar Joshi
Address: 16/A New Suryanarayan Society, Near Parasmani Flats, Rannapark, Ghatlodia, Ahmedabad 380061, INDIA
Phone: +91 8866458102 & +91 7927470131
Email: jigarjoshi1973@gmail.com
Website: www.youtube.com/watch?v=JqCAUJn_YS4

I have been filming Asiatic Lions in the wild for the past eight years now. I make purely wildlife short films. I am looking forward to broadcasting work internationally. I am able to deliver exceptional footage in the toughest of the conditions. I have been looking for working on showcasing the Asiatic lions in the wild habitat. Pure wildlife and conservation-themed films are very less in India, which I like to take up to a next level. Co-production is welcomed.

Richard Kemp – Producer/Director/Cameraman
Address: Valley Farmhouse, Whitwell, Norwich NR104SQ, UK
Email: augurfilms@gmail.com
Phone: +44 1603 872498

Veteran field producer and cinematographer of many years experience in difficult locations worldwide. Specialities: Spain, SW America, Russia, East & SW Africa. Experienced with HD, longlens, sync etc. Available: Canon 33:1 f4.5 with HD x2converter & microforce zoom controller; also Arri SR if required. No project too large or too small: at home in Norfolk or abroad. Also complete production of DVDs for charities/similar organisations. Made many Survival series documentaries 1973-2000, including *The Land of The White Fox*, "outstanding animal behaviour film" award at 1993 ABS Film Festival. Principal cameraman for Discovery's *Polar Bears: Hunters on Ice*, awarded Wildscreen Panda For Animal Behaviour 1998 and nominated for Best Photography Royal Television Society 1999.

Jin Pyn Lee – Producer/Director
Elemantree Media
Address: Blk 6, 12-430, Telok Blangah Crescent, 090006, SINGAPORE
Phone: +65 62726769 & +61 423662233
Fax: +65 62726769
Email: jinpyn.lee@elephantandtree.com
Website: www.elemantreemedia.com

Freelance television producer, director, writer, fixer, production management. Specialize in Asian natural history and conservation (over twenty years involvement). Jin Pyn's career spans across broadcaster and independent production companies. Credits include BBC Worldwide, Channel News Asia, and Animal Planet, across all genres – short-form interstitials, long-form factual documentaries, and animation. Geographically the programs have been distributed all over the globe, including Korea's Kids Talk Talk, US's Somos TV and India's Edumedia. In Japan, Jin Pyn has won the best animation award, and her children's picture book was the first from Singapore to garner multiple languages.

Hairy Frog
Productions

Mike Linley – Producer/Director
Hairy Frog Productions Ltd
Address: 4 The Paddock, White Horse Lane, Trowse, Norwich, Norfolk NR14 8TD, UK
Phone: +44 (0)7885964790
Email: hairyfrog@lineone.net
Website: www.hairy-frog.co.uk
Director/Producer/Cameraman: Mike Linley – mike_linley@yahoo.co.uk

Wildlife production company with full HD kit (BBC specs) + GoPro hero in flat optic housing + video-microscope and endoscopes + Canon 7D time-lapse kit. Over 400 credits mainly as a producer for Survival/Anglia Television. Now also producing Wildlife Interactive Touch-screens. Over forty International awards to date. Specialist in herpetology, entomology and UK wildlife. Large video, sound and stills library. Always happy to co-produce. Limited work experience opportunities, depending on current projects.

Vanessa Lucas – Producer/Director
Natural History Media
Address: Sandton, Johannesburg, SOUTH AFRICA
Phone: +27 827803840
Email: v.lucas@naturalhistorymedia.com
Website: www.naturalhistorymedia.com

Natural History Media specialises in wildlife, conservation and environmental documentary filmmaking and photography. In addition, we produce regular short ENG segments for international news agencies on environmental, conservation and wildlife current affairs throughout Africa and worldwide. With backgrounds in zoology and eco-tourism we can provide expertise and access to a variety of unique locations and offer professional location management services, facilitating shoots before, during and after filming. Natural History Media has a large HD stock library, with a broad range of footage and photography from around Africa and the UK. We have full HD broadcast cameras, audio and accessories. We are always interested in hearing new ideas and stories and are always happy to provide our expertise and contacts to develop ideas in the wildlife, conservation, adventure and cultural genres. We would be looking for collaborators and sponsors and always consider co-productions. We would consider work experience and internship applicants, but not actively looking. Please send CVs by email.

Daniel Vega Martínez – Independent Producer
E291 Science Films
Address: C/francisco Gomez Sierra 76, Villalbilla, Madrid 28810, SPAIN
Phone: +34 625248868 & +34 918859067
Email: dvegamar@gmail.com
Website: www.e291.info

Independent and new-coming producer of scientific films (physics, biology, geography, wildlife). We also offer photography courses in Spain, including short workshops in wildlife locations. Open to international collaborations and co-productions for filmmaking. Have a look in the web and vimeo channel.

Richard Matthews – Director/Producer/Cameraman
Wild Images
Address: Suite 255, Private Bag X16, Constantia 7848, SOUTH AFRICA
Phone: +27217940804 & +27217946618
Fax: +27217946618
Email: richard@wildimages.tv
Website: www.wildimages.tv

Wild Images is an independent media organisation specialising in aerial filming, wildlife sequence work and still image acquisition. Our main focus is in stabilised and inexpensive aerial filming from helicopters and light aircraft and we are building a stock library of superlative aerial images. Wild Images won an EMMY (2011) in Best Cinematography for work on National Geographic's *Great Migrations*. We have a range of specialist filming equipment available for hire. We are always open to new ideas for natural history or documentary films but now make these through our sister company Table Mountain Films. We regularly approach broadcasters to fund own programs and the programs from our collaborators. We offer some work experience positions. CVs should be emailed to us for consideration.

Paul Mills – Producer/Camera/Editing
Address: 1 Constitution St, Grahamstown 6139, SOUTH AFRICA
Phone: +27828509810
Email: rpmills@telkomsa.net

Shoot P2 HD, produced wildlife documentaries in the past. World's first African Wild-dog birth ever observed and recorded, have wide stock of wildlife & scenery available in 576 & HD & stills. I am passionate about production, and I have done a lot of art & social commentary documentary. I used to shoot hard news.

Rick Morris – Producer/Director
R.E.M Films
Address: 100 Huguenot Ave, Apt 6A, Englewood, NJ 07631, US
Phone: +1 1 508-237-4830
Website: www.vimeo.com/user1319269
Email: envirodiver@yahoo.com

I am a nature and marine science director/producer, cameraman and editor. I focus on underwater films but shoot all nature and wildlife as well as news and studio work. Won several film festivals with my work on the Census of Marine Life and now work as a studio cameraman in NYC on *Countdown with Keit Olbermann*. I have several series ideas and don't need more ideas to develop just films to work on and funding. My festival categories are nature & wildlife, science, exploration, sustainability and oceans. I only look for experienced filmmakers and have no internships. Seldom look at resumes.

Tom Mustill – Producer/Director
Address: London, UK
Email: tom.mustill@gmail.com
Website: www.neonotter.com

Freelance shooting producer/director – broadcast and online. Tom specialises in factual TV, currently as producer/director for the latest series of *Inside Nature's Giants* (winner of BAFTA, RTS and Broadcast awards). Excited by the possibilities of producing films specifically for online Tom directed two of the groundbreaking *'Cambridge Ideas'* films, *'NanoYou'* – Narrated by Stephen Fry (winner of SCINEMA Best Short award), as well as films for Wellcome Trust, Microsoft Research, Guerilla Scientists and Kew Gardens.

Vivian A. N. Nuhu – Producer/Coordinator
Address: P. O. Box OS3053, Osu-Accra, GHANA, WEST AFRICA
Phone: +233 244799749 & +233 302763308
Email: vannuhu@yahoo.co.uk

Coordinating notably for outside filming crews among them, BBC and NHK on wildlife locations, permits and local casts and logistics. As an experience wildlife conservationist, specialized in communication and education, I have been and still available as a presenter in wildlife adventure documentaries for general public and especially youth cum school groups. As a trained wildlife film-maker without own equipment/facilities have facilitated in the production of overseas documentaries for awareness creation in my home country, Ghana.
Not looking for proposals. Have already a number of ideas and proposals for wildlife adventure particularly for children and general Ghanaian public with conservation theme. Collaborators/sponsors most needed. Will welcome co-productions if it comes with funding.

Kathryn Pasternak – Executive Producer/Writer/Producer
Pasternak Media LLC
Address: 3323 Laurel Court, Falls Church, VA 22042, USA
Phone: +1 703 992 0449 &: +1 703 216 1746
Email: kathryn.pasternak@gmail.com
Website: www.pasternakmedia.com

Pasternak Media LLC specializes in supervision of wildlife and conservation films for broadcast television. We work for, and directly with, producers of wildlife programming. We will help you develop and pitch your concept, and supervise it through completion. Focus is telling the best possible story. Acting as an outside voice, we give the broadcaster confidence that your film will meet their needs, and at the same time, help make sure your original vision doesn't get lost in the process. Kathryn Pasternak has won two National Emmy Awards and has been nominated for two more, including most recently for *Swamp Troop* which was the product of first time, African-based producers. She has a twenty-year track record supervising projects for National Geographic Television, NGC, Animal Planet, and Smithsonian Networks. Looking for presenter-led, pure wildlife, and conservation-themed stories. Can consult on co-productions.

Luis Henrique Pereira
RTP – Radio e TV Portugal
Address: Rua do Belomonte, 405, Mafamide, Vila Nova de Gaia 4430-029, PORTUGAL
Phone: +351 962407468 & +351 967902766
Email: luis.henrique@rtp.pt
Website: www.rtp.pt or bloguedoluis.blogspot.com

I´m an author and wildlife film-maker in the Portuguese Public TV Station, Radio e Televisão de Portugal. I've made documentaries in São Tomé e Príncipe, Cape Verde, Portugal, Azores, Spain, Amazónia (Brazil, Colombia and Peru.) Lots of experience and lots of work in the field. I'm currently filming two new series about birds in Portugal and about wildlife in the four seasons. I'm editing two documentaries about the fossil treasures in Santa Maria Island (Azores) and another about great whales migration off-shore Pico Island (Azores). Of course I consider co-productions. I'm always Looking to improve my skills with books, like Wildeye books that I have, and other authors like David Attenborough, and Chris Palmer for instance.

Kate Raisz – Producer/Director/Writer
42°N Films
Address: USA
WebSite: www.42degreesnorth.com/

Will Ridgeon – Producer/Director
Country: UK
Phone: +44(0)7930 747 526
Email: will@willridgeon.com
Website: www.willridgeon.com

I am a freelance self-shooting producer/director specialising in wildlife television production and working predominantly at the BBC's Natural History Unit. I have worked on a number of award winning series such as the BBC's *Springwatch* and Channel Five's *Michaela's Wild Challenge* and I am currently making a new *Expeditions* series for the BBC.

Gianna Savoie – Documentary Filmmaker
Address: NY, USA
Website: www.giannasavoie.com

Phil Savoie – Producer/Director/Camera
Frog Films
Country: Montana, USA & UK
Email: phil@philsavoie.com & philshoots@gmail.com
Website: www.philsavoie.com

Werner Schuessler – Director/Director of Photography
Are U Happy? Films
Address: Gerda-Weiler-Str. 1, 79100 Freiburg, GERMANY
Phone: +49-177-761 6263
Email: info@areuhappyfilms.com
Website: www.areuhappyfilms.com

Currently in production: *Passion and Patience - Up Close with the World's Leading Wildlife Filmmakers*. We offer the following production services: experienced camera operator (Werner Schuessler) to hire and co-productions.

Hayley Smith – Series Producer/Director
Address: 109 Franciscan Road, London SW17 8DZ, UK
Phone: +44 7966 502062
Email: hayleysmith@me.com
Website: www.web.me.com/hayleysmith

Freelance Series PD and producer/director specialising in human stories and the natural world. Producer/Writer on wildlife 'soap' *Meerkat Manor* (winner of Grand Award NY Festival 2009); Producer/Director on psychological drama/doc *Fatal Attractions*; Series Producer/Director (self-shooting) on *Blonde vs Bear*; Series Producer on presenter-led format series *Wild on the West Coast*; Series Producer/Director on *Chimp Diaries*. Extensive overseas filming experience, HD self-shooter, trusted to deliver. GSOH. Popular science, natural history and drama-doc credits.

Kathleen Swalling – Producer/Director
Kathleen Swalling Photography and Film
Address: 483 Route des Nants, Chamonix Mont-Blanc 74400, FRANCE
Phone: +33 637 381 294 (Business) & +971 501 678 018 (Technical)
Email: kathleen@kathleenswalling.com
Website: www.kathleenswalling.com
Producer/Director/Line Production/Location Manager/Fixer: Kathleen Swalling

Services: Producer, Associate Producer, Line Producer, Location Manager. Wildlife, Marine/Island specialist. Media inspiring awareness and engagement with the natural and cultural world. Experience: *Revolution on the Reef part 1 and 2* (concept development, location manager, line producer, script supervisor, main character), *Lord Howe Island: Paradise at the End of the World* (location manager, line producer, 2nd underwater camera). Unique: capabilities stretch from boardroom to remote fieldwork. Science, Art, Law. Fisheries Prosecutor, Island Manager, Senior Lawyer/Strategist for Great Barrier Reef. Highly experienced diver, former competitive triathlete. Other: filmmaker, photographer, skier, mountaineer, team and individual sports. Board Member: Filmmakers for Conservation. Languages: English (Highly Proficient) and French (B1- Intermediate).

172

Dale Templar – Producer/Director
One Tribe TV
Address: Fairview, Charlcombe Lane, Bath BA1 5TT, UK
Email: Dale.Templar@OneTribeTV.co.uk
Website: www.onetribetv.co.uk

Series Producer from the BAFTA award-winning BBC landmark series *Human Planet* now heads up her own independent production company One Tribe TV. Based in Bath and Bristol, One Tribe TV specialise in foreign and remote filming, producing natural history, travel, expedition, anthropology and science content. The company also provides media training, corporate video production, media consultancy, guest lecturing and professional speaking. Our clients include the BBC Academy, Royal Geographical Society and Cunard.
One Tribe TV are always on the look out for exciting ideas and proposals with engaging stories, compelling context and new concepts. Our content focuses on wildlife, science, adventure, and human-interest stories whether they're presenter-led formats or traditional documentary. In addition to film and television content, we have started a corporate production and media training arm. We are always looking to collaborate with other production companies that have strong, engaging and compelling ideas both internationally and within the UK. We are currently working on television projects with the BBC, Dragonfly, RGS, BFI and Adventure Lifesigns.

Yusuf Thakur – Producer/Director
VFX Productions
Address: P.O. Box 49265, 3A Al Qouz, Shaikh Zayed Road, Interchange 3, Behind Times Square, Dubai DXB, UAE
Phone: +971 43471248 & +971 506521931
Fax: +971 43479335
Email: yusufwings@gmail.com
Website: www.vfxme.com

Visual Effects & Productions (VFX) is a twelve year old company based in Dubai and headed by Yusuf Thakur. We have been producing natural history based documentaries since our inception and have produced four HD based films in 2011. The last two have been shot on 4K RED ONE camera, which we own. All our work is based on subjects in the Middle East and specifically UAE. We have comprehensive production and post-production facilities including real time 2K/4K edit suites. Our work in the past has won awards at Jackson Hole, IWFF Montana, and Earth-vision. We have one of most comprehensive footage library on subjects from the region, 90% of which is HD/2K/4K. We would like to produce, work, collaborate, co-produce films on conservation, pure wildlife, children's based program. We would specifically work on films based on the Middle East, and the Indian Subcontinent. Past films have been based on birds, dugongs,

173

islands, mangroves and deserts. We attend pure wildlife film festivals. Would love to work with broadcasters/sponsors on co-productions. Will except Interns who will work in the Middle East region. Email CVs.

Alix Tidmarsh – Director
B8 media
Address: 34 St. Anns Road, London SW13 9LL, UK
Phone: +44 (0)208 876 0026
Email: alix.tidmarsh@b8media.com

Having worked as Marketing Director of BBC Worldwide for seven years, I led the investment strategy and marketing campaigns for the factual genres that BBCW bought. My particular interest is wildlife and as such I have spearheaded the global campaigns for *Walking with Dinosaurs* and follow-up sister series; *Planet Earth*, *The Blue Planet*, all David Attenborough series released since 1990 and *The Human Body* Imax. Since 2003 I have been producing wildlife films for theatrical release including: *Deep Blue* (BBC), *Earth* (BBC), *Wings of Life* (Disney Nature), *African Cats* (Disney Nature) and *Chimpanzee* (Disney Nature). I offer a unique strategic view on creativity and investment of big top-end projects for television and cinema release, having worked with BBC in-house and indies for over ten years, prior to this working in business marketing with Unilever and L'Oreal and we welcome approaches to work together from all film makers who believe they have strong ideas. I am looking for big ideas and strong stories for theatrical release and big event television release, ideally with a strong reason to exist, ie with a clear environmental message/belief. I am always looking for collaborators and co-production too. I am always on the lookout for new talent and prefer to accept CVs by email.

Nick Upton – Freelance Writer/Director/Producer.
Address: 5 Kingsdown House, Kingsdown, Corsham, Wiltshire SN13 8AX, UK
Phone: +44 1225 742300 & +44 7732 361521
Fax: +44 1225 742300
Email: nickupton@btopenworld.com

I'm a freelance director, writer and producer with over twenty years experience of working on wildlife films and series of many kinds, from high end to low budget, for a wide variety of broadcast/non-broadcast clients in Europe/USA/Asia. Films I've written, directed and produced have won nearly 100 awards including eleven Best of Festival wins in eight countries and I've contributed to many other award-winning productions. I'm interested to work on wildlife films on a very flexible basis, offering consultancy, directing, writing, producing or a combination of these. I also have extensive sound recording, stills photography and some 2nd camera experience. I'm looking for paid work on productions that need my input or backing for my own ideas, not for proposals to be sent to me. I don't run my own production company, but do seek to work with established companies on their productions or on projects I've initiated. I do not offer work experience.

Reece de Ville
Country: UK
Phone: +44 770943532
Email: reeceadeville@gmail.com
Website: www.reecedeville.com

I am a freelance filmmaker who has worked with the BBC, Absolute Radio, Mark Kermode, Thea Gilmore, Middlesex and Bournemouth Universities and many more. I shoot/edit exciting pieces for broadcast, online, advertising, wildlife studies and promos. Previous work includes advertisements for Apple Europe, broadcast packages for the BBC and promos for various digital companies. I'm exceptionally patient, which comes in handy when awaiting the perfect wildlife shot! I'm looking for wildlife projects that tell unique and vital stories · whether that's species conservation across the globe to individual animal study through to macro shot insects and creatures rarely seen on film. Also, if you're looking to create documentaries such as *Project Nim*, for example, with previously shot footage, I can be your editor and help pull together a stunning film. I'm looking to collaborate on projects that have the potential to be fascinating – from company promos to wildlife documentaries, day in the life pieces and features. I've a keen interest in working across the wildlife genre and have worked on projects for the National Trust in England and have shot various local wildlife pieces across the country. I love creating interesting and vibrant work and can offer my clients a cost-effective one-man shoot/edit package with HD cams, rapid editing and an open mind! I am open to projects large or small – lets chat! I'm happy to work with all collaborators and sponsors who are interested in creating rewarding pieces. You can hire me as a one-man shoot/edit or as part of a larger crew – happy to discuss your project and talk about what I can offer. I don't currently offer work experience placements or internships, but I'm happy to chat to anyone who'd like advice or has questions about the industry. I believe it's vital to share knowledge and even more vital to be approachable! I'm always looking to build up a contacts list of sound designers, cameramen, musicians etc, so drop me a line.

Bernard Walton – Producer
Aqua Vita Films
Address: Bristol UK
Website: www.aquavitafilms.com

175

Björn Welander – Producer
Björn Welander Photography
Address: 7628 Bayside Road, Chesapeake beach, MD 20732, USA
Phone: +1 301 910 1930
Email: b.welander@gmail.com
Website: www.bjornwelander.com and www.baldibis.org
Producer/Camera/Editor: Björn Welander

We produce films with strong conservation messages that have the local people's angle and involve those who live and work in valuable conservation areas or where threatened species occur. Currently looking for proposals that shows a success story in conservation and would work well as a presenter-led wildlife documentary. Conservation festival category. We are looking for sponsors that want to take an active part in our projects. We will consider co-productions. No work experience/internships for the moment since we have just relocated to Maryland, USA.

Thomas Wiewandt – Producer/Director
Wild Horizons Productions
Address: 5757 West Sweetwater Drive, Tucson, Arizona 85745, USA
Phone: +1 520 743 4551 & +1 520 743 4848
Fax: +1 520 743 4552
Email: info@wildhorizons.com
Website: www.wildhorizons.com
Producer/Director of Photography: Thomas Wiewandt – tom@wildhorizons.com

Experienced independent natural history photographer-storyteller with PhD in behavioral ecology, based in the Sonoran Desert. Now engaged in multimedia production. Special interests include conservation projects, children's programming, and new nature media. Inquire about stock video clips, project research/consulting, or location scouting. Awards: Emmy nomination in cinematography, 4 CINE Golden Eagles, Gold Apple from National Educational Film & Video Festival. Not looking for proposals or offering work experience. We are seeking sponsors for work in progress and are interested in speaking with potential collaborators or co-producers.

Norm Wilkinson – Producer/Director/Writer
Visionquest Entertainment international Pty Ltd
Address: P.O. Box 2097, Kelvin Grove, Queensland 4059, AUSTRALIA
Phone: +61 7 3369 5430 & +61 402 058 863
Fax: +61 7 33698119
Email: norm@visionquest.com.au
Website: www.visionquest.com.au

We are producers and executive producers. We are constantly looking for new ideas in all areas, including children's, of natural history, science, adventure and history storytelling. We are always looking for co-productions, consider sponsors/collaborations and prefer CVs to be delivered by email.

Kim Wolhuter – Producer/Cameraman
Mavela Media
Address: SOUTH AFRICA
Website: www.wildcast.net

Joe Yaggi – Director/Camera
Jungle Run Productions
Address: Jalan Raya Sanggingan #1. Ubud 80571, Bali Indonesia 80571, INDONESIA
Phone: +62 8123813887 & +62 361979109
Fax: +62 361975378
Email: joe@jungle-run.com & joeyaggi@yahoo.com
Website: www.jungle-run.com

I'm a freelance director and cameraman based in Indonesia. I've worked across the Indonesian archipelago and right across the region. Projects I've worked on range from wildlife to social issues, conservation to education. I've contributed to feature docs, factual programs and educational productions as well.

Some of my recent credits include: *History of the World*, BBC1 – Indonesia camera unit. *Trashed*, Blenheim Films: A feature documentary presented by Jeremy Irons – Indonesia camera unit. *Alien from Earth*, PBS Nova & ABC Australia – 2nd unit camera. *Heads Above Water*, BBC World – DOP, Co-Director Indonesia. *Age of Stupid*, Feature Documentary Launch USA – Greenpeace Director/DOP. Indigenous rights activist in a burned out forest beamed live to 600 screens across America. For more please see our website and IMDB.

ASSISTANT PRODUCERS

Gaby Bastyra – AP/Producer/Director
Address: 2, 147 Queens Drive, London N4 2BB, UK
Phone: +44 7941387314
Email: gabybastyra@gmail.com
Website: www.bee-productions.co.uk

Producer, director and AP specialising in wildlife documentaries. Have won Best Newcomer at Wildscreen 2008 and nominated at Jackson Hole 2009 in the same category for film *The White Wood*. Nominated in 2011 in the Best Short category for *Gloop*. Have been working on BBC *Natural Worlds* for the past two years at Passion Pictures.

Paul Dimmock – Self-Shooting Assistant Producer
Address: The Barn, Warren Farm, High Street, Ridgmont, Beds MK43 0TS, UK
Phone: +44 (0)7921848447
Email: pjdimmock@hotmail.com
Website: www.about.me/pjdimmock

I am a researcher, camera operator, photographer, self-shooting assistant producer, underwater photographer/videographer, production coordinator ... I create and research factual content with strong character-led stories involving wildlife. I photograph and film above and below the water, focusing on achieving captivating images and composition, which refreshes the viewers understanding. My determination and grit has enabled me to source valuable locations and professional cast on several productions and my creative ability means I always have ideas and can see how to pitch them. Experienced in directing crew and productions, producing drama and documentary, shooting DSLR and professional camera equipment. I am always on the look out for intriguing content and projects to work on as well as interesting people to work with. I am diverse in my outlook and like working on a variety of productions. I would consider working alongside or for any productions that have wildlife at their heart and which have a positive message that they are trying to achieve.

Claire Evans – Assistant Producer/Presenter/Editor
Address: Bristol, UK & CANADA
Email: clairepagan@hotmail.com

I specialise in natural history and environmental filmmaking. I have several years' experience working for companies such as the BBC and Halo Films. I hold three degrees including one in biology and one in creative arts/film studies. I hold UK and Canadian passports and have experience working with British and North American wildlife. I am currently planning a film about Tanzania. I make films for Friends of the Earth from time to time. I am frequently looking for sponsors and co-producers. I sometimes have availability to provide short-term work experience for camera operators and sound recordists. Prefer CVs by email. Some prior experience is usually necessary.

Freya Short (née Pratt) – Assistant Producer
Address: Bristol, UK
Email: freyapratt@hotmail.com
Phone: +44 (0)7968 843 086

I am a natural history assistant producer with seen years of production experience across blue-chip, children's, presenter-led and live productions. I am competent in self-shooting, script writing, directing, sound recording and edit producing as well as undertaking excellent research and development. My organisation, creativity and innovative visioning for shoots are all essential for the success of productions. I have extensive experience of setting up shoots and assisting on location in both the UK and abroad. Together with an MSc in Animal Behaviour, I have specialist knowledge of nocturnal carnivores, wild felid species, animal cognition and human-wildlife conflict.

Ed Watkins – Self-Shooting A.P/Editor
Address: 41 Brecknock Rd., Ground Floor, Bristol BS4 2DE, UK
Phone: +44 (0)7527 452 960
Email: e.m.watkins@gmail.com
Website: www.naturalscinema.com

I am a self-shooting assistant producer and editor with a strong background in science and natural history. I have worked on a wide range of productions from broadcast to commercial and corporate both in the US and the UK. I am very experienced with digital workflows and cameras.

179

PRODUCTION MANAGERS

Paul Dimmock – Production Coordinator
Address: The Barn, Warren Farm, High Street, Ridgmont, Beds MK43 0TS, UK
Phone: +44 (0)7921848447
Email: pjdimmock@hotmail.com
Website: www.about.me/pjdimmock

I am a researcher, camera operator, photographer, self-shooting assistant producer, underwater photographer/videographer, production coordinator ... I create and research factual content with strong character-led stories involving wildlife. I photograph and film above and below the water, focusing on achieving captivating images and composition, which refreshes the viewers understanding. My determination and grit has enabled me to source valuable locations and professional cast on several productions and my creative ability means I always have ideas and can see how to pitch them. Experienced in directing crew and productions, producing drama and documentary, shooting DSLR and professional camera equipment. I am always on the look out for intriguing content and projects to work on as well as interesting people to work with. I am diverse in my outlook and like working on a variety of productions. I would consider working alongside or for any productions that have wildlife at their heart and which have a positive message that they are trying to achieve.

Anya Klages – Line Producer
Address: 39 Skaife St, Hout Bay 7806, SOUTH AFRICA
Phone: +27 82 585 1188 & +27 21 790 4736

With over twenty-five years of invaluable experience in the production world, exceptional organisational skills, coupled with fluency in four European languages, Anya is at home in the bush. Highly regarded for her meticulous attention to detail and logical thinking, her energy and enthusiasm inspire all who work with her. Committed and hands-on, she has a passion for providing excellent service.

Rachel O'Reilly – Production Manager
Discovery Communications Europe
Address: Discovery House, bldg 2, Chiswick Park, 566 Chiswick High Road, London W4 5YB, UK
Email: rachel_oreilly@discovery-europe.com

180

Jin Pyn Lee – Production Manager
Elemantree Media
Address: Blk 6, 12-430, Telok Blangah Crescent, 090006, SINGAPORE
Phone: +65 62726769 & +61 423662233
Fax: +65 62726769
Email: jinpyn.lee@elephantandtree.com
Website: www.elemantreemedia.com

Freelance television producer, director, writer, fixer, production management. Specialize in Asian natural history and conservation (over twenty years involvement). Jin Pyn's career spans across broadcaster and independent production companies. Credits include BBC Worldwide, Channel News Asia, and Animal Planet, across all genres – short-form interstitials, long-form factual documentaries, and animation. Geographically the programs have been distributed all over the globe, including Korea's Kids Talk Talk, US's Somos TV and India's Edumedia. In Japan, Jin Pyn has won the best animation award, and her children's picture book was the first from Singapore to garner multiple languages.

Andrey Manirko
Address: London, UK
Phone: +44 7545051642 & +7 9161856110
Email: manirko@gmail.com
Website: www.manirko.com

Bilingual filmmaker based in London. Originally from Russia, living in UK, working in documentary production, both nature and ethnographical. Have been on shoots in Far East Russia, Kamchatka and other remote locations. Well connected in Moscow production/media scene. Looking to get involved in as many Russia-related productions as possible, but also willing to embark on adventures. I have some scripts for anthropological ob-docs bordering with natural world.

Dee Marshall – Production Manager
Address: 202 Chemin des Vachers 38410 Uriage, FRANCE
Phone: +33 611548112 & +33 476892053
Email: dee.marshall@gmail.com
Website: www.beneaththeskies.com

An experienced writer and photographer with extensive knowledge of wildlife and proven ability in wildlife filming and editing. Currently working on a short film about the Maasai in Tanzania and two books about wildlife and children. I have a diploma in Mammal Ecology and Conservation and have spent many years managing large complicated projects. Fluent in French and English and competent in Italian, German and Japanese. I am available to manage film productions on a freelance basis or short contract work.

RESEARCHERS

Karen Brooks: Researcher/Producer/Facilitator
Facilitation Southern Africa
Address: Suite 36, Private Bag X12, Cresta 2118, SOUTH AFRICA
Phone: +27 83 259-6324 & +27 11 880-4302
Email: karenvbrooks@gmail.com
Website: www.tinyurl.com/6l83cmw

Facilitation for all southern African countries: South Africa, Swaziland and Lesotho, Botswana, Namibia, Zimbabwe, Mozambique and Zambia. Madagascar. Wildlife films, documentaries and commercials. Over twenty-three years' experience in South African television.

Nicola Brown – Researcher
One Tribe TV
Address: Fairview, Charlcombe Lane, Bath BA1 5TT, UK
Email: Nicola.Brown@OneTribeTV.co.uk
Website: www.onetribetv.co.uk

Based in Bath and Bristol, One Tribe TV specialise in foreign and remote filming, producing natural history, travel, expedition, anthropology and science content. The company also provides media training, corporate video production, media consultancy, guest lecturing and professional speaking. Our clients include the BBC Academy, Royal Geographical Society and Cunard. One Tribe TV are always on the look out for exciting ideas and proposals with engaging stories, compelling context and new concepts. Our content focuses on wildlife, science, adventure, and human-interest stories whether they're presenter-led formats or traditional documentary. In addition to film and television content, we have started a corporate production and media training arm. We are always looking to collaborate with other production companies that have strong, engaging and compelling ideas both internationally and within the UK. We are currently working on television projects with the BBC, Dragonfly, RGS, BFI and Adventure Lifesigns.

Deep Fried Films – Researchers
Address: P O Box 659, Mossel Bay 6500, SOUTH AFRICA
Phone: +27 44 6903681
Email: admin@deepfriedfilms.com
Website: www.deepfriedfilms,com
Owner/Admin: Fiona Ayerst – fiona@deepfriedfilms.com
Owner/Strategy: Ryan Johnson – ryan@deepfriedfilms.com

Fiona, originally from Kenya, is a camerawoman specializing in underwater work, especially with sharks, and Ryan is a freelance presenter who has done work for NatGeo and BBC, inter alia. Ryan, originally a Kiwi, is a marine biologist with a PhD and is in demand for documentaries featuring sharks. We live in the beautiful Garden Route area of the Western Cape in RSA and have access to many pristine areas and wild animals. Fiona runs a photography internship program in South Africa and details are available on www.fionaayerst.com We do co-productions and we offer an internship.

Paul Dimmock – Researcher
Address: The Barn, Warren Farm, High Street, Ridgmont, Beds MK43 0TS, UK
Phone: +44 (0)7921848447
Email: pjdimmock@hotmail.com
Website: www.about.me/pjdimmock

I am a researcher, camera operator, photographer, self-shooting assistant producer, underwater photographer/videographer, production coordinator ... I create and research factual content with strong character-led stories involving wildlife. I photograph and film above and below the water, focusing on achieving captivating images and composition, which refreshes the viewers understanding. My determination and grit has enabled me to source valuable locations and professional cast on several productions and my creative ability means I always have ideas and can see how to pitch them. Experienced in directing crew and productions, producing drama and documentary, shooting DSLR and professional camera equipment. I am always on the look out for intriguing content and projects to work on as well as interesting people to work with. I am diverse in my outlook and like working on a variety of productions. I would consider working alongside or for any productions that have wildlife at their heart and which have a positive message that they are trying to achieve.

Sara Douglas – Researcher
Country: UK
Phone: +447813801141
Email: sara.l.douglas@gmail.com

Thorough ability to extract salient and most 'film-able' points from vast amounts of scientific research. Key skills include: self-shooting on Sony Z1, EX1 and DSLR, Final Cut Pro, Soundtrack Pro, Shotput Pro, GoPro HD operation, P2CMS, managing tape and tapeless media formats, full clean driving licence (extensive 4WD experience), basic French and German, field craft and survival.

Natalie Gilbert – Anthrozoology Researcher/Writer
Country: UK
Website: www.nataliegilbert.net
Email: animaltheory@gmail.com

I'm a researcher, writer, photographer and online manager with a postgrad in Anthrozoology. I'm expressly interested in the human-animal bond and keen to assist any efforts made in wildlife film-making that supports exploration of human-animal relationships of every kind. I have many contacts in this field and an abundance of knowledge to assist planning, production and marketing of Film. I have previously worked for Wildeye and Wildlife-film.com and have undertaken a course in Wildlife Film-making.

Mundy Hackett – Researcher
Mundy Hackett Photography
Address: 130 Colony Trail, Lanexa, Virginia 23089, USA
Phone: +1 804 349 6501
Email: mundy@mundyhackett.com
Website: www.mundyhackett.com

I have a PhD in Wildlife Biology and Conservation, I am a published author and wildlife photographer, and I am an experienced researcher in the areas of applied field research. I have worked with groups such as Nature Conservancy, Tigers 4 Tigers, National Fish & Wildlife Foundation, and Smithsonian. I am looking for opportunities to utilize my skill sets to benefit and promote conservation of rare, threatened and endangered habitats and species. I am also looking for opportunities to travel and assist in anyway with research projects focused on carnivores and carnivore ecology. I will consider pro bono assignments if they benefit and further my professional goals and objectives.

Arlo Hemphill – Writer, Filmmaker, Science Consultant
Address: 1419 Roosevelt Avenue, Melbourne, Florida 32901, USA
Phone: +1 202·746·3484
Email: arlo@arlohemphill.com
Website: www.arlohemphill.com

Producer, writer and researcher for science, wilderness and conservation topics. Subject matter expert on tropical marine ecosystems, Sargassum, Sargasso Sea, Amazon, Caribbean, tropical Andes and coastal Ecuador/Peru. Available for short and long-term work in production.

Clive Huggins – Consultant Entomologist/Photographer
Address: Surrey, UK
Phone: +44 (0)20 8942 7846
Email: clivehuggins@ymail.com

Insects & Spiders Worldwide, Consultant.
Research and develop ideas; access to specialists and local contacts; field support; macro and habitat stills photography. Assisted BBC NHU productions. Previously entomologist at Natural History Museum London, with published material, speciality butterflies. Padi Advanced Scuba Diver.

Clova Jurk – Researcher/Marine Biologist
Address: Hout Bay, Cape Town 7806, SOUTH AFRICA
Phone: +27 (0)73 996 3293
Email: clovajurk@gmail.com

Marine biologist with experience in invasive species management.
Four years of wildlife film experience: January 2006: Production Assistant on National Geographic TV & Film shoot; June – October 2006: Course Co-ordinator, Wildlife Film Academy, Cape Town; November 2006 – January 2010: Researcher and Production Manager for Wild Images, Cape Town.

Jin Pyn Lee – Researcher
Elemantree Media
Address: Blk 6, 12-430, Telok Blangah Crescent, 090006, SINGAPORE
Phone: +65 62726769 & +61 423662233
Fax: +65 62726769
Email: jinpyn.lee@elephantandtree.com
Website: www.elemantreemedia.com

Freelance television producer, director, writer, fixer, production management. Specialize in Asian natural history and conservation (over twenty years involvement). Jin Pyn's career spans across broadcaster and independent production companies. Credits include BBC Worldwide, Channel News Asia, and Animal Planet, across all genres – short-form interstitials, long-form factual documentaries, and animation. Geographically the programs have been distributed all over the globe, including Korea's Kids Talk Talk, US's Somos TV and India's Edumedia. In Japan, Jin Pyn has won the best animation award, and her children's picture book was the first from Singapore to garner multiple languages.

Tamara Lodge – Researcher/Assistant Camera
Address: 21 Shaftesbury Avenue, Bristol BS6 5LT, UK
Phone: +44 7977 001 848
Email: tamara@tamaralodge.co.uk
Website: www.tamaralodge.co.uk

Interested in adventure/travel/natural history/ob docs. Marine biology background with three years experience as location runner/camera assistant and junior researcher. Previous employers: BBC, Tigress, Ten Alps Vision, JJ Stereo.

Lisa Nupen – Researcher/Doctoral Candidate
Address: 2 Chemlsford Court, Vredehoek, Cape Town 8001, SOUTH AFRICA
Phone: +27216503619 & +27725122143
Email: lisa.nupen@uct.ac.za
Website: www.fitzpatrick.uct.ac.za/docs/lisa.html

I would like to offer my skills as a researcher to help players in the film industry make meaningful wildlife documentaries. I get enormously frustrated when I see documentaries based on flawed logic and/or science. I have a Masters degree in conservation biology and a (seemingly) bottomless interest in the intricacies in nature that evolution has produced. I also have a broad knowledge of relevant global environmental issues. I'd like to work on adventure films, wildlife documentaries, even if they're targeted at kids. Looking for collaborators.

Claire Thompson – Freelance Researcher
Address: 1 Redland Court Road, Bristol BS6 7EE, UK
Phone: +44 (0)7979 693975
Email: claire_t009@yahoo.co.uk

I am an experienced freelance researcher with an in-depth understanding of a wide range of natural history subjects. I have worked for the BBC Natural History Unit, Azara Film, ITV Studios, Aardman and Wildscreen; have a Masters of Research from Cambridge University in primate ecology and many years experience working in Africa and Asia under challenging conditions in the field. I have a proven history of providing thorough, in-depth research and comprehensive practical support for wildlife productions and am a passionate, resilient team member; enthusiastic in my work, with an established record of achievement.

Thomas Wiewandt
Wild Horizons Productions
Address: 5757 West Sweetwater Drive, Tucson, Arizona 85745, USA
Phone: +1 520 743 4551 & +1 520 743 4848
Fax: +1 520 743 4552
Email: info@wildhorizons.com
Website: www.wildhorizons.com
Producer/Director of Photography: Thomas Wiewandt – tom@wildhorizons.com

Experienced independent natural history photographer-storyteller with PhD in behavioral ecology, based in the Sonoran Desert. Now engaged in multimedia production. Special interests include conservation projects, children's programming, and new nature media. Inquire about stock video clips, project research/consulting, or location scouting. Awards: Emmy nomination in cinematography, four CINE Golden Eagles, Gold Apple from National Educational Film & Video Festival. Not looking for proposals or offering work experience. We are seeking sponsors for work in progress and are interested in speaking with potential collaborators or co-producers.

Marleen van der Werf - Researcher
Wild Work Productions
Email: info@wildworkproductions.com
Website: www.wildworkproductions.com

Filmmaker, Marleen van der Werf, has a Msc in Biology and MA in Wildlife Documentary. Her combined background in biology and filmmaking enables her to understand and capture the beauty of the natural world and sciences at all levels. As a wildlife filmmaker she has specialised in using camera techniques such as macro, underwater, infra red, high speed and aerial filming as well as time-lapse and animation. Furthermore she is a skilled researcher, scriptwriter, director, sound recordist and editor that works worldwide. Marleen van der Werf is also founder of Wild Work Productions.

187

ASSISTANTS/RUNNERS

Yusuf Akhtar – Young Wildlife Filmmaker and Photographer

(NB Yusuf was 15 years old at time of publication and is looking to become a wildlife film-maker when he finishes school)
Address : London, UK
Email: yaproductions@hotmail.co.uk
Website: www.yusufakhtar.wordpress.com/

I'm Yusuf and I'm a wildlife filmmaker and photographer. I have a passion for filming wildlife. I make short wildlife documentaries but I am starting to experiment with making longer films. I like films that are informative and my aim is to uncover the secret lives of wild animals so people appreciate them more. I'm currently working on projects of my own but am always looking for new opportunities to film for people. I mainly have experience in presenter led documentaries but I am learning to make more pure wildlife films. I am looking for sponsoring for my films and I will consider co-productions. I am looking for work experience and will appreciate any help and advice.

Tatiana Biktimirova – Film-maker Assistant

Address: Flat 49 Whinchat Road, Thamesmead SE28 0DZ, UK
Phone: +44 (0)7703692740
Email: Tatiana_wonderland@hotmail.co.uk

Multi-skilled in everything from camera operation to production, research and editing. I'm available to assist on any level of production. Happy to get stuck in with any tasks, whether on a voluntary or paid basis.

Will Bolton – Assistant Camera/Photographer

Address: Bristol, UK
Website: www.willbolton.co.uk

Marcus Brent-Smith – Camera Assistant

Country: UK
Email: marcusbrentsmith@hotmail.com
Website: www.marcusbrentsmith.co.uk

Young, enthusiastic camera assistant specialising in wildlife productions. Zoology degree, extensive camera training, time-lapse expertise and wide-ranging experience in all areas of television production.

Tom Burn – Videographer/Photographer/Assistant
Tom Burn Photography

Address: Dorset, UK
Website: www.tomburnphotography.net
Email: t.burn24@gmail.com

Wildlife photographer and videographer based in Dorset, UK. Available for hire to work in many different production roles, with the main focus being camera operator. Completed Wildeye Introduction to Wildlife Filmmaking and the Wildlife Film Academy course. I am eager to support or co-produce wildlife films in the UK or abroad.

Adam L Canning – Wildlife Filmer Adam
Nature On Screen
Address: West Midlands, UK
Email: WildlifeFilmerAdam@live.co.uk
Website: www.NatureonScreen.webs.com

'Wildlife Filmer Adam' is a film maker who directs, produces, presents, films and edits. Up for any kind of natural history documentary film. Have made documentaries for Reader's Digest in the form of a web-series called *Wildlife Monthly*. Experience: directing, producing, presenting, camerawork and editing, plus will happily assist with any of those roles. Keen to learn and experience new things. Would love to be sponsored and happy to do co-productions. Anyone who would like to write scripts for *Wildlife Monthly* are very welcome and anyone wanting their footage or pictures featured are welcome too.

Peter Cayless – Camera/Field Assistant
Address: Bristol, UK
Website: www.petecaylessfilms.com

Andrew Chambi – Assistant Director
Country: UK
Phone: +44 7947828979 & +44 2084461419
Email: Andrewchambi@gmail.com

I have made various independent wildlife films for organisations and individuals from concept to completion – including producing, filming, directing and editing. I am constantly looking for new projects to be involved in especially if the subject is animal behaviour – my specialism and the subject of my studies. I am currently helping a wildlife presenter deliver his demo to a commissioner and would be happy to help any other budding presenters. I am also currently looking for the opportunity to be involved with a professional, experienced director/company to help me gain valuable experience. I am planning on entering festivals in the newcomer category and would love to encounter likeminded film-makers to collaborate with.

Francis Chee – Assistant/Lighting Cameraman/Biologist
Address: Bristol, UK
Email: info@francischeefilms.com
Website: www.francischeefilms.com

Jade Childs – Assistant
Address: 29 Buccaneer Court, Kestrel Road, Farnborough, Hampshire, UK
Phone: +44 (007805018318
Email: jade.childs@sky.com

I am currently a student at Sunderland University studying Television and Radio and have an extremely keen interest in wildlife and documentary production. As I also live in the South I have access to the Hampshire/London, Midlands and Northeast areas. I am an extremely willing, conscientious and hard-working individual who strives to learn new things and achieve her best. I already have some camera experience under my belt and am currently working on a team that produces documentaries and promotional videos (www.northernangelmedia.tv/news.php) and have had runner/assistant work experience also. I would love the opportunity to be a part of future wildlife film developments.

Karla Munguia Colmenero – Camera/Production Assistant
Address: Jesus del Monte, MEXICO
Phone: +52 5516679565
Email: karla.munguia@gmail.com
Website: www.karlamunguia.tv

I am a Mexican wildlife camerawoman open to assist in nature films. I am fluent in both Spanish and English. My experience as production assistant includes Animal Planet's and Barron TV's series *Unearthed, Film School Wild 2*, filmed in South Africa. I am currently looking for productions focused in conservation, adventure, human-interest or pure wildlife.

Ryan Farnes – Assistant
Address: Washington, DC, USA
Website: www.ryanfarnes.com

Ricardo Guerreiro – Wildlife Photographer/Cameraman
Country: PORTUGAL
Phone: +351 910732177 & +351 969336964
Email: zevimetal@gmail.com
Website: www.zevi.cabine.org/rgfoto/

Freelance natural history photographer and cameraman working in Portugal. May also work as assistant to foreign production teams coming to Portugal. Main interests: NH filmmaking and stills photography, including the rural traditional practices of agriculture and their interaction with wildlife. Some experience in film editing also.

Samuel Guiton – Camera Assistant
Address: 9 rue mélusine, 79310 Verruyes, FRANCE
Phone: +33 664319816 & +33 549644360
Email: s.guiton@gmail.com
Website: www.dailly-guiton.jimdo.com

I'm a French freelance camera operator specialising in wildlife and time-lapse shots. I have been involved in shooting for several series as *Wild France* (Gédéon Programmes) and *Life in Fire* (Saint Thomas Productions). You can have a look to my showreel here: http://vimeo.com/24957539

Mundy Hackett – Assistant
Mundy Hackett Photography
Address: 130 Colony Trail, Lanexa, Virginia 23089, USA
Phone: +1 804 349 6501
Email: mundy@mundyhackett.com
Website: www.mundyhackett.com

I have a PhD in Wildlife Biology and Conservation, I am a published author and wildlife photographer, and I am an experienced researcher in the areas of applied field research. I have worked with groups such as Nature Conservancy, Tigers 4 Tigers, National Fish & Wildlife Foundation, and Smithsonian. I am looking for opportunities to utilize my skill sets to benefit and promote conservation of rare, threatened and endangered habitats and species. I am also looking for opportunities to travel and assist in anyway with research projects focused on carnivores and carnivore ecology. I will consider pro bono assignments if they benefit and further my professional goals and objectives.

Dick Harrewijn – Assistant Cameraman
Address: Utrecht, NETHERLANDS
Phone: +31 618182655
Email: ik@dickharrewijn.com
Website: www.dickharrewijn.com

From the start of my first days in film-making I've gained much experience from pre- to post-production. I'm best described as a young cameraman with good knowledge of (digital) post-production workflows and a huge passion for wildlife. Besides being a cameraman I'm working as a colorist and on location sound recordist. Skills: adventure, animal behaviour, blue/green screen, camera loading and assistant work. Data workflow, DVD authoring, editing, field audio gathering equipment, Final Cut Pro, HD, Open Water Dive Licence, RED ONE, sound recording, stills photography, time-lapse.

Siyabulela Jabavu – Assistant/Aspiring Wildlife Filmmaker
Address: 8745 Mandleni Street, Kwazakhele, Port Elizabeth 6205, SOUTH AFRICA
Email: jabavus@yahoo.com

I have completed the month-long Wildlife Film Academy course in Cape Town and I am fascinated about the relationship between human beings and animals. This I see as an ongoing process that has to be filmed on a continuous basis. Passionate about human-interest stories. Stories about the co-existence between human beings and animals.

Jin Pyn Lee – Assistant
Elemantree Media
Address: Blk 6, 12-430, Telok Blangah Crescent, 090006, SINGAPORE
Phone: +65 62726769 & +61 423662233
Fax: +65 62726769
Email: jinpyn.lee@elephantandtree.com
Website: www.elemantreemedia.com

Freelance television producer, director, writer, fixer, production management. Specialize in Asian natural history and conservation (over twenty years involvement). Jin Pyn's career spans across broadcaster and independent production companies. Credits include BBC Worldwide, Channel News Asia, and Animal Planet, across all genres – short-form interstitials, long-form factual documentaries, and animation. Geographically the programs have been distributed all over the globe, including Korea's Kids Talk Talk, US's Somos TV and India's Edumedia. In Japan, Jin Pyn has won the best animation award, and her children's picture book was the first from Singapore to garner multiple languages.

Tamara Lodge – Assistant Camera/Locations Assistant
Address: 21 Shaftesbury Avenue, Bristol BS6 5LT, UK
Phone: +44 7977 001 848
Email: tamara@tamaralodge.co.uk
Website: www.tamaralodge.co.uk

Three Years location running and camera assisting experience. Looking to get involved with productions setting up foreign shoots. I specialise in natural history/adventure/travel. Padi Master Diver and environmental/marine biology background.

Jim Manthorpe – Freelance Wildlife Film-maker
Address: Scottas Cottage West, Knoydart, Mallaig PH41 4PL, Scotland, UK
Phone: +44 (0)1687 460318
Email: info@jimmanthorpe.com
Website: www.jimmanthorpe.com

I am an aspiring film-maker looking for camera assistant roles or work as a runner. As a child I appeared in three episodes of *Wildabout*, a Children's ITV series. I went on to do work experience in post-production at Partridge Films. I live in Knoydart, a remote part of the Highlands where I film my local wildlife for my website. I worked as a ranger here for five years and have in depth knowledge of Scottish wildlife and locations. I am the author of a guidebook to hillwalking so I know the region very well. Recently I have worked as a camera mentor on two films made by children, one of which came first in its category at the First Light Movie Awards.

Thomas Marks – Camera Assistant
Address: 62b Grosvenor Terrace, London SE5 0NP, UK
Phone: +44 (0)7740 682 425
Email: tom@thomas-marks.com
Website: www.thomas-marks.com

Camera assistant looking for experience to work on any project. Good technical ability with DSLRs, lenses and camera techniques. Passionate about making it in wildlife filmmaking, will work very hard and will be an enthusiastic addition to your team. Very good organisational and IT skills. Have absorbed a wealth of knowledge about the field over many years now. Regularly practice filming to improve my techniques and understanding. Please contact me if you can offer a spare place on your team for any sort of production. Will work for free depending on circumstances. Can be available for several months if needs be.

Luke Massey – Camera Assistant
Address: 112 Lancaster Road, St Albans AL1 4ES, UK
Phone: +44 (0)7519 175553 & +44 (0)1727 831344
Fax: +44 (0)1727 831344
Email: lmassey91@hotmail.co.uk
Website: www.lmasseyimages.com

I am a young conservationist with experience in identifying most British, Fijian and Canadian wildlife. I am able to offer help with filming documentaries, short films and showreels. I know basic rope skills for tree climbing and am competent in off-road driving.

193

I also make a mean cup of tea! Starting out in the trade I am looking for as many chances as possible in wildlife filmmaking. Contact me for a showreel.

Jo McIvor
Address: Cheshire, UK
Email: jomcivor@yahoo.co.uk

A recent graduate of the MA Wildlife Documentary Course at the University of Salford, Jo has several years experience working on television dramas, commercials, documentaries and films. Since 2006 she has been working her way up the ladder in the camera department and wants to break in to the wildlife industry. She is currently entering her MA final film in to wildlife festivals around the world. The film has been screened at a local wildlife conference, where it received great feedback. Several Wildlife Colleges have requested a copy to show their students.

Pim Niesten – Assistant/Cameraman/Zoologist
Address: Mechelen, BELGIUM
Phone: +32 (0)485 593049
Email: pimniesten@hotmail.com
Website: pimniesten.skynetblogs.be

After getting a Masters degree in Zoology, Marine Biology and a Bachelor in Cinematography I've been working as a camera operator, camera and field assistant and sound operator for wildlife film projects since 2006, mainly in Europe and Africa. During my first experiences in the professional world of wildlife filmmaking I was involved in pre- and postproduction: doing research, logging footage and editing trailers for wildlife documentaries. With the ever-present aspiration to become a wildlife camera operator and in order to get more hands-on experience in the field I became a camera assistant, sound recordist and second camera operator for various wildlife film productions. Besides assisting jobs, I'm also gaining experience as a wildlife cameraman for various productions. Currently filming nature and wildlife in the Durmitor Mountains and Tara River Canyon in Montenegro (2010-11).

John Oteng Ochuodho – Zonal Forest Inspector
Kenya Forest Service
Address: BOX 114, Transmara-Kilgoris 40700, KENYA
Phone: +254 (0)720845171
Email: oteng2000@yahoo.com
Website: www.kenyaforestservice.org

I am involved in conservation as a forest inspector for the enforcement and compliance of forest protection and its benefits, arresting and prosecution of the culprits, writing report on forest activities, educating the community on the important of forest conservation. I would like to be considered in environmental documentary, as it requires public relation knowledge and communication skills I acquired in the work field and in my course-regional environmental journalism and communication and community-based biodiversity conservation film-making. I have made a documentary on soil erosion. Selling of films will be done through forest community association advocacy. I am looking for film ideas especially conservation-themed. I consider sponsors and co-production with any partner. I will offer work experience placement in forest conservation, protection and advocacy. I am actively looking for talent in documentary film production. I would prefer CV by email. I have work experience in environmental conservation, certificate in environmental film-making, Diploma in Administration and Public Relation, work experience in forest and wildlife protection.

George Pillas
Country: England, UK
Phone: +447923387537
Email: Georgepillas@gmail.com

I hold a zoology degree and I have just completed an MA in wildlife documentary production at the University of Salford. I have been trained in many aspects of wildlife film-making such as production, camera operation, script-writing, sound recording and post-production. I have used telephoto and macro lenses, infrared cameras and camera traps to name a few. Interested in getting involved with anything related to wildlife documentaries.

Daniel Pinheiro – Assistant Camera Operator
Country: UK and Portugal
Phone: +351 964376768 & +44 (0)7519945823
Email: dpinheiro80@gmail.com

Freelance assistant camera operator and sound recordist. Graduated in audiovisuals. Post-graduated with an MA in Wildlife Documentary Production from University of Salford. Eight years experience as sound operator and editor for radio and in live recordings of orchestras. Member of the Wildlife Sound Recording Society. Skills: Final Cut Pro, Pro Tools, animal behaviour, tracking wildlife, editing, field audio gathering equipment, sound recording, stills photography, time-lapse. In 2011 I produced a film about the wildlife of the Mondego River in Portugal and also worked as sound recordist and camera assistant in a film about Macaws in Tambopata Peru.

Plane Viewing Ltd
Address: 39 The Vineries, Burgess Hill, West Sussex, RH15 0ND, UK
Phone: +44 (0)1444 870894
Email: bryangrayson@ymail.com
Director/Cameraman: Bryan Grayson – bryangrayson@ymail.com
Cameraman/Editor: Nigel Jefferies – njefferies52@gmail.com

Wildlife filmmaker and cameraman. Credits from Animal planet "Shark Night" and the only UK selected contestant for the Animal Planet 2006 "Unearthed" series. Able to offer cameraman and editing service using final cut pro.
Looking for presenter in local area and story tellers

Alex Rhodes – Wildlife and Conservation Camera Operator/Assistant
(NB Alex was 15 years old at time of publication and is looking to become a wildlife film-maker when he finishes school)
Address: Bristol, UK
Phone: +44 (0)1275 373382
Email: all@rhodesinternet.com

195

Alex Rhodes is a young, enthusiastic camera operator, based near Bristol, UK. He wishes to pursue a career in wildlife documentaries and productions. He has had a deep-rooted interest for natural history since a young age, and is actively looking for work experience and part-time placements as a camera operator or field assistant in this sector. His skill and talent for camera operation whether from a hide or at night belies his age, reflecting his true appreciation for the natural world. In addition, his interests extend to conservation and wildlife photography; he is accumulating an ever-increasing portfolio.

Adam Charles Scott – Camera Facilities Assistant
Address: Half Moon Cottage, Stoke Climsland, Callington, Cornwall PL178NY, UK
Phone: +44 (0)1579370131 & +44 (0)7527804828
Email: adamscott_402@fsmail.net

I am looking for work as a camera assistant, B camera, or production assistant. I currently work as a camera facilities assistant within a large production company based in the Southwest. I am familiar with both tape based and solid-state cameras and workflows, I also have a wide knowledge of grip and lighting. I am open to anything wildlife, outdoor, adventure-related, the more extreme the environment the better. Please email or call for more info.

Steve Spence – 2nd camera and PA
Spence Media International
Address: Bozeman, Montana, USA
Phone: +1 6156680454
Email: steven@stevenmarkspence.com
Website: www.stevenmarkspence.com

I am interested in any natural history project. I have HD camera experience, topside and underwater. Currently at wildlife film Masters program but have worked on professional films.

Pedro Uviedo – Camera/Sound/Filming Assistant
Address: 178 Gilbert Road, Cambridge CB4 3PB, UK
Phone: +44 (0)7897915988
Email: uviedo@gmail.com

Responsible, dedicated and proactive with a broad range of expertise and abilities in production and video camera/sound assistant filming wildlife, cultural and adventure travel documentaries on location with the director/producer in very remote and often inhospitable conditions throughout South America rainforest, assisting with all aspects of filming and camera operation, including transporting and mounting film equipment in extreme and obscure sites (eg mountain peaks, raging rivers, jungles, treetops, inside nests) and inventing tactics for filming complicated shots without disturbing wildlife. Interested in all aspects of production in wildlife travel and adventure, I am currently looking the opportunity to take part in a project or idea related with film documentaries.

Jessica Wagner – Freelance Film Maker
Address: Leicester, UK
Phone: +447837917758
Email: jess_wager@hotmail.co.uk

I am a student studying Media Production BSc at De Montfort University in Leicester. I am incredibly passionate about wildlife conservation and hope to pursue a career in this field. I have experience as a camera operator, editor and stills photographer. I am most interested in making films that aim to protect and raise awareness of the natural world. I believe the media has an amazing power to influence and inspire people and I hope that through my own passion for the films I make I can motivate a positive change, as the work of other film makers has motivated me. I am interested in all projects that aim to have a positive impact and am especially interested in working on media campaigns for charitable organisations. I would be happy working within a production team of any size. I do not have much experience working as a producer or in directorial roles and so I feel at this time I would be most comfortable in an assisting role, however on smaller projects I would consider myself able to take on larger responsibilities.

Marleen van der Werf – Filmmaker
Wild Work Productions
Email: info@wildworkproductions.com
Website: www.wildworkproductions.com

Filmmaker, Marleen van der Werf, has a Msc in Biology and MA in Wildlife Documentary. Her combined background in biology and filmmaking enables her to understand and capture the beauty of the natural world and sciences at all levels. As a wildlife filmmaker she is a specialist in using camera techniques such as macro, underwater, infra-red, high-speed and aerial filming as well as time-lapse and animation. Furthermore she is a skilled researcher, scriptwriter, director, sound recordist and editor that works worldwide. Marleen van der Werf is also founder of Wild Work Productions.

Stuart Westfield – Ranger Expeditions Ltd
Address: 62 Creek Road, Hayling Island, Hampshire, PO11 9RE, UK
Phone: +44 (0)2392 469003 & +44 (0)7890 620274
Email: rangerexped@hotmail.co.uk
Website: www.stuartwestfield.co.uk
Expedition Leader: Stuart Westfield

Freelance mountain and wilderness expedition leader/assistant (MLTUK qualified & Remote 1st Aid). Environments: desert, jungle, volcanic, tundra, altitude (6000m) and 4X4 driving. Extensive Africa & Iceland experience. Base camp, expedition project, field study support and in-country fixing. Degree qualified in science/engineering and project management. Stills photography (published) and feature writing (published). MiniDV camera operation. Pre-expedition navigation, wilderness skills and camp craft training offered.

197

WRITERS/SCRIPT EDITORS

Amy Brown – Script Writer
Björn Welander Photography
Address: 7628 Bayside Road, Chesapeake beach, MD 20732, USA
Phone: +1 301 910 1930
Email: amysusanbrown@gmail.com
Website: www.bjornwelander.com and www.baldibis.org

We produce films with strong conservation messages that have the local people's angle and involve those who live and work in valuable conservation areas or where threatened species occur. Currently looking for proposals that shows a success story in conservation and would work well as a presenter-led wildlife documentary. Conservation festival category. We are looking for sponsors that want to take an active part in our projects. We will consider co-productions. No work experience/internships for the moment since we have just relocated to Maryland, USA

Adrian Cale – Writer
Address: London, UK
Phone: +44 (0)77 8920 5211
Email: ade.cale@gmail.com
Website: www.adriancale.co.uk

I am an independent wildlife film-maker who has written a wide variety of natural history content for various international broadcast and production partners. Content includes press releases, programme pitch documents, synopsis, treatments, scripts and script editing.
Credits include: *Baboon Boot Camp*: Parthenon Entertainment, *International Animal Rescue: Orangutan*: IAR, *Gibbons: Back in the Swing*: 5 x 30' - Animal Planet/Discovery Networks, *Woolly Jumpers: Made in Peru*: Animal Planet/Discovery Networks. Winner BEST NEWCOMER AWARD at the International Wildlife Film Festival (IWFF) 2006. *Make me a Monkey*: Electric Sky Distribution.
My combination of skill sets can compliment a number of crewing options and allow me to accommodate flexible and demanding budgets. I also develop my own independent film projects, which affords me a clear understanding of what it takes to carry a good program idea through from concept to completion.

Alice Clarke – Scriptwriter
NHU Africa
Address: PO Box 12317, Mill Street, Gardens, Cape Town 8010, SOUTH AFRICA
Phone: +27 214221054 & +27 729642281
Email: alice@nhuafrica.com
Website: www.nhuafrica.com

Wildlife documentary production unit. Hire of Panasonic HD camera equipment. Wildlife Film Academy for aspiring wildlife filmmakers. Wild Talk Africa, International Wildlife Film Festival. African-based stories only. Broad remit of subjects, styles. We co-produce and commission producers. Send CVs by email for work experience placements.

Jamie Crawford – Script Writer
Address: London, UK
Email: info@jamiecrawfordmedia.com
Website: www.jamiecrawfordmedia.com

I work on both sides of the camera as a presenter and as a producer, director and writer. On screen I work mostly on the BBC's *One Show* fronting stories on wildlife, adventure and photography, previous credits include wildlife adventure shows for Animal Planet, Discovery and Five. We won a BAFTA with one series and I was nominated as Best Presenter at the Wildsceen Panda awards with another. Behind the camera I produce and direct docs on everything and anything from Tornado outbreaks in the USA to epic survival tales in Borneo for Discovery, National Geographic, BBC, Sky and others. As a freelancer, I'm always on the lookout for interesting new projects to work on, be it as a presenter or producer/director, as script writer or narrator. As long as the content is interesting, I don't mind what I do (well ... to a point)!

199

BAOBAB TREE PRODUCTIONS

Jenny Devitt – Script Writer/Editor/Consultant
Baobab Tree Productions
Address: 21 Sydling Road, Yeovil, Somerset BA21 5LH, UK
Phone: +44 1935 410511 & +44 7707 007099 Fax: +44 1935 410511
Email: jenny.devitt@virgin.net
Website: www.jennydevitt.com

Freelance script writer/editor/consultant, script translator (French to English), narrator/voice-over artist specialising in wildlife and factual programming.
Script credits include: *Jewels of the South*, *Secrets of the North*, *Grand Canyon - From Dinosaurs to Dams*, *Crater - Africa's Predator Paradise*, *Mountain of the Sea*, and other programme scripts for BBC *Natural World* strand: *City Slickers*, *Whale Induna*, *The Whole Story* (series), *Young and Wild* (series): for Off The Fence for Discovery/Animal Planet; *Eye of the Storm* (series): ABC Australia/Channel 4, *Guy Pearce's Ultimate Guide to Tigers*: Universal Studios – documentary tie-in with feature film *Two Brothers Egypt: Splendours of the Golden Age*, *Natural Wonders*: Reader's Digest, Sydney. Previously employed by Partridge Films. My scripts for *Whale Induna* and one episode of *Whole Story* won international awards in South Africa. I am fluent in French (having lived and worked in France for fourteen years), and can translate and re-work scripts from French to English. Also help with re-versioning. I am willing and able to assist with developing ideas and/or proposals for documentary films (wildlife, conservation, human-interest and children's).

Jen Grace – Writer
Jen Grace Productions
Address: 501 S 15th Ave #3, Bozeman, Montana 59715, USA
Phone: +1 406 249 2153
Email: minisuperjennifer@yahoo.com
Website: www.jengrace.com

Producer, director, writer, multimedia designer Jen Grace has an MFA in Science and Natural History Filmmaking from MSU. Specializing in conservation, sports and dance film and live production. Clients include the Smithsonian Institution, The Jim Henson Company, Patrick Leonard, 4H and the Montana Ballet Company. Winner IWFF, Jackson Hole, Lunafest, College Television Awards, HATCHfest. Collaborators/sponsors/co-productions all welcome on children's, experimental and conservation subjects. I do not offer work experience/internships.

HAWNT Media
Address: P.O. Box 1872, Byron Bay, NSW 2480, AUSTRALIA
Phone: +61 421573262
Email: info@hawntmedia.com
Website: www.hawntmedia.com
Director: Rowena Mynott

HAWNT Media specialises in natural history photojournalism. We are happy to provide writing services for wildlife documentary projects. We invite communication from sponsors and are open to collaborations. We are always interested in hearing from people that might like to contribute. CVs and publication content can be sent via email or post.

We would prefer contributors to be experienced writers, photographers and/or scientists but are happy to hear from anyone interested in being part of our publication. We would also consider work experience placements.

Jin Pyn Lee – Writer
Elemantree Media
Address: Blk 6, 12-430, Telok Blangah Crescent, 090006, SINGAPORE
Phone: +65 62726769 & +61 423662233 Fax: +65 62726769
Email: jinpyn.lee@elephantandtree.com
Website: www.elemantreemedia.com

Freelance television producer, director, writer, fixer, production management. Specialize in Asian natural history and conservation (over twenty years involvement). Jin Pyn's career spans across broadcaster and independent production companies. Credits include BBC Worldwide, Channel News Asia, and Animal Planet, across all genres – short-form interstitials, long-form factual documentaries, and animation. Geographically the programs have been distributed all over the globe, including Korea's Kids Talk Talk, US's Somos TV and India's Edumedia. In Japan, Jin Pyn has won the best animation award, and her children's picture book was the first from Singapore to garner multiple languages.

Mike Linley
Hairy Frog Productions Ltd
Address: 4 The Paddock, White Horse Lane, Trowse, Norwich, Norfolk NR14 8TD, UK
Phone: +44 (0)7885964790
Email: hairyfrog@lineone.net
Website: www.hairy-frog.co.uk
Director/Producer/Cameraman: Mike Linley – mike_linley@yahoo.co.uk

Wildlife Production Company with full HD kit (BBC specs) + GoPro hero in flat optic housing + video-microscope and endoscopes + Canon 7D time-lapse kit. Over 400 credits mainly as a Producer for Survival/Anglia Television. Now also producing Wildlife Interactive Touch-screens. Over forty International awards to date. Specialist in herpetology, entomology and UK wildlife. Large video, sound and stills library. Always happy to co-produce. Limited work experience opportunities, depending on current projects.

Vanessa Lucas: Writer
Natural History Media
Address: Sandton, Johannesburg, SOUTH AFRICA
Phone: +27 827803840
Email: v.lucas@naturalhistorymedia.com
Website: www.naturalhistorymedia.com

Natural History Media specialises in wildlife, conservation and environmental documentary filmmaking and photography. In addition, we produce regular short ENG segments for international news agencies on environmental, conservation and wildlife current affairs throughout Africa and worldwide. With backgrounds in zoology and eco-tourism we can provide expertise and access to a variety of unique locations and offer professional location management services, facilitating shoots before, during and after filming. Natural History Media has a large HD stock library, with a broad range of footage and photography from around Africa and the UK. We have full HD broadcast cameras, audio and accessories. We are always interested in hearing new ideas and stories and are always happy to provide our expertise and contacts to develop ideas in the wildlife, conservation, adventure and cultural genres. We would be looking for collaborators and sponsors and always consider co-productions. We would consider work experience and internship applicants, but not actively looking. Please send CVs by email.

Dee Marshall – Writer/Photographer
Address: 202 Chemin des Vachers 38410 Uriage, FRANCE
Phone: +33 611548112 & +33 476892053
Email: dee.marshall@gmail.com
Website: www.beneaththeskies.com

An experienced writer and photographer with extensive knowledge of wildlife and proven ability in wildlife filming and editing. Currently working on a short film about the Maasai in Tanzania and two books about wildlife and children. In addition to a diploma in Mammal Ecology and Conservation, I have wide experience in visual and written communication. I have spent many years editing texts and writing for scientific journals. I am fluent in French and English and competent in Italian, German and Japanese. I am available to work as a writer or script editor on a freelance basis or short contract work.

Kathryn Pasternak: Writer/Producer
Pasternak Media LLC
Address: 3323 Laurel Court, Falls Church, VA 22042, USA
Phone: +1 703 992 0449 &: +1 703 216 1746
Email: kathryn.pasternak@gmail.com
Website: www.pasternakmedia.com

Pasternak Media LLC specializes in supervision of wildlife and conservation films for broadcast television. We work for, and directly with, producers of wildlife programming. We will help you develop and pitch your concept, and supervise it through completion. Focus is telling the best possible story. Acting as an outside voice, we give the broadcaster confidence that your film will meet their needs, and at the same time, help make sure your original vision doesn't get lost in the process. Kathryn Pasternak has won two National Emmy Awards and has been nominated for two more, including most recently for *Swamp Troop* which was the product of first time, African-based producers. She has a twenty-year track record supervising projects for National Geographic Television, NGC, Animal Planet, and Smithsonian Networks. Looking for presenter-led, pure wildlife, and conservation-themed stories. Can consult on co-productions.

Nick Upton – Freelance Writer/Director/Consultant/Producer
Address: 5 Kingsdown House, Kingsdown, Corsham, Wiltshire SN13 8AX, UK
Phone: +44 1225 742300 & +44 7732 361521
Fax: +44 1225 742300
Email: nickupton@btopenworld.com

I'm a freelance director, writer and producer with over twenty years experience of working on wildlife films and series of many kinds, from high end to low budget, for a wide variety of broadcast/non-broadcast clients in Europe/USA/Asia. Films I've written, directed and produced have won nearly 100 awards including eleven Best of Festival wins in eight countries, and I've contributed to many other award-winning productions. I'm interested to work on wildlife films on a very flexible basis, offering consultancy, directing, writing, producing or a combination of these. I also have extensive sound recording, stills photography and some 2nd camera experience. I'm looking for paid work on productions that need my input or backing for my own ideas, not for proposals to be sent to me. I don't run my own production company, but do seek to work with established companies on their productions or on projects I've initiated. I do not offer work experience.

Sue Western – Script Editor/Writer/Story Consultant
Country: UK
Telephone: +44 (0)117 9735473 or +44 (0)7870 977762
Email: sue.western@blueyonder.co.uk

When it's difficult to see the wood for the trees, I'm the *fresh pair of eyes* that provides clarity, or nudges a project back on track. I can supply story advice from the outset, act as a mid-production sounding-board, offer structural guidance in the cutting room, write or script edit the final commentary, or even provide a full remedial service for films in distress. My aim, always, is to add value – to unlock the full potential of a story and make a film the *best* it can be. Credits on over sixty films for television and cinematic release, many of which have won, or been nominated for, top industry awards.

PRESENTERS

Nick Baker – Naturalist/Television Presenter
Country: UK
Agent: David Foster Management, PO Box 1805, Andover, Hampshire SP10 3ZN, UK
Phone: +44 (0)1264 771726
Email: talent@dfmanagement.tv
Website: www.nickbaker.tv

Adrian Cale – Narrator/Presenter
Address: London, UK
Phone: +44 (0)77 8920 5211
Email: ade.cale@gmail.com
Website: www.adriancale.co.uk

Adrian Cale is a television presenter with a vast knowledge of the natural world. As a curious adventurer and self-confessed animal geek he has explored the planet filming wildlife and uses his experience and observation to communicate his passion on camera. Adrian is equally at home on location or in the studio, scripted or unscripted and very much in the moment. He is a diverse and adaptable television broadcaster who can be counted on to deliver.

Press reviews include: "Endearing to watch" Radio Times, "Adrian is an engaging presenter" BBC Wildlife Magazine.

Credits include: *Tarsier Towers*: 25 x 30'series – Channel 5, *Baboon Boot Camp*: Parthenon Entertainment, *Gibbons: Back in the Swing*: 5 x 30' – Animal Planet/Discovery Networks, *Rural Matters*: Aquavita Films, *Woolly Jumpers: Made in Peru*: Animal Planet/Discovery Networks – Winner BEST NEWCOMER AWARD at the International Wildlife Film Festival (IWFF) 2006, *Make me a Monkey*: Electric Sky Distribution

Adam L Canning – 'Wildlife Filmer Adam' - Presenter
Nature On Screen
Address: West Midlands, UK
Email: WildlifeFilmerAdam@live.co.uk
Website: www.NatureonScreen.webs.com

'Wildlife Filmer Adam' is a film maker who directs, produces, presents, films & edits. Up for any kind of Natural History documentary film. Have made documentaries for Reader's Digest in the form of a web-series called 'Wildlife Monthly'. Experience: directing, producing, presenting, camerawork and editing, plus will happily assist with any of those roles. Keen to learn and experience new things. Would love to be sponsored and happy to do co-productions. Anyone who would like to write scripts for 'Wildlife Monthly' are very welcome and anyone wanting their footage or pictures featured are welcome too.

205

Andy Casagrande IV – Presenter/Camera Operator
Address: Naples, Florida, USA
Phone: +1 202 4154472
Email: andycasagrande@yahoo.com & abc4explore@yahoo.com
Website: www.abc4explore.com

A veteran field producer and cinematographer, Andy B. Casagrande's passion for wildlife, as well as his experience as a naturalist and documentary filmmaker, have taken him around the world to capture the behavior of some of the planet's most fascinating creatures and fiercest predators. Andy risks everything to get the shot, including swimming uncaged with Great White Sharks, on foot with lions, face to face with king cobras, and jumping out of helicopters to film Polar Bears. Presenter on Nat Geo Wild's *Killer Shots*.

Karla Munguia Colmenero - Wildlife Camerawoman/Presenter
Address: Jesus del Monte, MEXICO
Phone: +52 5516679565
Email: karla.munguia@gmail.com
Website: www.karlamunguia.tv

Beating 34,000 applications worldwide, I was one of the six participants on Animal Planet's 'docu-reality' show *Unearthed, Film School Wild*. After that I spent three years in South Africa working as camera operator and offline editor for Animal Planet's Series *Shamwari: A Wild Life* and *Wild and Woolly*, as well as *Ocean Rescue*, filmed at the Gold Coast, Australia. I am now keen on presenting my concerns and passion for wildlife, as well as working as production assistant or camera assistant. I have a level 5 SSI scuba diving expertise, including Night Limited Visibility. I am currently looking for presenter-led films with a high conservation content. I am not looking for a production based on misleading audiences. For example shows based on animal attacks. What we need is people looking after the survival of our species, not people terrified of them.

Jamie Crawford – Presenter/Narrator
Address: London, UK
Email: info@jamiecrawfordmedia.com
Website: www.jamiecrawfordmedia.com

I work on both sides of the camera as a presenter and as a producer, director and writer. On screen I work mostly on the BBC's *One Show* fronting stories on wildlife, adventure and photography, previous credits include wildlife adventure shows for Animal Planet, Discovery and Five. We won a BAFTA with one series and I was nominated as Best Presenter at the Wildsceen Panda awards with another. Behind the camera I produce and direct docs on everything and anything from tornado outbreaks in the USA to epic survival tales in Borneo for Discovery, National Geographic, BBC, Sky and others. As a freelancer, I'm always on the lookout for interesting new projects to work on, be it as a presenter or producer/director, as script writer or narrator. As long as the content is interesting, I don't mind what I do (well ... to a point)!

BAOBAB TREE PRODUCTIONS

Jenny Devitt – Narrator/Voice-over Artist
Baobab Tree Productions
Address: 21 Sydling Road, Yeovil, Somerset BA21 5LH, UK
Phone: +44 1935 410511 & +44 7707 007099
Fax: +44 1935 410511
Email: jenny.devitt@virgin.net
Website: www.jennydevitt.com

Freelance script writer/editor/consultant, script translator (French to English), narrator/voice-over artist specialising in wildlife and factual programming.
Script credits include: *Jewels of the South*, *Secrets of the North*, *Grand Canyon - From Dinosaurs to Dams*, *Crater - Africa's Predator Paradise*, *Mountain of the Sea*, and other programme scripts for BBC *Natural World* strand: *City Slickers*, *Whale Induna*, *The Whole Story* (series), *Young and Wild* (series): for Off The Fence for Discovery/Animal Planet; *Eye of the Storm* (series): ABC Australia/Channel 4, *Guy Pearce's Ultimate Guide to Tigers*: Universal Studios – documentary tie-in with feature film *Two Brothers Egypt: Splendours of the Golden Age, Natural Wonders*: Reader's Digest, Sydney. Previously employed by Partridge Films. My scripts for *Whale Induna* and one episode of *Whole Story* won international awards in South Africa. I am fluent in French (having lived and worked in France for fourteen years), and can translate and re-work scripts from French to English.

207

Also help with re-versioning. I am willing and able to assist with developing ideas and/or proposals for documentary films (wildlife, conservation, human-interest and children's).

Ed Drewitt – Naturalist/Broadcaster/Wildlife Detective/Consultant
Address: Bristol, UK
Phone: +44 (0)777 2342 758
Email: ed@eddrewitt.co.uk
Website: www.eddrewitt.co.uk

Ed's been a naturalist for over twenty years and works as a freelance naturalist, broadcaster and wildlife detective. Ed's excellent communicating skills translate difficult messages or concepts into interesting and accessible broadcasts. He is able to offer his communication/presenting skills, wildlife advice, and resources (eg feathers, skulls, wings). Ed is particularly good at identifying birdsong and wildlife tracks and signs. He is a frequent contributor to TV and radio, a reporter for BBC Radio 4's *Savings Species* series and BBC West's wildlife expert. Ed is also a contributor and consultant for the BBC's *Springwatch* and *Autumnwatch*.

Claire Evans – Presenter/AP
Address: Bristol, UK & CANADA
Email: clairepagan@hotmail.com

I specialise in natural history and environmental filmmaking. I have several years experience working for companies such as the BBC and Halo Films. I hold three degrees including one in biology and one in creative arts/film studies. I hold UK and Canadian passports and have experience working with British and North American wildlife. I am currently planning a film about Tanzania. I make films for Friends of the Earth from time to time. I am frequently looking for sponsors and co-producers. I sometimes have availability to provide short-term work experience for camera operators and sound recordists. Prefer CVs by email. Some prior experience is usually necessary.

Simon King – Presenter/Cameraman
Country: UK
Email: promotions@simonkingwildlife.com
Website: www.simonkingwildlife.com
Promotions Manager: Debbie Cripps

Ryan Johnson – Presenter/Marine Biologist
Deep Fried Films
Address: P O Box 659, Mossel Bay 6500, SOUTH AFRICA
Phone: +27 44 6903681
Fax: +44 86 7195309
Email: ryan@deepfriedfilms.com
Website: www.deepfriedfilms,com

Ryan is a freelance presenter who has done work for Nat Geo and BBC, inter alia. Ryan, originally a kiwi, is a marine biologist with a PhD and is in demand for documentaries featuring sharks. He lives in the beautiful Garden Route area of the Western Cape in RSA and has access to many pristine areas and wild animals.

Vivian A. N. Nuhu – Presenter/Narrator
Address: P. O. Box OS3053, Osu-Accra, GHANA, WEST AFRICA
Phone: +233 244799749 & +233 302763308
Email: vannuhu@yahoo.co.uk

Coordinating notably for outside filming crews among them, BBC and NHK on wildlife locations, permits and local casts and logistics. As an experienced wildlife conservationist, specializing in communication and education, I have been and still available as a presenter in wildlife adventure documentaries for general public and especially youth cum school groups. As a trained wildlife film-maker without own equipment/facilities, I have facilitated in the production of overseas documentaries for awareness creation in my home country, Ghana.
Not looking for proposals. Have already a number of ideas and proposals for wildlife adventure particularly for children and general Ghanaian public with conservation theme. Collaborators/sponsors most needed. Will welcome co-productions if it comes with funding.

Neil Owen – Presenter/Narrator
Country:UK
Email: neilcroc@hotmail.com
Website: www.baldibis.org
Documentary maker, Presenter, Narrator, Scriptwriter, Zoo Keeper, Educational lecturer. Co-producer Bjorn Welander (Camera, Editing, Scriptwriter, Photography)

I have been working with wildlife for twelve years now following a life-long passion. I have worked at zoos in Australia (Crocodylus Park) and England and filmed wildlife documentaries in Morocco, Sweden, Australia, Turkey and England. I believe that one of the best forms of conservation is positive, fun and inspirational education. I have lectured to hundreds of thousands of people of all ages throughout the last twelve years. My primary species are Crocodilians, however I have worked with hundreds of species since 1999. Inspirational films with a strong conservation message are high on the agenda. We are looking for all of the above. I have extensive experience working with children, my work with crocodiles in Australia led to a lot of adventure and fast-paced action. I have presented pure wildlife in the lecture theatre, and in front of camera. And in Morocco (www.baldibis.org co-produced with Bjorn Welander) we integrated the wildlife and rare Bald Ibis with the culture and human interest. We are looking for collaborators and sponsors and would definitely consider co-productions. We are always keeping an eye out for talent and as far as qualifications go the only things I look for are a fantastic attitude, hard working individual who is willing to learn and the most important thing ... Passion!!

Michaela Strachan – Wildlife Presenter
Country: UK/SOUTH AFRICA
Agent: Jo Sarsby Management, 58 St Johns Road, Clifton, Bristol BS8 2HG, UK
Phone: +44 (0)117 973 8589
Email: jo@josarsby.com
Website: www.josarsby.com/presenters/michaelastrachan

Swati Thiyagarajan – Presenter/Director/Writer
Countries: INDIA/SOUTH AFRICA
Website: www.ndtv.com

Gavin Thurston – Cameraman/Director/Presenter
Country: UK
Website: www.gavinthurston.com

Ashleigh Young – Co-Presenter/Narrator/Co-Producer
Extinction Sucks
Address: PO Box 845, Kalamunda, WA 6926, AUSTRALIA
Phone: +61 404305431 & +15 039989255
Email: ashleigh_young@hotmail.com
Website: www.natgeotv.com.au/tv/extinction-sucks

Australian voice over/narration, presenter, producer. Interested in conservation, adventure, wildlife, human interest, fast-paced, raw & real! Looking for collaborators/sponsors.

EDITORS

Andrew Chastney – Film Editor
Address: Bristol, BS6, UK
Phone: +44 7976 644454
Email: andychas@blueyonder.co.uk
Website: www.andrewchastney.com

I've been a freelance film editor for the last twenty years working mainly in wildlife film-making for the BBC Natural History Unit. Recent credits include *Planet Earth*, *Life*, *Human Planet* and the upcoming epic *Frozen Planet*. I have extensive field experience, please see my website for more details. Always interested in new programme ideas, styles and proposals. Very happy to try and help keen newcomers to the industry.

Alice Clarke – Editor
NHU Africa
Address: PO Box 12317, Mill Street, Gardens, Cape Town 8010, SOUTH AFRICA
Phone: +27 214221054 & +27 729642281
Email: alice@nhuafrica.com
Website: www.nhuafrica.com

Wildlife documentary production unit. Hire of Panasonic HD camera equipment. Wildlife Film Academy for aspiring wildlife filmmakers. Wild Talk Africa, International Wildlife Film Festival. African-based stories only. Broad remit of subjects, styles. We co-produce and commission producers. Send CVs by email for work experience placements.

Steve Cummings – Avid/FCP Editor
Address: 5 Bracewell Grove, Halifax, West Yorkshire, HX3 5HP, UK
Phone: +44 (0)1422 360 548
Email: steve_cummings@btinternet.com
Website: www.stephencummings.co.uk

Freelance cameraman, Avid/FCP editor. Stock images available. Material may be viewed on thebaldibis You Tube Channel: www.youtube.com/TheBaldIbis.
Awards: Sonderpreis des Tierschutbeirates von Rheinland-Pfalz in Naturale 2004/2005 International Nature Film Festival for *Return of the Waldrapp*. Honorable Mention For Conservation Message for *Birds, Bins and Bullets* in IWFF 2009. Honorable Mention for Portrayal of a Critical Issue in IWFF 2008 for *The Honey Buzzard*. Have had material broadcast on PBS Malta and webcast by Birdlife Malta. Aside from regular corporate shoots, wildlife clients include RSPB and Natural England.

Martin Elsbury – Editor
Address: Bristol, UK
Email: melsbury@aol.com

Martin Elsbury is an award-winning BAFTA and Emmy nominated editor with more than twenty-five years experience of film editing. His work for the BBC includes many major series such as *Kingdom of the Ice Bear, Trials of Life, Life in the Freezer, Alien Empire, The Private Life of Plants, Life of Mammals* and *Blue Planet* and he edited Disneynature's new film, *African Cats*.

Claire Evans – Editor/AP
Address: Bristol, UK & CANADA
Email: clairepagan@hotmail.com

I specialise in natural history and environmental filmmaking. I have several years experience working for companies such as the BBC and Halo Films. I hold three degrees including one in biology and one in creative arts/film studies. I hold UK and Canadian passports and have experience working with British and North American wildlife. I am currently planning a film about Tanzania. I make and edit films for Friends of the Earth from time to time. I am frequently looking for sponsors and co-producers. I sometimes have availability to provide short-term work experience for camera operators and sound recordists. Prefer CVs by email. Some prior experience is usually necessary.

Matt Meech – Editor
Address: Bristol UK
Email: mm@mattmeech.com
Website: www.mattmeech.com

I am an award winning, freelance, offline editor working in Bristol and London, as well as overseas. Over the past ten years I have made documentaries for BBC, ITV, Channel 4, FIVE, Animal Planet & Discovery. I am a creative storyteller with a natural editorial instinct. In October 2007 I won Best Editing at Jackson Hole Wildlife Film Festival for the film *Paranormal Pigeons*. Since then nearly all of the programmes I have edited have picked up an award somewhere in the world. I love working with other creative people and crafting rushes into gold.

Ben Please - Editor
Address: 18 Edward Street, Lower Weston, Bath, BA1 3BP, UK
Phone: +44 (0)7789348165
Email: benplease@hotmail.com
Website: www.benedictplease.co.uk

Ten years experience with environmental film making, directing, producing and training in East Africa. I can offer film production mentoring to individuals and groups, as well as editing services.

Sue Scott - Editor
Country: SOUTH AFRICA
Phone: +27 82 400 5525
Email: suescott@gmail.com
Website: www.susanscott.com

For over fifteen years, Susan Scott has cut documentary films for National Geographic, Animal Planet, PBS, Discovery Channel, NBC, NHK, Canal+, ZDF, ORF, France 5 and UK's FIVE. Graduating from Baylor University (Texas) with a BA degree in Telecommunication (TV & Film studies), Susan won an apprenticeship with Tony Black, A.C.E., in Washington, DC. She went on to spend the next six years cutting documentaries with Tony, as well as beta-testing software for Avid Technology. Susan now lives in South Africa where she cuts for several wildlife filmmakers, most notably Dereck & Beverly Joubert (National Geographic Explorers in Residence). She won Best Editing at the Jackson Hole Wildlife Film Festival in 2011 for the Joubert's feature film, *The Last Lions*. Susan is a full member of the South African Guild of Editors (SAGE) and received her acronym from the guild in 2010.

Laura Turner - Freelance Editor/Camera Operator/Filmmaker
Ant Farm Films and The Wildlife Garden Project
Address: Nottingham, UK
Phone: +44 (0)7948 377224
Email: laura@antfarmfilms.com
Website: www.antfarmfilms.com

I am an Apple-certified FCP editor, camera operator and filmmaker specialising in wildlife and conservation films. I have worked on documentaries, promos and charity videos, and as an editing tutor on the Wildeye Big Cat Film Safari in Kenya. I was also the in-house editor for CTV Perth, Australia, where a conservation documentary I edited won a WA

Screen Award. In 2010 I set up The Wildlife Garden Project: a film and a website which aim to inspire people to make their gardens more wildlife friendly (www.wildlifegardenproject.com). Take a look at my websites or get in touch to discuss my services!

Reece de Ville
Country: UK
Phone: +44 770943532
Email: reeceadeville@gmail.com
Website: www.reecedeville.com

I am a freelance filmmaker who has worked with the BBC, Absolute Radio, Mark Kermode, Thea Gilmore, Middlesex and Bournemouth Universities and many more. I shoot/edit exciting pieces for broadcast, online, advertising, wildlife studies and promos. Previous work includes advertisements for Apple Europe, broadcast packages for the BBC and promos for various digital companies. I'm exceptionally patient, which comes in handy when awaiting the perfect wildlife shot! I'm looking for wildlife projects that tell unique and vital stories – whether that's species conservation across the globe to individual animal study through to macro-shot insects and creatures rarely seen on film. Also, if you're looking to create documentaries such as *Project Nim*, for example, with previously shot footage, I can be your editor and help pull together a stunning film. I'm looking to collaborate on projects that have the potential to be fascinating – from company promos to wildlife documentaries, day in the life pieces and features. I've a keen interest in working across the wildlife genre and have worked on projects for the National Trust in England and have shot various local wildlife pieces across the country. I love creating interesting and vibrant work and can offer my clients a cost-effective one-man shoot/edit package with HD cams, rapid editing and an open mind! I am open to projects large or small – lets chat! I'm happy to work with all collaborators and sponsors who are interested in creating rewarding pieces. You can hire me as a one-man shoot/edit or as part of a larger crew – happy to discuss your project and talk about what I can offer. I don't currently offer work experience placements or internships, but I'm happy to chat to anyone who'd like advice or has questions about the industry. I believe it's vital to share knowledge and even more vital to be approachable! I'm always looking to build up a contacts list of sound designers, cameramen, musicians etc, so drop me a line.

Ed Watkins – Editor/Self-Shooting AP
Address: 41 Brecknock Rd., Ground Floor, Bristol BS4 2DE, UK
Phone: +44 (0)7527 452 960
Email: e.m.watkins@gmail.com
Website: www.naturalscinema.com

I am a self-shooting assistant producer and editor with a strong background in science and natural history. I have worked on a wide range of productions from broadcast to commercial and corporate both in the US and the UK. I am very experienced with digital workflows and cameras.

Stefanie Watkins – Offline Editor
Address: 41 Brecknock Rd, Bristol BS4 2DE, UK
Phone: +44 07837591777 & +1 720-545-7643
Email: stef@stefaniewatkins.com
Website: www.stefaniewatkins.com

I am an award-winning offline editor specializing in natural history, science, and factual progamming. My broadcast credits include UK, US, and international shows. I'm a strong independent storyteller who thrives on collaboration and loves mixing the edgy flair of music videos with the elegant grace of wildlife films.

Zed Creative
Address: Tan Yr Allt, Trefriw, Conwy LL27 0RJ, Wales, UK
Phone: +44 (0)7789 071 038
Email: ant.zed@mac.com
Website: www.iamzed.co.uk
Main Contact: Anthony Roberts

I am a graphic designer who has recently moved into digital media, including editing and motion graphics. I have a very keen interest in wildlife and conservation and am eager to get involved in the field. As a wildlife photographer, I am also capable of producing some of my own footage. Based in North Wales, I am particularly keen on wildlife in the UK and Africa.

MUSIC COMPOSERS

Brollyman Productions
Country: UK
Phone: +44 (0)7887 508973
Email: brolly@brollyman.com
Website: www.brollyman.com
Main Contact: Brolly

We write lots of music to picture for lots of lovely wildlife programmes but are always looking for new people to work with. There's plenty of clips on our website as well as our full CV and our blog/newsletter keeps people up to date with what we do. Email me to be added to the list.

Juan Camilo Arboleda
Address: Cra 19a #122-46, COLOMBIA
Phone: +57 1 214 8782 & +57 301 452 9228
Email: juancamilo@arboleda.co
Website: www.arboleda.co

My name is Juan Camilo Arboleda, and I'm a Colombian composer, I have worked with orchestras, ensembles and electronics to create music for many genres. I'm also an experienced orchestrator. I love wildlife documentaries, and I'm looking forward to be involved in this industry, making the best possible soundtracks for them. I have a master in music composition and I have produced several projects over the years, the OSCN and several Colombian ensembles have played my works. Please feel free to view my work and contact me through my web page. I'm currently looking to work in the film industry, writing music best suited for the ideas represented in the film. I'm a versatile composer that can adapt to any genre and budget available.

MT Music
Address: 25 Ollands Road, Reepham, Norwich, Norfolk NR10 4EL, UK
Phone: +44 (0)1603 870255
Email: music@mtmusic.co.uk
Website: www.mtmusic.co.uk
Composers: Tobie Rudd and Mark Twine

From classic score to the latest cutting edge music, MT Music use the latest technologies to create the perfect soundtrack for TV, film, and game productions.

James Muxworthy – Composer/Sound Designer
Address: West Yorkshire, UK
Email: james@helicalblue.com
Website: www.helicalblue.com

James works as a creative composer and sound designer as part of running his audio and multimedia production company Helical Blue. His musical & sound design influences are wide ranging and he has an extensive understanding of field recording. Wildlife credits: include *Beauty and the Parasite* 2010 (music, sound design and narration). Contribution to various wildlife film showreels. He is always interested to collaborate on wildlife related film and has contributed music, sound design and voice-over to video in other areas such as documentary, corporate and training video. Does not offer work experience.

Matt Norman – Composer
SilverScore Productions
Country: UK
Phone: +44 (0)7761 332084
Email: matt@silverscoreproductions.com
Website: www.silverscoreproductions.com/audio.htm

Original music composed and produced by Matt Norman for natural history documentaries, TV & film. Credits include *Bandits of Selous*, *Humpbacks – Cracking the Code* and *21st Century Shark* – National Geographic Channel. All music composed to picture and produced in 5.1 surround for HD broadcast. Further credits include *This is Your Life Simon Cowell* – ITV1, *Hitler's Bodyguard* – UKTV History and *The Dark Heart of Italy* – BBC 4. Please see the website for video and audio samples.

Natural Magic Music
Address: P.O. Box 150643, Florida 33915, USA
Phone: +1 239 849 3536
Email: singinfortheearth@gmail.com
Website: www.jptaylormusic.com
Contact: JP Taylor

Nature, wildlife, conservation songs available for documentaries (instrumental versions also available).

Fraser Purdie
Country: UK
Email: fraser@fraserpurdie.com
Website: www.fraserpurdie.com

"Thanks again so much for the music, you've been effective, quick and delivered great quality. Hope we can work on other projects, too." Renate Farkas (Director, *The 6th Child*)

UK based composer for film, television and new media. Has composed for numerous short films, natural history films, documentaries and corporate productions.

Phoenix Benedict Aesthetics (Pty) Ltd
Address: PO Box 44212, Linden, Johannesburg 2195, SOUTH AFRICA
Phone: +27 82 346 9776
Email: info@phoenixbenedict.com
Website: www.phoenixbenedict.com
CEO: Phoenix Benedict – audio branding guru, film music for specific visuals and even epic narratives!

We provide audio branding (sonic identity creation and proliferation) for all types of documentaries including full-length film and series. We have worked on numerous local films as well as three South African TV series, of which one (*Death of a Queen*) won the South African Film and TV Award in 2010. Our passion is to create an audio identity to the visual and the narrative that serves both the purpose of the narrative and the overall multi-media product. CVs welcome via email.

Ben Please – Composer
Address: 18 Edward Street, Lower Weston, Bath, BA1 3BP, UK
Phone: +44 (0)7789348165
Email: benplease@hotmail.com
Website: www.benedictplease.co.uk

All audio production services provided for film, from Foley, live recording to orchestral scores. Particular experience working with animations, but all types considered. Credits include BAFTA for short animation in 2011 (provided Foley and orchestral score). Also have ten years wider experience as a film editor/producer for environmental films.

Jobina Tinnemans – Music Composer/Wildlife Sound Recordist
Country: Pembrokeshire, UK
Phone: +44 (0)7779235442
Email: mail@jobinatinnemans.com
Website: www.jobinatinnemans.com

If you are looking for music compositions with an edge, get in touch for some quick suggestions to see how my work would compliment your film to help it stand out. Preferred way of working is recording on location to incorporate situational sounds into the soundtrack. Independent production company for BBC3 Radio, first radio work was broadcast by ABC Australia and selected for the ISCM World New Music Festival 2010. Sound recordings are in Griff Rhys Jones' *Pembrokeshire Farm* TV programmes. Currently in collaboration with Peter Zinovieff. Since 2002 I'm working in all facets of sound production. Media concepts which are keen on the vivid use of wildlife sound, next to commentating, to bring the message across, would have my special interest. With smaller productions we can discuss whether I will do all sound tasks needed, including engineering.

Twisted Jukebox Ltd.
Address: Suite 34, 272, Kensington High Street, London W8 6ND, UK
Phone: +44 (0)20 33974848
Email: library@twistedjukebox.com
Website: www.twistedjukebox.com
Sync Licensing & Business Affairs: Adrian Augustin – adrian@twistedjukebox.com
Music Director and Management: Matt Welch – matt@twistedjukebox.com

Twisted Jukebox is a music publishing and production music library. We have a range of music suitable for nature themed documentaries that cover different moods and scenarios as well as a team of talented composers that can write bespoke music to fill clients briefs.

Cody Westheimer – Composer
Address: 3127 Glendon Ave, Los Angeles, CA, USA
Phone: +1 213 709·5643
Email: cody@codywestheimer.com
Website: www.codywestheimer.com

Cody Westheimer is a noted film and television composer. A multi-instrumentalist and magna-cum-laude graduate of the music composition program at USC's Thornton School of Music, his gift for thematic writing and creative instrument choices has made him a sought after composer for both studio and independent projects. A passion for wildlife and the son of a veterinarian, Cody's love of nature gives him a unique perspective scoring such projects. Equally comfortable with the orchestra and the rock band, his blend of contemporary musical styles has taken over 100 films to the next level of storytelling.

Josh Wynter – Film & TV Composer
Josh Wynter Music
Addresses: Flat 6, 9 Manilla Road, Clifton, Bristol BS8 4ED, UK
& Camps Bay, Cape Town, South Africa
Phone: +44 (0)7792401368 & +44 (0)1243 551320
Email: contact@joshwynter.co.uk
Website: www.joshwynter.co.uk

Bespoke scores and soundtracks for film and television. Interested in being a part of new exciting projects, especially in historical & wildlife documentary film.

PRODUCTION STILLS PHOTOGRAPHERS

Tom Burn – Photographer/Videographer
Tom Burn Photography
Address: Dorset, UK
Website: www.tomburnphotography.net
Email: t.burn24@gmail.com

Wildlife Photographer and Videographer based in Dorset, UK. Available for hire to work in many different production roles, with the main focus being camera operator. Completed Wildeye Introduction to Wildlife Filmmaking and the Wildlife Film Academy Course. I am eager to support or co-produce wildlife films in the UK or abroad.

Ethan Daniels – Photojournalist
OceanStockImages.com
Address: 2920 Benvenue Ave., Berkeley, CA 94705, USA
Phone: +1 510 332 9740
Email: ethanadaniels@gmail.com
Website: www.oceanstockimages.com

OceanStockImages.com offers the highest quality still imagery focusing on aquatic ecosystems, animals, behaviors, and conservation issues. We also offer text stories based on marine subjects. We have published hundreds of stories in publications worldwide and have two books now available: *Under Cape Cod Waters* (2010) and *Coral Triangle Seascapes* (out in March 2012).

Paul Dimmock – Underwater Photographer/Videographer
Address: The Barn, Warren Farm, High Street, Ridgmont, Beds MK43 0TS, UK
Phone: +44 (0)7921848447
Email: pjdimmock@hotmail.com
Website: www.about.me/pjdimmock

I am a researcher, camera operator, photographer, self-shooting assistant producer, underwater photographer/videographer, production coordinator ... I create and research factual content with strong character-led stories involving wildlife. I photograph and film above and below the water, focusing on achieving captivating images and composition, which refreshes the viewers understanding. My determination and grit has enabled me to source valuable locations and professional cast on several productions and my creative ability means I always have ideas and can see how to pitch them. Experienced in directing crew and productions, producing drama and documentary, shooting DSLR and professional camera equipment. I am always on the look out for intriguing content and projects to work on as well as interesting people to work with. I am diverse in my outlook and like working on a variety of productions. I would consider working alongside or for any productions that have wildlife at their heart and which have a positive message that they are trying to achieve.

Ricardo Guerreiro - Wildlife Photographer/Cameraman
Country: PORTUGAL
Phone: +351 910732177 & +351 969336964
Email: zevimetal@gmail.com
Website: www.zevi.cabine.org/rgfoto/

Freelance natural history photographer and cameraman working in Portugal. May also work as assistant to foreign production teams coming to Portugal. Main interests: NH filmmaking and stills photography, including the rural traditional practices of agriculture and their interaction with wildlife. Some experience in film editing also.

Mundy Hackett – Wildlife Photographer
Mundy Hackett Photography
Address: 130 Colony Trail, Lanexa, Virginia 23089, USA
Phone: +1 804 349 6501
Email: mundy@mundyhackett.com
Website: www.mundyhackett.com

I am a freelance wildlife photographer and research biologist. My research has focused on rare and endangered forest species in North America. My recent publications range from my own book on birds in Missouri to the plight of tigers in India. I am interested in offering my services wherever they may be needed, as a photographer and a researcher. I would prefer wildlife and conservation-themed assignments. I am always on the lookout for a good idea to focus my efforts upon, and would love an opportunity to get immersed more in-depth into the conservation photography world, both at home and abroad.

HAWNT Media
Address: P.O. Box 1872, Byron Bay, NSW 2480, AUSTRALIA
Phone: +6 421573262
Email: info@hawntmedia.com
Website: www.hawntmedia.com
Director: Rowena Mynott

HAWNT Media: A natural history photojournalism company that offers photographic services for natural history or documentary projects. We invite communication from sponsors and are open to collaborations. We are always interested in hearing from people that might like to contribute. CVs and publication content can be sent via email or post. We would prefer contributors to be experienced writers, photographers and/or scientists but are happy to hear from anyone interested in being part of our publication. We would also consider work experience placements.

Sandesh Kadur – Wildlife Photographer
Felis Creations
Address: #295 39th 'C' Cross 10th Main 5th Block, Jayanagar, Bangalore 560041, INDIA
Phone: +91 9448059209
Email: sandesh@sandeshkadur.com
Website: www.sandeshkadur.com

Sandesh Kadur has a passion for visual imagery and has made his mark as both a wildlife photographer and documentary filmmaker. His films have been shown on television networks including National Geographic, BBC, Discovery and Animal Planet. Currently based in India, Sandesh is documenting the Eastern Himalaya, another endangered ecosystem in critical need of conservation. He is a member of the International League of Conservation Photographers and director of Felis Creations, a visual-arts company based in India, which focuses on creating content that inspires conservation.

Pawel Kot – Still Photographer/Camera Operator
Address: P.O.Box 70878 Bryanston 2021, SOUTH AFRICA
Phone: +27 +83 7163553 & +27 +11 4679677
Website: www.pawelkotphotography.com
Email: mail@pawelkot.com

Cristina Goettsch Mittermeier – Photographer
Cristina Mittermeier Photography
Address: 3357 Coho Lane, Nanoose, BC V9P 9H9, CANADA
Phone: +1 7033041440
Email: cmittermeier@gmail.com
Website: www.cristinamittermeier.com

Robin Moore - Wildlife/Nature/Conservation Photographer
Robin Moore Photography
Address: 3155 Mt Pleasant St NW, Apt 302, Washington 20010, DC, USA
Phone: +1 2023605339 & +1 57123163455
Email: robin@robindmoore.com
Website: www.robindmoore.com

I am an Associate of the International League of Conservation Photographers and hold a PhD in amphibian conservation. I am widely published and have won awards for my images of wildlife, landscapes and cultures including first place in 2011 Nature's Best International Photo Awards, second and third place in National Geographic Traveler's Photo Contest in the past two years, and gained recognition for a series of portraits from Haiti in *Photo District News*. I run photo safaris in Kenya and expect to expand to other parts of the world. I am always interested in ideas for projects centered around a conservation theme. I do consider co-productions and am open to invitations to collaborate.

Chris Perrett
Natures Art
Address: Surrey, UK
Phone: +44 (0)1932 348117
Fax: +44 (0)1932 348117
Email: naturesart@me.com
Website: www.naturesart.co.uk

Stills photographer, thirty-years experience – hung out of helicopters and hot air balloons, walked through the rainforest, trekked in the South African bush and hiked in the Arctic.

Ramnivas
Address: Plot No.6, Andalpuram, T.P.K Road, 625003, INDIA
Phone: +91 4522373997 & +91 9894432859
Email: ramni.rg@gmail.com & ramnivasphotography@yahoo.com
Website: www.flickr.com/photos/ramnivasphotography

I am a photography student. I have completed a film-making course at Balumahendra Film Institute (Chennai). I am very passionate about wildlife photography, film-making and conservation. As I am passionate about photography I want to work as assistant and learn the art of wildlife photography.

Thomas Wiewandt - Photographer
Wild Horizons Productions
Address: 5757 West Sweetwater Drive, Tucson, Arizona 85745, USA
Phone: +1 520 743 4551 & +1 520 743 4848
Fax: +1 520 743 4552
Email: info@wildhorizons.com
Website: www.wildhorizons.com
Producer/Director of Photography: Thomas Wiewandt – tom@wildhorizons.com

Experienced independent natural history photographer-storyteller with PhD in behavioral ecology, based in the Sonoran Desert. Now engaged in multimedia production. Special interests include conservation projects, children's programming, and new nature media. Inquire about stock video clips, project research/consulting, or location scouting. Awards: Emmy nomination in cinematography, 4 CINE Golden Eagles, Gold Apple from National Educational Film & Video Festival. Not looking for proposals or offering work experience. We are seeking sponsors for work in progress and are interested in speaking with potential collaborators or co-producers.

FURTHER READING

Wildlife Film-making: Looking to the Future edited by Piers Warren, foreword by Neil Nightingale – published by Wildeye 2011

What does the future of wildlife film-making hold for us all? Whether you are a budding film-maker, an experienced amateur or a seasoned professional, this new book – an accompaniment to the hugely successful *Careers in Wildlife Film-making* – attempts to answer this question. As technology advances rapidly and viewers' options increase, this book presents a unique collection of views and advice that make it an invaluable resource for everyone who wishes to succeed as a wildlife film-maker in years to come. With articles from many leading figures in the industry and case studies of numerous skilled practitioners.
(see www.wildeye.co.uk/shop.html)

Careers in Wildlife Film-making by Piers Warren – published by Wildeye 2002, 2006

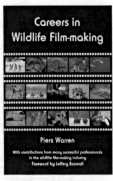

The essential book by Piers Warren, packed with guidance and advice for aspiring makers of natural history films. Described as 'long-overdue' and 'much-needed', this is not just an essential book for newcomers and wannabes – the fascinating case studies of well-known individuals, and unique discussion of the future of the industry from top professionals, make this an important read for those already working in the fields of wildlife, underwater and conservation film.
(see www.wildeye.co.uk/shop.html)

Go Wild with your Camcorder - How to Make Wildlife Films
by Piers Warren – published by Wildeye 2006

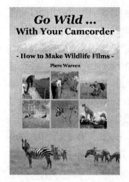

Whether you want to film wildlife as a fascinating hobby, or are hoping for a career as a professional wildlife film-maker, this book and a basic camcorder are all you need to get started! Packed with information and advice acquired over years of teaching wildlife film-making Piers Warren guides you through all aspects of making a wildlife film from choosing a camcorder to editing the final product.
(see www.wildeye.co.uk/shop.html)

Shooting in the Wild: An Insider's Account of Making Movies in the Animal Kingdom by Chris Palmer – published by Sierra Club Books 2010

Longtime producer Chris Palmer provides an in-depth look at wild animals on film, covering the history of wildlife documentaries, safety issues, and the never-ending pressure to obtain the "money shot." Marlin Perkins, Jacques Cousteau, Steve Irwin, Timothy Treadwell, and many other familiar names are discussed along with their work, accidents, and in some cases, untimely deaths. Chris Palmer is highly critical of Irwin, and offers fascinating revelations about game farms used by exploitative filmmakers and photographers looking for easy shots and willing to use caged animals to obtain them. He also considers the subliminal messages of many wildlife films, considering everything from *Shark Week* to *Happy Feet* and how they manipulate audiences toward preset conclusions about animal behavior. In all this is an engaging and exceedingly timely look at a form of entertainment the public has long taken for granted and which, as Chris Palmer points out, really needs a fresh and careful reconsideration.

Africa's Big Five And Other Wildlife Film Makers by Jean Hartley – published by Twaweza Communications 2010

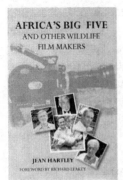

Jean Hartley, born in Kenya, is acknowledged as being the first to legitimise "fixing" for wildlife film crews. Over the last 25 years, she has worked on over a thousand films, the vast majority being about wildlife and nature. In this insightful book she features five of the great film-makers who all started their careers in Kenya in the 1950s, legends whom she is proud to call personal friends. Watching all their films, and many more, she became fascinated by the history of film-making in Kenya and determined to find out when it all started. She traces the roots of wildlife film back a hundred years, drawing on accounts of the original film makers and the professional hunters who guided those early safaris. She tracks the changes from those grainy, speeded up, silent films through to the technologically perfect High Definition and 3D films that are being made today.
(see www.wildeye.co.uk/shop.html)

Wildlife Films by Derek Bousé – published by University of Pennsylvania Press 2000

This book is a scholarly analysis of the development of wildlife films up to the 21st century. Derek Bousé's exploration of wildlife film-making over the last few hundred years is fascinating, and the book is littered with behind-the-scenes anecdotes. Although the book focuses on the industry in the USA and UK, the discussions (to what extent are wildlife films documentaries for example) are applicable to wildlife film-makers the world over. There are so many well-known names – both companies and individuals – in the business today, and it's hard to keep track as units change name, merge or disappear. This book certainly helps piece the jigsaw together as the genre's development is analysed.

100 Years of Wildlife by Michael Bright – published by BBC Books 2007

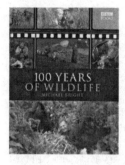

Ever since 1907, when a flickering film about birds enthralled a cinema audience, we've been fascinated by watching the natural world on film. For 100 years wildlife films have taken us to places and shown us things we would never be able to see – the excitement, the strangeness, the danger of the wild. Today, our interest in the wonders of the natural world is stronger than ever. Discover the history of the wildlife moving image: the first heady days when an ant juggling a matchbox was big box office; the charismatic and sometimes controversial celebrity presenters; the astonishing behaviour of animals and plants; the boggling oddities of nature; the animals now extinct that poignantly only exist on film. Explore 100 years of revelation – from the black-and-white silent footage that started it all to the almost magical photography techniques seen today in programmes like *Planet Earth*. From famous faces of wildlife TV to extraordinary animal (and plant) behaviour, natural history filming has changed the way we look at and think about our world. It's all here – so weird, you couldn't make it up; so wonderful, you wouldn't want to miss it.

Reel Nature by Gregg Mitman – published 1999 by Harvard University Press

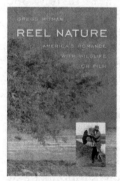

In this book Gregg Mitman explores the history of nature films focusing on the conflict between the desire for scientific authenticity and the demand for audience-pleasing dramatisation. He discusses the driving forces behind the evolution of nature films over the decades, highlights good and bad nature film-makers, explores the relationship between scientific establishments and Hollywood, and analyses Disney's contributions to this genre and the huge success of natural history on TV. He finishes by concluding that while nature films help us to understand the natural world, the truth about our place in the web of life has been left on the cutting-room floor.

Celebrity and the Environment by Dan Brockington – published by Zed Books 2009

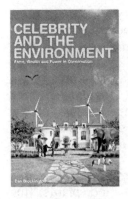

The battle to save the world is being joined by a powerful new group of warriors. Celebrities are lending their name to conservation causes, and conservation itself is growing its own stars to fight and speak for nature. In this timely and essential book, Dan Brockington argues that this alliance grows from the mutually supportive publicity celebrity and conservation causes provide for each other, and more fundamentally, that the flourishing of celebrity and charismatic conservation is part of an ever-closer intertwining of conservation and corporate capitalism. Celebrity promotions, the investments of rich executives, and the wealthy social networks of charismatic conservationists are producing more commodified and commercial conservation strategies; conservation becomes an ever more important means of generating profit. 'Celebrity and the Environment' provides vital critical analysis of this new phenomena.

Media, Ecology and Conservation: Using the media to protect the world's wildlife and ecosystems by John Blewitt – published by Green Books

Media, Ecology and Conservation focuses on global connectivity and the role of new digital and traditional media in bringing people together to protect the world's endangered wildlife and conserve fragile and threatened habitats. By exploring the role of film, television, video, photography and the internet in animal conservation in the USA, India, Africa, Australia and the United Kingdom John Blewitt investigates the politics of media representation surrounding important controversies such as the trade in bushmeat, whaling and habitat destruction. The work and achievements of media/conservation activists are located within a cultural framework that simultaneously loves nature, reveres animals but too often ignores the uncomfortable realities of species extinction and animal cruelty.

Missouri in Flight by Mundy Hackett – published by University of Missouri Press 2007

With its rugged Ozarks, rolling plains, big rivers, and wetlands, Missouri offers a diversity of habitats for native birds, and its location along a major migration route attracts many avian visitors. Wildlife biologist and photographer Mundy Hackett offers more than one hundred spectacular color images, along with his thoughts on the beauty of birds, the subtleties of their behavior, and all of the elements that make them the ultimate photographic subject. Along with interesting facts about the various birds of Missouri, he shares tips on how amateur shutterbugs can improve the overall quality of their photos. Mingled with his amazing photos of coots, crows, kestrels, and more are Hackett's thoughts about choosing cameras, taking photos from cars, visualization, composing an appealing scene, using contrasting colors—a host of practical tips that can help birders and photographers better capture those elusive images. He even passes along suggestions on the most challenging of photos, those of birds in flight. Through its examples and subtle instruction, the book can help readers record their own timeless moments and rediscover the beauty in the skies.

Wildlife Stalker: Days in the Life of Filmmaker Bob Landis
by Kevin G. Rhoades – published: Five Valleys Press 2011

Recording wildlife behavior on movie film and video is the hallmark of Bob Landis' films. He has filmed wildlife in Yellowstone for over 40 years – a place dear to his soul. This book is comprised of two stories wound into one: a depiction of days afield with a wildlife cinematographer who has filmed and co-produced stories about Yellowstone's iconic species – the bear, the wolf, the bison – films that have aired on *PBS*, *Nature* and on *National Geographic Television*. This book also is a collection of flashbacks to Landis' past – growing up as a small-town Wisconsin boy where he followed his destiny to become a football player, teacher, diehard Green Bay Packers fan, and wildlife filmmaker. Bob Landis is one of America's premier wildlife filmmakers.

INDEX

232

Films that Make a Difference

~ The online library of conservation films.

A collaborative project to document conservation films that have proven to have made a real and tangible difference to a conservation issue.

http://www.filmmakersforconservation.org

"Showing the truth on some minority channel is not the answer. Showing it where it counts is." Richard Brock, The Brock Initiative.

Filmmakers for Conservation
*"Using The Power Of Film
And Media To Conserve Our Natural World"*

CELEBRATING TEN YEARS OF FFC SUCCESS

Our Code of Ethics
Conservation Filmmakers Award
FFC Fund
Guidelines to Pitching
Graduate Research
The Great Ape Film Initiative (GAFI)
Code of Best Practice in Sustainable Filmmaking

Support FFC: www.filmmakersforconservation.org

Since the late 1990s **Wildlife-film.com** has been the leading source of information for the wildlife film-making industry worldwide. For over twelve years the site has been Google's number one ranking site for 'wildlife film' and related searches. The website is viewed in over 175 countries.

The newsletter, **Wildlife Film News**, is read every month by thousands of people involved in wildlife film-making - from broadcasters and producers to freelancers and newcomers - we encourage readers to submit their news.

Wildlife-film.com also serves as an online resource for industry professionals and services. Find producers, editors, presenters and more in the **Freelancer** section, and find out about festivals, training and conservation in **Organisations**. We encourage amateur and professional freelancers to join our network and welcome all wildlife-film related organisations to join our team.

www.wildlife-film.com

Lightning Source UK Ltd.
Milton Keynes UK
UKOW031817230812

197995UK00004B/6/P